Spots, Pimples
and
Bum fluff

By John Fagan

First Published 2007 by Appin Press,

Appin Press is an inprint of Countyvise Limited

14 Appin Road, Birkenhead, Wirral CH41 9HH.

British Library Cataloguing in Publication Data.

A catalogue record for this book is available from the British Library.

ISBN 978 1906 205 06 5

Acknowledgements.

My thanks to Malcom Young, for his proof reading and inspirational ideas, which have been a great help in bringing the book to fruition. Also his humorous character drawings that grace the front and back cover of the book.

I'm grateful to our dear friend, the late Tony Eccles, for his wonderful sketches which have certainly enhanced the stories.

Also Mark Yates, for reading my initial draft copy, and for his progressive suggestions.

To Ken Hatton, my computer guru, who has diligently improved my basic P.C skills.

And, as always, to my better half Pat, for her unending support and patience.

Contents

The Pitts	7
Initiation	10
Eggo	22
On the buses	27
The window dresser	36
Church street drama	44
Suspension	51
The Artful dodger	56
Pastures new	60
The raid	66
Leisure	72
Harry's domain	79
Rock Ferry Frank and the lost brew	84
On Guard	90
Time served, or tool wise	93
Last in, first out	97
The Quisling	102
Bonso's misfortune	105
Joining the union	119
Moving on	125
Temptation	132
The boss poser	143
Nobby's revenge	151
The Mill and a new set of characters	168
Sid Shortwick, ex Mariner and master story teller	172
Extra hands	179
Nipper and his final plunge	192
Summer holidays and the noble art of self-defence	205
More gaffers, more changes	217
Tails and spooks	232
Sussed out by the Chancer	249
Re-union	273
Electrocution	291
Curtains	311

Preface

'Name,'

'James Reilly.'

'And you want to become a spark?'

'Yes sir.'

'Don't call me sir, it's Mac to you an' everyone else round here.'

'Yes er...erm Mac.'

'You're not very big are you lad.'

'I'm nearly five foot, an' as me mam always says, there's good stuff in small parcels.'

'I'm sure your mam's right. How does eight pence an hour sound young Reilly?'

'Eight pence an hour, you mean you're offerin' me the job?'

'I suppose so. I'll expect you'll come in handy for workin' under floorboards.'

'I'll work anywhere 'onest ter God.'

And so I became an apprentice electrician, of a kind. It's often been said that the first couple of years in the contracting game are spent running messages, in making tea, and larking about, which I think is a fair assessment. However, serving your time is also to do with growing up and learning about life, and delving into taboo subjects that weren't discussed at home. And of course it was about meeting and working with characters of all types.

Take Eggo for example. Funny and original, he was one who had definitely slipped through that net which trawled up so many of Liverpool's natural comedians across the years, and was impossible to forget. In all the time I spent in the contracting industry since those formative years, I've yet to meet anyone to match him, as you will learn.

This, then, is a light hearted account of days when a tradesman considered it his solemn duty to pass on his experience and knowledge to the still 'wet behind the ears' apprentices, always a thankless task in anyone's book. It also reflects on a period when becoming a journeyman was a step up the ladder, particularly for someone from a working class family, where previously the bread winner could only aspire to become a casual labourer, a docker, a navvie or a shipyard worker.

The downside of being an apprentice, of course was the lowly wage rate; but it was a sacrifice worth enduring, for the end result meant having a coveted trade at your fingertips.

Most of the characters and locations in this book are as real as you and me, but for obvious reasons, identities and exact places have been altered to spare some embarrassments.

But then, the incidents described bring to mind aspects of the old adage which says, 'never let the truth spoil a good story.'

The boy maketh the man,
Who maketh the apprentice?

The Pitts

I left school at Easter 1953, a fifteen-year-old pimple-face lad ambitious to travel the world, and hoping to join the merchant navy like my mates Nacker Ryan and Teddy Bowie. Unfortunately, a certain person didn't share my enthusiasm or my ambition, because according to dad the idea of going to sea as a galley-boy just wasn't going to happen. And we all knew that his word was law in our house, no arguments accepted.

'Get yourself an apprenticeship and then go away to sea, otherwise you'll end up on the docks like me,' he'd preach

'Just as if,' I thought. Without a tradesman in our family to 'put in a good word' it was easier said than done, so what chance did I have?

For the last two years at school I'd worked part-time delivering milk, and on reaching my fifteenth birthday I'd decided to plod along with this on a permanent basis until a suitable opportunity came my way. That is until I met up with my schoolmate Chunkie Harlowe, who was employed by a Liverpool contracting company, which was in the process of expanding, and looking for young lads to join their books.

Whether they were recruiting cheap labour, or had a genuine desire to assist youngsters become tradesmen wasn't at all clear, but it didn't bother me at the time. So even when Chunkie told me in confidence that lads working for his firm - and indeed many other small contractors - were neither indentured, nor, for that matter, guaranteed the prospect of finishing an apprenticeship, I had already made up my mind.

'Chunks, it's a chance I'm willing to take,' I said. As far as I was concerned, the glamour and potential of becoming a tradesman far outweighed that of being a part-time milkman. Brimming with confidence I crossed the River Mersey from Birkenhead for my first interview, which is where I met Mac.

The Pitts Electrical Company' was located in one of the many large Victorian terrace houses that graced Duke Street, a once affluent district of Liverpool in earlier and wealthier times. After the interview and somehow convincing Mac - the Supervisor - that my four-foot eleven stature would not be detrimental nor a disadvantage to company profits, I joined a workforce consisting of a handful of journeymen who were significantly outnumbered by a gaggle of young apprentices.

Most days at Pitts were predictable. The 'sparks' would gulp swift mouthfuls of thick brown tea from stained 'billy cans,' climb three flights of stairs to receive jobs from Mac, re-enter the large parlour-cum workshop to select one of the lads who in their considered opinion was blessed with sufficient gumption, strength and personality to tackle the allocated daily tasks, and then set off for the site.

When it came to juggling for positions to assist the more easy-going and jovial sparks, and dodging those who were less popular, the older lads had the advantage of being more street-wise than us newcomers. It didn't take long for me to realise that one character to avoid like the plague was old Ted Snypy.

Apart from being the most elderly workman employed by the firm, he was by far the most miserable. Grumpy and impatient by nature, he moaned consistently, and was a dab hand at passing the buck to the unlucky lad assisting him when some unpleasant job landed in his lap. Little wonder then that the older lads ducked and dived whenever Snypy entered the room.

Not knowing how to avoid him nor having the skills of my more experienced mates, I was singled out by Ted on a couple of occasions during my first two weeks at Pitts. Not being the finest of orators, nor possessing any semblance of tact, his monotone patter rarely altered as he collared some lad to work with him. On the first occasion he captured me I was daydreaming, leaning on a vice when Ted's whinging voice brought me back to earth with a crash.

'HEY, short arse. Wake up an' lift me toolbox on yer shoulder an' don't drop it,' he roared.

As it was approaching eight fifteen, the apprentices paired with their respective tradesmen were already making tracks to leave the shop, while those remaining made themselves scarce. Showing little enthusiasm, I bent to take hold of the huge toolbox, struggling to lift it past my waist, but then I lost my grip and it crashed to the floor with a shattering noise, spilling spanners and other essentials in all directions.

A few of the lads tittered as I tried explaining to Ted that the box was too heavy and too awkward to carry. But he was in no mood for excuses.

'You'd better buck your ideas up if you're comin' with me for the day,' he scowled, grabbing the handle of the box in a sudden burst of temper and striding out of the office. I trailed a few yards behind, muttering under my breath.

'Anymore lip out of you m'lad an' I'll put me boot up yer bloody arse. D'yer 'ear me?' he bawled.

Looking over my shoulder I clocked a couple of the lads emerging from the backyard, and others sneaking out of the storeroom. They were grinning like Cheshire cats.

Already it was us against Ted, and I had become one of us.

Initiation

During slack periods, or when we were waiting for contracts to begin, the sparks and the lads spent their time in the workshop carrying out repairs to light fittings, to motor starters and the like. These were long days, and to relieve the boredom and to work off our excess energy we'd indulge in a game of football during the dinner hour. The venue for these games took place on a small patch of ground situated behind the yard of the office.

Nailers Cardboard Carton Company occupied the adjacent house to Pitt's Electric and, unfortunately for the enthusiastic players, Nailers employed an all female workforce. As soon as a match began all the girls from the Carton company would flock from their workplace to take up positions on a dividing wall, then shower the budding stars with a rising crescendo of ribald and uncomplimentary remarks. As the teenagers amongst them screamed their foul-mouth banter, the older women relaxing on comfortable wooden chairs placed out of the wind, gossiped together  and occasionally remonstrated with their younger colleagues about their unsavoury language.

On Thursday of my second week at Pitts I was approached by an older apprentice named Bonso who asked if I fancied a game of footy. Before I had time to reply, one of the sparks interjected, 'check the winder lad, to see if the fat, the thin an' the ugly are out there supportin'. 'Cos if they are then steer clear. With that mop of black curly 'air they'll make for you straight away. An' woe betide you if yer captured an' initiated. Take my advice or leave it, it's up to you lad.'

Alarmed by this news I turned to Bonso, who reassured me. 'It's not that bad, take no notice of 'im, he's only tryin' ter put the wind up yer.'

'Initiate, I wonder what that means,' I asked myself as I traipsed behind Bonso across the yard and onto the pitch. Feeling slightly nervous I glanced to the left then to the right, and couldn't help noticing a number of heavily tattooed girls congregated just a few yards behind the wooden gate that separated our yard from theirs. One in particular was scraping her toenails with an evil looking pen-knife which she flicked in my direction when our eyes accidentally made contact.

The game began and as the intensity of the contest increased my fears were soon put to one side, and I even managed to ignore the screeching and mickey-taking, which occurred whenever I threw my four feet eleven in the air in an attempt to head the ball. Shrieks of 'a bit higher short-arse', and 'Come over here an' we'll give yer leg up' were par for the course, along with a spattering of four letter obscenities with every catcall.

By the second half buckets of sweat dripped from both teams but then as the tempo increased, and with the score at three goals apiece, disaster struck. Volleying from the halfway line, Burkey belted the ball so hard that it cannoned off Chunkie's head and shot high into Nailers yard. Before we had time to do anything, mayhem broke out. With an almighty roar the foul-mouthed spectators clambered off the wall, screaming deliriously, while all we could do was to stand in silence with our mouths wide open and our hands on our hips.

'If yer want your ball back come an' gerrit,' a large and hefty girl suggested. There was no movement from the team, just a squabble between Chunkie and Burkey as to the merits of hitting the ball so hard at one of his own players. After a few minutes of quiet deliberation as we congregated in the goalmouth, Bonso took the initiative by volunteering to try to retrieve the ball by negotiation. This seemed fair enough to me, for after all he was the oldest and tallest.

'It's the 'ard faced one that's comin' over,' an elderly turbaned woman observed as Bonso approached the gate.

'Come on girls, let's 'ave the ball back,' he yelled from a safe distance. 'We're drawin' three each an' there's money on the result.'

'Who d'yer think yer are, Stanley Matthew's?' growled Gail, a thin featured and fervent Evertonian.

'Ah rey, come on now girls, don't be mingey,' Bonso pleaded. 'Just throw us the ball back, we've only gorra couple of minutes before the final whistle, an' it's worth half a dollar to the winners.'

'Pull the other one lad, yer 'aven't got a tanner between the lorra of yer,' Gummy Gerty replied.

In desperation Bonso threw his hands in the air reluctantly accepting defeat. 'Okay, there's no cash on the game, but we need the ball. So where is it then?'

The girls nudged each other and began laughing.

'Guess where it's bounced Bonso?'

'I 'aven't a clue an' I don't bleedin' care,' he replied angrily.

Big Bertha, weighing in at well over twenty stone, stepped forward, pointed her middle finger at her tent-like dress and said, 'try lookin' up 'ere lad.'

As she moved towards him, Bonso, was off in a flash, yelling that the game was now abandoned because the ball had landed in 'no mans land.'

'No mans land? That's a new one on me,' I said, scratching my innocent head. 'Whereabouts in the yard is that?' The lads looked at me and then at Bonso.

'Somewhere you wouldn't take your granny,' he replied laughing.

A despondent team trudged back into the workshop. As there was at least ten minutes before the end of the dinner hour it was obvious to the sparks that something drastic - or at least out of the ordinary - had taken place.

'What's up with you'se lot?' Billy Chancer asked, lowering his newspaper and removing his glasses at the same time.

Bonso immediately plonked himself on one of the spare toolboxes and began relating the story of his confrontation with Big Bertha. Before he had time to finish, however, Gormless Ginger Moorfield interrupted.

'What! A big lad like you scared to go in amongst all those judy's to get the ball? Why when I was your age I'd still be in there now,' he chortled.

'With big Bertha, the famous nutcracker. You're jokin aren't yer?' Bonso snapped back. 'You know what her party piece is don't yer?'

'No, worr is it? Come on tell us,' said Frankie Focus smiling broadly.

'Well rumour 'as it she can crack walnuts between the cheeks of 'er arse.'

'Judgin' by the ring piece on 'er, she'd crack a bloody walrus,' Tom Baines observed, enjoying the crack.

'Go way, you don't believe that crap, do yer?' said Ginger.

It's a well-known fact, isn't it lads?' Bonso replied, winking slyly to the older apprentices. Mindful of Ginger's gullibility and the whisper that he wasn't a full shilling, they nodded approvingly.

'Which ball were you playin' with anyway?' Freddy Focus asked.

'The old casey,' Chunkie replied.

'That's not too bad then. The worst thing that can happen to that is that she'll puncture it,' Frankie said.

'You're lucky it wasn't the tennis ball you were playin' with last week,' interrupted Ginger. 'Cos that would 'ave been swallowed up straight away, and never see the light of day again.'

A mutual roar of dirty laughter greeted his analysis.

'What d'yer mean?' I asked, 'wouldn't 'ave seen the light of day?'

'Stick with us Jimmy,' Bonso said, 'we'll teach you where balls go kid; when you get initiated.'

On my way home from work I couldn't help thinking about all the different experiences I'd encountered during that one afternoon, and for the life of me I still couldn't fathom out the meaning of the word 'initiate.'

'Mam'll know' I thought, and so after devouring a couple of platefuls of proper scouse in record time I put the question to her.

'Initiate? You've caught me out there son,' she said 'I've not heard that one before. Not to worry though, I'll get me medical book out later an' look it up.'

But I couldn't wait, so I slipped out the back and went round to see Spud, my mate from school. I knew he'd read lots of things, and wasn't he already well on his way to becoming a priest. He would surely know what it was, because I reckoned that 'initiate' had something to do with rituals – which I knew from experience was a subject the Catholic Church was more than familiar with.

'Can I pick your brains Spud?' I said, when he came to the door in answer to my knock.

'If you can find them,' he replied, still acting the fool like we'd always done.

'D'yer know what initiate means?' I asked. 'I think it's something to do with your nudger and two McNally's, from what I've heard.'

He thought for a long moment, looking very solemn. 'Could be what the Jews do,' he said in a low whisper.

'The Jews!' I exclaimed. We'd been brought up close to the docks, in the terraces where there were clear demarcations between Catholics and Proddies, but little or no contact with the Jews.

'It's when a Jewish baby boy is sort of christened; only of course it's not christened with it being a Jew. And they cut the end of its nudger off – it's called 'circumcision.' And there's a ritual with a Rabbi an' all that.

'You're kiddin' me,' I said, squirming and rubbing my groin at the thought of it.

'No, it's true. Remember Gordon Goldberg whose father had the pawnbrokers, and his sisters, Ruth an' whatsername.'

'Gordon Goldberg, who used to play goalie in the matches down the park?'

'That's him. He was circumcised. I never saw it, of course. They don't flash things like that.'

'I'm not surprised,' I told him.

I didn't think Mam would find what I'd just heard about in her medical dictionary, and when she didn't mention it again I didn't remind her. 'Initiation' it seemed was a bigger and more dreadful thing than I'd anticipated; something I might well try and do without.

'No, No, No, Yaaah! Gerraway from me,' I yelled, pulling my shirt tail between my legs, and almost kicking our Tommy out of the bottom half of the bed, as the huge figure of a woman dressed in green and looking too much like Big Bertha for comfort came steadily towards me, gripping a long, crooked knife clasped in a blood covered hand.

'Charlie...Charlie...wake up.   Our...Jimmy's havin' a nightmare.'

'Bloody 'ell woman, what time is it?' Dad grumbled, as he covered the few yards to the back bedroom door were I lay shivering with fright.

'Jimmy you're only dreamin', he whispered, 'now turn over off yer back an' go ter sleep.'

However, long after Dad had returned to bed I lay there thinking of the vivid apparition that had frightened the life out of me. Eventually I did drop off to sleep, but even at breakfast the thought of an initiation by 'circumcision' put me right off my toast.

Later that same morning, still feeling unsure and a little queasy, I couldn't muster any real enthusiasm for work as I lumped my journeyman's tools to a small factory a hundred yards or so from the office.

'You're quiet this mornin' lad, what's up? Haven't you 'ad your breakfast?' Billy Chancer asked.

'No, and I hardly slept at all last night.'

'You must 'ave 'ad a soft day if you couldn't sleep, unless something else is worryin' you.'

I remained silent for a minute, wondering whether to continue the conversation or to keep my thoughts to myself. 'Billy, what does initiate mean?' I finally blurted.

'Ah! That's what's worrying you. I knew it was somethin'', he said, showing genuine concern and even appearing to feel sorry for me. 'You'se kids should have lessons about the real world before leavin' school,' he muttered, stroking his fingers across his chin.

'M..m..n..n.. Let me see,' he continued in a fatherly way, 'what's the best way to explain it to you Jim? Now don't ask me why, but for some reason, certain youngsters 'ave an urge to strip each other off, mob like. D'yer know what I mean?'

I maintained a bland expression, waiting for him to explain.

'Take birds for instance, like that crowd next door. Now if they were all together, and say for arguments sake that a couple of lads worked in there, well it would be like a red flag to a bull with some of them. They'd think nothing of attackin' the lads, and not be satisfied 'til they've had their kecks down and smothered their balls with grease, or tallow, or anything sticky or somethin' that stinks. Now don't ask me why lad, there's no logical reason for it. It's a thing that 'appens all the time, particularly in factories where there's all wimmin.'

'They're worse than fella's, you know Jim. Of course in the shipyards all the young lads get a dose of the same treatment from the older ones. But that's just a workin' ritual, not the same as a crowd of wimmin goin' wild and getting' a grip of your plums an' throwin' all sorts of rubbish at them. I mean ter say, it's not only embarrassing, there's always the danger of permanent damage.'

I was shocked at the revelation, but in a sense relieved to hear that it wasn't a fine blood sport with knives or sharp weapons used in the attacks.

'Well son, that's what's known as initiation. Did yer follow me?'

'I think so Bill,' I said, somewhat chastened, 'and that's the last time I'll be playin' football at the back of the office.'

'A wise move son, a wise move,' said Billy, who seemed rather chuffed that his way of thinking had put me on the right road.

At lunchtime on the following Monday, with the rain relentlessly pounding the city centre, all hands were confined to the workshop, where we sprawled in various positions of comfort. As usual on such occasions, most of the tradesmen had their heads buried in the daily newspapers, while the lads were playing draughts using nuts and washers on improvised plywood boards made from sections of old China tea chests.

'It's a bloody good job it's dinner hour,' old Snypy remarked, as a shower of hailstones momentarily battered the windows. 'It would just be my lousy luck ter be given an outside job in all that,' he added, gazing at the rain pouring from out of a leaking downspout and cascading onto the sandstone sill. Suddenly, at ten minutes to one the back door burst open with such ferocity that everyone almost suffered heart failure, including Teddy Roberts who was supposedly stone deaf.

Bonso, who's absence had not been noticed or commented on, staggered into the room out of the raging storm, his hair flattened like a wet mop, the rain streaming down his face onto the shoulders of his long grey shirt and from the tail his lily-white legs disappeared into a pair of odd socks. In one hand he grasped his crumpled trousers, in the other he held the ball we'd lost to the Nailers girls on the previous Thursday.

'Christ worr 'appened there?' Ginger said, watching Bonso squelch towards the sink.

'I thought it would be a good idea to try an' get the ball back, seein' that it was rainin' an' all that,' he replied, with his back to us. 'So when I looked over the wall, an' with the coast bein' clear, I just crept across the yard with me 'ead down low and picked the ball up from the grid. But then how was I supposed to know that the Tank an' Sweaty Betty were in the lavvie together 'aving a fag? Anyway, before I had time to think, or to leg it back, the Tank gripped me round me waist an' Betty 'eld me in a head lock. Bloody 'ell she didn't half pong. Stank like a Greek wrestler's jock strap,' he continued, as if it was obvious we would know what that was like.

Old Snypy tutted, shook his head and after wrapping his remaining butties in greaseproof paper he plonked his pipe under the brown stained moustache adorning his upper lip and closed his eyes. Bonso carried on with the story.

'ERE GIRLS WE'VE GORR'IM,' they yelled. 'And then all 'ell broke loose. Next minute I was being dragged into the kitchen by at least ten of them.'

He paused to rinse a worn out towel under the cold water gushing from the tap.

'Worr 'appened next?' Tommy Baines asked.

'I was wrestled to the floor an' pinned on me back. Two 'eld me legs an' two 'eld me arms. Suddenly big Bertha appeared an' stood right over me. Worra a sight.'

The audience was mesmerised, with the exception of Snypy who paced the workshop puffing at his pipe, showing not the slightest interest in the on-going drama.

The narrator continued gleefully. 'Right girls altogether now,' she said, and they chanted ONE, TWO, THREE, as she sat down on me face. I had no chance then. Even though I struggled for at least five minutes the others finally pulled me kecks off, and plastered me bollocks with marmalade an' jam.'

'Bloody 'ell, am I 'earing things. She sat on yer face? Are you tryin' ter tell us the nut cracker sat on yer face?' Freddy Focus repeated, astonished at what he'd just heard.

'Honest ter God it's the truth. I wouldn't tell lies,' Bonso pleaded. Everyone looked shocked, lost for words, until Ginger Moorfield broke the silence.

'It's a bloody good job she didn't fart when yer face was stuck under her arse, 'cos she'd 'ave blown that bit of bum fluff right off yer chin.'

'Aye and wiped that stupid grin off yer face at the same time,' muttered Snypy, which surprised everyone. He was the last person in the shop to comment on tomfoolery or anything of a smutty nature.

Later that afternoon I was assisting Billy Chancer on a small job at a shop in Slater Street when the subject of Bonso's escapade came up.

'What do yer think about poor Bonso's experience?' I asked.

'You didn't fall for that claptrap, did yer lad? If you did I'm surprised at yer.'

'Why's that Bill?' I replied, genuinely puzzled by his dismissal.

'Because anyone with brains in their 'ead could see the little bugger was lyin'. What you've got to do son is analyse it. It's the same with any situation in life. Believe it or not Jim that was the first lesson my journeyman taught me when I was your age.'

'Let's just sit down and go through it step by step', Bill continued, pleased that he was once again assuming the role of tutor and able to give me the benefit of his years of experience.

'First of all what time did he go missin'? No one knows for certain, but he wasn't away for long that's for sure. So let's give 'im the benefit of the doubt an' say he was in there for ten minutes at the most, right? Now think about it. How long does it take to drop yer kecks? I'm not talkin' about emergencies like when yer taken short, just ordinary situations. What d'yer reckon? About ten seconds? And a damn sight quicker if someone drags them off yer.'

I agreed.

'Now then, Bonso said he struggled with the girls for at least five minutes as they tried to pull his kecks off. I ask yer, five minutes. Now add that to the time of the initiation, so were talkin' about another seven or even eight minutes on top. And then there's at least three more minutes to walk back 'ere.' He paused to let his analysis sink in and begin its task of showing me how many beans make five. 'I'll tell you what he's done James. He's whipped his kecks off on purpose, an' lay back and let the girls initiate him, that's what he's done. He's at it Jim, take it from me he's givin' us the madam.'

'What's more,' Bill continued. 'Ask yourself. How tall is Bonso?'

'Er, about eight inches bigger than me, which would make 'im five foot seven.'

'Correct, and he's twice as broad as you, right?

I nodded.

'So tell me how the Tank was able to grab a strong lad like him with just the help of Sweaty Betty? And as we all know, there's more meat on a butcher's pencil than's on 'er. And then to actually hold 'im down 'til the mob arrived. It stinks to high heaven as far as I'm concerned.'

'Now then Jim, here we come to the technical part of the analysis. I don't know whether you'll understand the logic son, because I know yer 'aven't been to night school yet; but I'm sure a bright lad like you will get the gist. Just say for arguments sake that a little stone fell off that shelf up there an' landed on yer 'ead, it would leave a nasty lump wouldn't it? And if, for example, a huge rock weighing two tons fell off the lower shelf on to your 'ead we'd probably 'ave to shovel you off the floor. Agreed?'

I nodded, wondering what this had to do with Bonso's initiation.

'Okay, we're gettin' into the theory of gravitation now, masses, an' foot pounds and the like. But don't worry son, you'll soon see what I'm gettin' at.'

'So let's see. In Bonso's own words, he said that Big Bertha had sat on 'is face, right? But just think about it Jim. If the weight of her fat arse fell on your face - even from two foot away - apart from smotherin' yer, what else would it do? Think carefully son.'

I shook my head and said, 'what could it do Bill?'

'It would flatten your nose, wouldn't it?' he replied triumphantly.

I immediately thought of Bonso's huge conk and burst out laughing.

'What's up?' Bill asked, seemingly surprised that I'd found his meticulous analysis to be so funny.

'I was just picturin' Bonso's nose under all that weight. That's all,' I giggled.

'Exactly lad. That's it; you've got me point. His nose wasn't bruised or even red, was it? So you see Jim, it pays to break everything down in a methodical way, like I've just showed yer. It's the only way to get to the truth. I hope you remember the lesson lad.'

'But what I can't make out, is why did he do it in the first place?'

'I'll tell you why. Because he's a show-off, an exhibitionist if you like. And what's more that's the third time he's been gripped by that crowd next door in the last twelve months that I know of.'

'He must be a glutton for punishment,' I replied.

Bill smiled smugly. 'There's a bit more to it than punishment though,' he said with a sideways look.

'What d'you mean?' I asked.

'Well, sitting on a conk as big and as proud as that one for a minute or two is probably all that someone as ugly as Big Bertha can hope for.'

'I don't follow. What d'you mean?' I asked again. This lesson seemed to be taking off in directions I'd not expected.

'Well lad, the girls have got to have their own initiations ceremonies don't they? They need a bit of fun as well, you know.'

'Do they,' I said all adrift now.

'Look Jim, you're a bright lad, so stick with me an' you'll be alright. Eventually!'

Eggo

As the weeks turned into months I settled into a routine of learning the basic rudiments of life as an apprentice electrician and, of course, attuning my mind and body to enduring a forty-eight hour week. Within short period of time my body bore the ravages of change, with visible traces of hammer rash, two blackened fingernails, and a septic big toe inflicted when a rusty nail easily penetrated the paper-thin sole of a cheap Bata shoe. During those first few months I worked with most of the tradesmen at Pitts, travelling to various sites in the city, from the cast-iron shore of the Dingle to as far north as Seaforth, often by means of the overhead railway system.

In the early fifties, with petrol still rationed and vans still a rarity for small contractors, we had no alternative but to use public transport to carry the materials needed for those jobs beyond walking distance from the office. This practice had obvious drawbacks, particularly if, during the rush hour, we were forced to use the overhead railway. This was universally and aptly known as the 'docker's umbrella', because it ran the length of the docks and gave shelter to those workers lashed by the wind and rain whipping off the River Mersey. On these occasions the apprentices had to be sharp enough to manoeuvre heavy tool boxes, various pieces of conduit, coils of cable, and lengths of tray from out of the paths of the dockers employed on the numerous ships berthed along the main waterfront, as they stampeded past.

One late August morning when Pitts were having problems recruiting tradesmen, I, along with a number of other apprentices, was confined to the workshop for the day. With no experienced journeyman to supervise, Mac had taken the responsibility of dishing out menial tasks to keep us occupied and, of course, out of mischief. As the morning dragged on, and with the time ticking over at a caterpillar pace, our enthusiasm for work dwindled accordingly, until someone flicked an elastic band and stung Arnie's ear. Before long a full scale battle was in progress, with everyone bombarding each other with bits of cardboard, pieces of putty and other chunks of waste materials. With the melee now totally out of control, no one noticed the workshop door open slowly and a genial character enter the room. He coughed loudly - we looked round - but too late. Realising we'd been caught red-handed and, of course, fearing repercussions from Mac, we skulked back to the jobs we were supposed to be doing.

'Good morning gentlemen,' the visitor greeted us. 'Will one of you lads be kind enough to direct me to your supervisor's office?' The stranger, about six-foot tall, dressed in a smart worsted suit, addressed the group in a loud and rather posh voice.

Chunkie, feverishly cleaning a fluorescent light fitting, pointed nervously to the upstairs.

'Thank you very much young man,' the newcomer replied, passing through the workshop and leaving the door to the upstairs slightly open. We turned to one another and began tittering.

'Who d'yer reckon he is Bonso?'

'Haven't a clue,' Bonso said, cocking his ear to the sound of footsteps echoing up the creaking staircase. From the darkest part of the stairwell we suddenly heard the visitor yell out, 'SO, THIS IS AFRICA.'

We crept into the hallway, positioning ourselves at the bottom of the stairs, curious to hear how Mac would react to this oddball's approach.

'Good morning Sir,' the man boomed. 'According to last night's Echo I believe you're looking for electricians? '

'Indeed we are,' Mac replied. 'What's your name young man?'

'Surely you've heard of me. I'M EGGO,' he bawled. 'THE GREATEST SPARK IN THE UNIVERSE.'

Despite crawling halfway up the stairs to the landing we couldn't hear Mac's response, which left us wondering whether he'd collapsed with shock.

'James Aigburth, at your disposal Sir,' the newcomer continued, 'but feel free to call me Eggo, everyone else in town does.'

After what seemed like an eternity we were pleased to hear Mac assuring Eggo that there was indeed a vacancy for a suitable electrician, stressing that Pitts would not tolerate cowboys, nor, under any circumstances accept low standards of workmanship.

Life at Pitts was never the same after this. Those apprentices fortunate enough to work with Eggo not only learnt from a first class journeyman, but also were able to enjoy his madcap humour, and the pranks and wild cavorting of an extrovert, whose skylarking lifted the gloomy atmosphere, which had existed before his arrival.

'Which of you lucky lads is coming with me today?' he'd bellow, and there was never a shortage of volunteers, even if the work was in some unsavoury tannery or abattoir.

Eggo's jokes, innuendoes and exploits became a main topic of conversation in the months that followed, as the apprentices became experts at imitating his cultured voice and enjoyed describing his antics, and the seemingly endlessly bazaar activities which made him tick.

He was forever escorting elderly ladies across the road, which is a thoughtful gesture by any standards. However, it was his theatrical manner that everyone found so amusing. 'That looks to me like a damsel in distress,' he'd announce loudly to his apprentice. 'Keep your eye on the tools lad while I do the honours,' he'd say, and then trot off to where the lady was standing.

'May I have the pleasure of assisting you across this busy thoroughfare my dear,' he'd bellow, holding out his arm like a bride's father escorting a daughter down the aisle. At the same time he'd raise his other hand to stop the oncoming traffic - or give a two-finger salute if they showed no sign of slowing. Once across, the lady would invariably thank him for his courtesy, at which he would remove his arm, bow his head and reply in a deep voice, 'You're welcome madam, the pleasure is all mine.'

One morning, not long after he'd started working at Pitts, I was honoured to be his assistant on a job situated near the bottom end of Dale Street. We were carrying the toolbox in the usual fashion - supported by a piece of conduit, held firmly between us. Half way down the street Eggo's attention was drawn to a character walking boldly towards us. Dressed in a double breasted blazer with badge, a military striped tie, and sharply pressed cavalry twill trousers, the red-faced occupant sported a clipped moustache, iron-grey short back and sides, and was carrying a briefcase, a rolled umbrella and a copy of the Daily Telegraph, which looked as if it had been ironed flat.

'Put the tools down, Jimmy,' said Eggo, stopping short and coming smartly to attention and saluting with an exaggerated swing of the arm.

'Good morning major, long-time no see.'

The man stopped dead, scrutinised Eggo from head to toe, placed his briefcase and umbrella on the ground before him and fumbled in his pocket to extract a spectacle case. From this he produced a thick pair of horned rimmed glasses and, after slipping them on, scanned Eggo's face at close range.

'I'm afraid you have the wrong person old boy.'

'But you are my ex-commanding officer, Major Bull of the Grenadier Guards, are you not Sir?'

'Certainly not. I'm afraid you've made a mistake my man.'

'Perhaps he's a relation of yours sir.'

'No, no relation,' the victim insisted.

'If I may say so, you are his double sir,' Eggo said.

'Sorry old chap, wrong uniform. Ex Flight Lieutenant Wallace of the Royal Air Force, but good day to you anyway,' he added, lifting his briefcase and striding off.

Eggo, smirking as usual, glanced after the Flight Lieutenant. 'Lesson there, young Reilly,' he said. 'Know what you've just seen?'

'No idea,' I said.

'Observation, young Reilly, observation. Brylcream boy, you can tell 'em a mile away.'

'I didn't know you were in the army Eggo?'

'Me! Of course I was. And that's why when I see someone like Flight Lewy Wallace there; well you know for certain he's done nowt. All blazer and badges and stripey ties and clipped moustache, hoping to impress all and sundry that he was in the RAF; wouldn't be surprised if he says 'Jolly good show and whacko old boy' every other sentence. And as for being a Flight Lewy; I'll bet he was just a buckshee corporal.'

'What's happened there, young James, is a lesson in deflating pomp and circumstance and playing Flight Lieutenant Wallace at his own game. Y'see those who were at El Alamein or flying above the Atlantic convoys don't need to wear badges and ties and the medals, because they know they were there. Those types usually don't brag about it.'

'Do you talk about your time in the army Eggo?' I asked tentatively, for surely that would be a tale here for the telling.

'You wouldn't think to look at me now,' he said gravely as we slid the conduit through the toolbox handle and picked it up. 'At one time I happened to be a high-ranking officer in the army, but then my voice broke and they had the cheek to relegate me to third reserve to a trumpet player in Clayton Square.'

'Clayton Square,' I said uncomprehending.

'Sally Army, James! Sally Army,' Eggo grinned as we set off for the job.

On the buses

As the first whiff of autumn crept across the cobbled streets of town, the firm bid successfully for a number of contracts slightly larger than the usual 'run of the mill' jobs they'd normally price for. To save valuable time, Mac instructed the lads working on these projects to make their way direct to site, rather than report to the office, and to supplement the labour force, Eggo and Bonso were sent to a job located in the Edge Lane district of the city.

Now the buses on that particular circuit tended to carry a majority of female passengers employed by Littlewoods Football Pools Company. Having used the route on numerous occasions Eggo was acutely aware of this overwhelming female presence, and had craftily made last minute arrangements to meet Bonso on the seven thirty bus.

Considered by many to be the firms most experienced apprentice, Bonso joined the bus at the Pier Head, well versed to keep a sharp look out for Eggo boarding somewhere along the route.

Leaving the terminal at ten minutes to eight, the bus began its journey, chugging between the stops, where shivering passengers waited to climb aboard. Meanwhile Bonso, surrounded by gossiping women of all ages and sizes, was slouched upstairs in the front seat, wiping the steam off the side windows, peering into a bleak morning mist. Eventually as the bus braked sharply at a stop, Eggo emerged from a shadowed doorway, clambered aboard, and within seconds had silenced the chattering women with his booming voice.

'GOOD MORNING LADIES,' he yelled. 'IT'S YOUR LUCKY DAY. Come on now girls, don't be shy, let's have a glimpse of your Colgate pegs.'

A number of the women perched on the top deck tittered loudly, while a couple even left their seats to glance in the mirror at the top of the stairs, hoping to see the face of the 'screw-ball' who'd boarded the bus.

In the meantime, to prevent himself from laughing out loud, Bonso stuffed his sleeve into his mouth and began chewing the cuff; he had no doubt who the new arrival was.

Screams of female laughter were now echoing from below, with the exuberant Eggo in full swing, flirting, uttering a string of 'near to the bone' innuendoes and all the while prancing about, drawing everyone into his mayhem whether they wanted to or not.

'Got to share myself out ladies,' he bawled, as he made his way through the jostling chaos to head upstairs. 'Can't let you have all the fun, can I? See you tomorrow girls.'

'Well, well, well, what a pleasant surprise. Now don't all shout at once, but which of you girls would like the pleasure of my company?' he greeted the top deck, before plonking his huge frame alongside a plump young woman huddled in the back seat.

'Now there's luck for yer,' the big man gasped in mock surprise. 'This is what I call a pretty face,' and he pinched her cheek playfully.

'BEAT IT YER PERVERT,' the girl yelled, blushing with embarrassment.

'HERBERT?' said Eggo deliberately switching the 'P' for an 'aitch'. 'No young lady, I'm not Herbert, I'm, EGGO, the great Eggo...o ...o...o,' he yodelled, beating the palms of his hands against his chest like a gorilla.

Within seconds the atmosphere on the top deck had changed dramatically for now a dark skinned girl, obviously enjoying the occasion joined in and screamed, 'Eggo, worra name. An' you've gorra a bleedin' 'ead like an egg, as well.'

Chiming in to support this rebuff of the great man, a young blonde shrieked, 'beat it Dad! You're a bit old for us lot, aren't yer?'

From further up the bus, a brunette, eager to get in on the action, bawled 'which zoo 'ave you escaped from, anyway?'

As the clamour increased and more women ganged together to batter him with verbal onslaughts, Eggo remained sitting besides the plump girl on the rear seat, his arms folded, his eyes closed, his face a calm and tranquil picture of placid and unruffled contentment.

Suddenly his eyes opened and he sat up at attention. 'BONSO' he bawled, his colossal voice shattering the first bit of quiet to have settled since he'd climbed on board the vehicle. Right on cue, Bonso stood to attention at the front of the bus. Then he turned with an artistic swivel and gave a little bow down the aisle towards his mentor sitting in the rear.

'Now then girls, what do you reckon to him? Smart lad isn't he? By the way, Bonso me'lad, what did you get up to last night with that blonde piece I introduced you to?'

'She wasn't all blonde, Eggo,' Bonso shouted back down the aisle as instructed.

'Bloody hell, don't tell me we've got two nutters on board,' an older lady said, looking around for support.

'Yeah, we've got an Eggo and a Bonso,' tittered the woman sitting next to her.

'Thinks he's a Bonker, not a Bonso,' a ginger wench giggled, openly giving the eye to Bonso who was still facing the crowd with a silly grin on his face

'Let's leave him to his blonde date, Ginger,' chuckled one of the girls as they got up, clattered down the stairs and filed from the bus.

This time the little charade hadn't produced a result for Bonso, though Eggo had pulled out all the stops. But just occasionally the drama paid dividends when a blonde or brunette would be caught in the playful trap and Bonso would have a night out, courtesy of the maestro.

The contract - a re-wire job - located in a section of a car parts factory, involved the installation of a conduit system. The bending of conduit in those days entailed the use of a block of wood, drilled with holes of various sizes with the pipe placed in the hole of the relevant size, ready to shape. According to the experienced tradesmen this was a skill you either had or you didn't have. Ted Snypy and Billy Chancer were the journeymen assigned to the project with Arnie Royal and Harry Burkey as their apprentices. However, after a few weeks of slow progress they'd began to realise that certain parts of the installation would take considerably longer than anticipated. Fearing their reputations were at stake, and that the company could lose money on the job, they'd contacted Mac to request additional labour. When he'd eventually had time to consider their concerns Mac resolved the problem by sending Eggo to pull the job out of the mire.

As a result the bold Eggo entered the site like a proverbial whirlwind, proclaiming to all and sundry that the 'A' team had arrived to sort out the job. In the circumstances, even old Snypy permitted himself the pleasure of a half-hearted smile at Eggo's bluster.

'What's this then? A teapot spout factory?' Eggo cried, casting his critical eye in the direction of a heap of discarded conduit lengths, which contained more than the usual variety of kinked bends and dog legs.

'Come on lads, who's the black pudding bender?' he scoffed, looking in disbelief at a piece of conduit someone had attempted to bend into a circle and now completely flattened in the middle.

'The lad's just been gettin' a bit of practice, that's all,' Snypy muttered, furious that the heap of incriminating evidence hadn't been hidden from Eggo's prying eyes.

'It's a bloody good job Mac hasn't showed up, otherwise there'd be a right inquest over the amount of material wasted here,' Eggo mumbled to himself under his breath.

Realising he'd need to make amends, Snypy changed tack, stood with his legs apart, his chin thrust out, and took charge of the apprentices.

'Right lads,' he growled, 'you're goin' to 'ave ter get a grip of yourselves if you wanna progress in this game. So pay attention to what I tell yer in future, d'yer hear me? Otherwise neither of you will make a spark while you've got an 'ole in yer arse.'

During the dinner hour Billy and Ted relaxed on an improvised bench made from a plank of wood resting on two small oil drums. Having read their newspapers, they'd started to complain and grumble about the decline in the industry since they'd been apprentices. Out of earshot, across in a corner on the far side of the room, Eggo was asleep, stretched out on a sheet of corrugated cardboard placed on the floor. Nearby the lads were playing cards for imaginary money.

'We didn't 'ave all this trouble with conduit in the old days,' Ted whinged. 'Straight pieces, an' proper solid bends. None of this crap we've got ter put up with today. An' using bits of bloody wood to bend it. Bloody primitive, I call it. It's a good job the old timers 'ave passed on; they'd 'ave gone ape-shit. Old Barney Bubbler, my journeyman, what a right-so- an' -so he was. Talk about graft, I never stopped from mornin' 'til night. Give 'im 'is due though, he taught me properly. I'll tell yer what Billy, when I came out of me time, there was nowt I didn't know about this game. Not like those lazy buggers over there,' he added, pointing in the direction of the lads. 'All they're interested in these days is football an' girls, an' getting' pissed outa their minds at weekends. I don't know what the worlds comin' to.'

'Aye, yer right there Ted, I've got to agree with yer,' Billy said. 'I served me time down at Lairds shipyard an' it was bloody tough, believe me. But it was only when I went away ter sea as an engineer that I appreciated just what a good apprenticeship I'd had.'

'This lot 'ere wouldn't 'ave the gumption to go ter sea. There's no bloody go in them at all. That's the trouble with them,' Snypy moaned.

'Fancy Billy bein' an engineer an' goin' away ter sea,' Bonso said later, as he helped Eggo pull cables in the roof space during the afternoon.

'Sea-going engineer! I've been longer on a wave,' Eggo replied sarcastically. 'The furthest he's sailed is just past New Brighton Lighthouse. And then, as soon as the chief sussed him out, he was transferred back to the Co-op as second engineer on the bacon slicer.'

Bonso chuckled at this response. 'But what about Snypy knowing the game inside out by the time he was twenty one?' he continued mischievously.

'Don't make me laugh lad. He still only knows the game from A to B, and he's sixty-one going on ninety-one. What's more he couldn't wire a bloody telegram, the black pudding bender.'

The following week I was sent to the site to assist Eggo when Bonso's mother contacted Mac to inform him her son was suffering from a bad dose of flu. News of Eggo's early morning pranks on the Edge Lane bus had long since circulated round the shop, so I was under no illusion as to what lay in store. Joining the bus at James Street Station I managed to secure an upstairs front seat, hoping against hope that when he boarded I'd be as far as possible from the clutches of my high-spirited colleague. At each stop as more girls joined the bus I heard Bonso's name being constantly mentioned again and again, usually followed by fits of laughter and hysterical giggling.

As we approached the fifth stop the bus slowed and the conductor yelled out, 'get ready girls, the nut case is about to gerron.'

Eggo climbed aboard, and within seconds had taken charge of the bus.

Dolly and Millie, two grossly overweight fifty-year-old women who occupied the side seats each morning for comforts sake, glared at Eggo as he approached, obviously hell-bent on having some fun.

'Come on girls, move over and allow me the pleasure of squeezing my little bum next to yours,' he cajoled. Crouching down he pushed his backside out and attempted to wriggle into a gap no more than six inches wide. A young girl sitting opposite cried out, 'it's your lucky day Millie.' Her friends, sitting on either side shouted a warning, 'watch 'im Dolly you know worr 'es after.'

'I'll 'ave no messin' out of you lad, d'you hear me?' Dolly warned him. 'I'm a 'appily married woman. An' don't be tappin' her up, either,' she added, glancing in the direction of the po-faced Millie. 'Cos she's hitched to our Billy, an' he'll batter yer for even just lookin' at her.'

She turned to the bus conductor. 'You know our Billy, don't yer Tom? So tell this bugger what he's like.'

'Know 'im?' The conductor said, staring pensively at

the women. 'He's one of the hardest cases in the south-end, six foot four and built like a brick shit 'ouse, if you'll excuse me expression. Got arms like tree trunks, a head on him like Birkenhead, an' a gob like a robbers dog,' he added, then seemed to experience a twinge of conscience or apprehension because of his less than flattering description. Millie, however, didn't seem to notice, but sat there as if she was again about to break wind, which was what usually happened whenever the bus rattled across tram lines or the wheels slid into some deeper crater on the un-even roads.

The conductor's blunt assessment of their Billy seemed to please the sisters-in-law who nodded approvingly, and then Dolly immediately went back on the attack.

'You 'eard what he said didn't yer? So watch it lad,' she growled, prodding a heavily nicotine stained finger under Eggo's chin.

'Okay...Okay girls. I know when I'm beat,' Eggo spluttered, pulling a crumpled white handkerchief from his jacket pocket and waving it backwards and forwards in mock surrender, to the great delight of all those on the bottom deck.

As if someone had a revolver in his back and with both hands held above his head, Eggo got to his feet and climbed the stairs, as little Aggie - a friend of Dolly's - yelled after him, 'Yer nothing but a yeller belly Eggo.'

'Some poor woman's had ter rear 'im,' Millie said ruefully, shaking her grey mop of Toni-permed hair.

'I'd poison 'im if he was my fella,' someone else observed coldly and clinically. 'Or I'd have to work night shift; one of the two.'

At this point the discussion was interrupted by the sounds of hysterical laughter drifting down from the top deck.

'There he goes again tryin' to tap off with the young girls. He wants ter grow up an' act his age,' muttered one of the few women on the bus who didn't work for the Pools firm.

'He'll be alright if Big Ginger get's a grip of 'im,' remarked Aggie, who was reputed to be the Pools firm's number one gossip. 'I hear she was out with that young lad Bonko, or Bonso, all last week,' she continued.

'What!' Dolly tutted. 'She's old enough to be 'is mother, the dirty cow.'

'No wonder there's no sign of 'im this mornin,' said Millie.

Meanwhile, Eggo was stealthily creeping along the upstairs aisle of the bus. Of course, given the fact that all the girls were giving out comments and broad hints as to his progress, I had sensed what was coming and tried sliding down in the seat to escape his clutches.

'Gotcha!' He yelled, gripping my ear and hauling me into view.

'Here he is ladies. Young Jimmy Reilly. Bonso's replacement. And guess what? He's only trying to grow a moustache like Errol Flynn. Or is it Clarkie Gable? But Reilly, you can't be Errol Flynn, 'cos that's who Bonso wants to be. An' he's a big, big lad, isn't he girls?'

'See the conk and know the rest,' someone shouted.

'Cock! Did you say cock or conk,' another girl added without much finesse, and then fell about laughing.

'Ask Ginger, she knows what he's got,' another squealed, and the place collapsed in a mood of general hilarity.

'So ladies, worrabout this one?' Eggo asked, holding me up for inspection.

'Good things in small parcels,' a blonde girl yelled.

'Does he make up for lack of height in other departments?' another asked, and again the bus was rocked by gales of laughter.

The saucy suggestions from the younger girls even made me smile and my cheeks felt as if they were on fire.

'The best thing you can do with this thing,' Eggo continued, trying to grip the fair hairs growing above my upper lip, 'is to put a bit of 'connie onnie' milk on it tonight, and with a bit of luck the cat will lick them off.'

As we reached our destination I stood up to leave, but in my haste I failed to notice that Eggo was nodding slyly at a girl sitting near the back. As I passed alongside her I suddenly felt her fingers move across the back of my trousers to touch me up.

'OUCH,' I yelled, more from the shock than the pain.

'What's up with you Reilly?' Eggo asked as we stepped onto the pavement.

'That big woman near the back pinched me arse, just when I was walkin' past 'er.'

Eggo chuckled loudly.

'You're lucky it wasn't the dark girl sittin' next to her, 'cos she would 'ave gripped your 'ollies so hard, that this little fella would have shot up and choked yer.' And he tittered as he searched my thin neck for the tiny lump of my adams apple.

The window dresser

Before the work in Edge Lane reached its final stage of completion Eggo received a call to report to the office for a discussion on a job showing signs of getting out of hand. A lighting and power installation at 'Waring and Gillows,' the up-market furniture store in Bold Street, had run into problems, with the contract exceeding the agreed date by two weeks. Mac wasn't too bothered about being a fortnight over, but he was concerned that the store manager had complained about the misbehaviour of the apprentices. This was an altogether different matter. Apart from effecting payment for work already completed, such activity could well influence the chances of gaining future contracts; a situation which Mac decided needed to be rectified at once.

Tom Baines - the spark in charge had mentioned his concern at the snowballing amount of extra work when he filled in his weekly report, and as a result, to ease the position, it was decided five apprentices would be dispatched to finish minor jobs such as installing light switches and socket boxes; tasks which were well within their capabilities.

However, with little or no experience of accepting responsibility or for maintaining standards of self-discipline, the five of us found time to wander throughout the store whenever the opportunity arose, showing off and acting the goat.

Such behaviour, coupled with a blatant lack of respect shown towards the assistant floor manager and window dresser, Mr. Max Unterlanze, had earned us few plaudits.

A stickler for position and discipline, Max had spent twenty and more of his adult years in the glossy world of retail sales. And being of German origin possessed a Teutonic rigidity in the principle that the paying customer was always right. What's more, he believed firmly in setting an example and championing the concept of rank and status in the world of shop management. In truth he was just not used to contractors – or their apprentices - especially when the latter treated his polished showroom as if it were some back-street workshop.

Although not much bigger than either Arnie or myself,

Max patrolled the shopfloor like a tyrannical sergeant-major protecting his sacred parade ground; but in his case wearing a uniform of black 'claw-hammer' jacket, camel waistcoat, 'dickie' bow-tie, pin-striped trousers, and highly polished, tightly laced shoes.

Constantly moving around his manor he dominated the place, appearing here there and everywhere, and all the time peeping out from a pair of dark, suspicious eyes that were deep-set beneath a patina of close-cropped shiny black hair parted severely down the middle. His sharp pointed nose, reached out overshadowing a pencil-thin waxed moustache that sniffed and snuffled ready to seek out trouble.

Small as he was, he stood out like a sore thumb, while his draconian appearance made him an obvious target for us lowly apprentices. But then again, his attitude earned him few favours. He was often brusque and ill-tempered, even to his own staff. And so it didn't take a great deal of imagination for us to dub him with the derisory nickname of Marmaduke.

Eggo, always respectably dressed for work compared to most electricians at the time, strolled into the store. The first person he bumped into was Max, standing 'four-square' by the furniture display.

'Good morning my man, may I have the pleasure of a word with a Mister Percy Fairclough,' Eggo requested in his most cultured voice.

'Most certainly Sir, come this way,' Max said, and led Eggo to the manager's plush office.

'How do you do Sir,' our hero addressed the manager. 'My name's Eggo and I'm here on behalf of Pitts Electrical Company to finish this contract in a most efficient manner, and at the same time to discipline those scallywags, who, I believe, have been making a nuisance of themselves.'

'Glad to make your acquaintance, Mister ...erm Eggo - a strange name if I may say so.' The manager paused, mildly surprised by Eggo's unusual appearance and his air of superiority. 'Out of curiosity, from which part of the globe does your clan originate?' he enquired, shaking Eggo's hand in an attempt to show he was unconcerned as to why this huge electrician was so different to the rest.

Eggo stroked his chin and after a moments silence replied. 'According to my dear old daddy, we originate from a small hamlet called Roosterville. This, I believe, is located somewhere in the lower regions of Feather Creek.

'Ah,' said Percy, impressed by what he'd heard. 'Is that in America then old boy?'

'America! It's in the deep, deep south of HENsylvania,' Eggo beamed.

Max, who'd heard this exchange, came into the room in answer to a call from his boss.

'Something tells me your troubles are only just beginning, Mister Unterlanze,' Percy told his floor manager. 'Take this gentleman downstairs to join the rest of the undesirables.'

We were made up to see Eggo when he popped his head round the door to the basement. His timing was perfect; it was breaktime.

Phil, Scullo and Arnie were sharing an ancient Victorian divan between them, Chunkie had commandeered the easy chair, and with my short legs dangling above the floor I sat on a roll of Axminster stair carpet. Tom had the best speck in our small out-of-the-way den. Sunk deep in the comfort of an old rocking chair, with one-foot on top of the other, his long legs stretching to rest on a dusty mahogany stool, he was deeply absorbed in the sports page of the Daily Herald and in his element.

An old somewhat battered table, discarded as junk by the shop management, formed the centrepiece to our den. On it we'd placed a piece of cardboard, a sort of forlorn gesture of concern for what little remained of a long-since-applied coat of beeswax polish. And on this our billy-cans and tea mugs were laid out.

After lifting an empty mug from the table Eggo swilled it out with a drop of tea from the billy-can, then topped it up and sipped a few mouthfuls of the heavy sugary brew.

'Perfect,' he said, rolling the brew round his mouth and smacking his lips as if tasting a glass of vintage wine.

'Now what have you lads been up to? Mac's had some bad reports from old Percy about you lot. And who's been a cheeky boy to Waxie Underpants? Was it you Chunkie?' he asked, leaning across me to grab Chunkie by the ear.

'Honest Eggo, you want to see the way he performs. The other day he bollocked me an' Scullo in front of everyone for nothin', just because we had some dust on our kecks an' sat on the carpet to wire a 5 amp socket.'

'Would you remove your scruffy clothes from that carpet at once,' Chunkie mimicked, in a posh accent.

'Why don't yer go an' stand in the winder, Marmaduke, like the rest of the dummies. That's all I said. There's nowt wrong with that, is there Eggo?'

'Of course not. What's the matter with the man, hasn't he got a sense of humour?'

'Sense of 'umour...you must be jokin', Tom said. 'No wonder the lads 'ave been messin' about, the way that creep follows you around. And then the cheeky bugger times yer. Just wait till you've been here a few days an' see for yourself.'

Although the work-rate did improve over the following week and things were less tense, it was the daily clashes between Eggo and Marmaduke that was the highlight for both the shop staff and the contractors alike.

'I'd be obliged if you will use the tradesman's entrance', Max replied frostily to Eggo's greeting of 'Good morning Marmaduke,'on his first full day at the store.

'Tradesman! Tradesman!' Eggo replied, with exaggerated dignity. 'I'll have you know that I am a journeyman of the highest esteem and if the front door is good enough for you, my man, then it's certainly good enough for me.'

Always ready to spring to the offensive against anyone challenging his authority Max spread his short arm across a section of the main door and growled, 'I'm not telling you. I'm ordering you to use the tradesman's entrance.'

'Steady on lad. If you don't behave yourself, I'll be obliged to go to old Percy and make a formal complaint about your attitude, Mister Underpants,' Eggo said, leaning forward and tickling the floor manager under his raised arm.

'U..N..T..E..R..L..A..N..Z..E. My name is Mister Unterlanze,' Max screamed at his tormentor.

'Fair comment my man,' Eggo replied sagely. 'But what's a little 'p' between friends. You do have a little 'p' I take it?' Eggo said.

The shop staff could be heard giggling in the background, a lack of loyalty, which proved to be the final straw for Max. After glaring in the direction of the offenders, he stomped angrily and made his way upstairs, muttering to himself. Meanwhile, not one to be flustered or upset by anything, Eggo wandered through the store singing, 'Oh what a beautiful morning, Oh what a beautiful day.'

Despite reeling from the continuous banter Eggo threw at him, the encounters between the two of them showed no sign of dropping off, as Max persisted in checking the times we commenced and hovering in the background on every job we undertook. On more than one occasion, when Max pushed him to the edge, Eggo would vow to 'fix the little bugger before the end of the contract.'

Even when the work in the furniture showroom was dwindling to a close, Max's attitude towards us never slackened or improved. Always aloof, he would swagger around with an exaggerated air of self-importance, although we felt he was definitely not as arrogant as he'd been in the past. Finally, there came a point when Eggo, believing he'd seen his opponent's moustache quiver slightly as if he was about to smile, decided now was the time to begin plotting Marmaduke's downfall. And so the big man approached Mavis, the girl in charge of the carpet section.

'What's happened to my little friend Marmaduke?' he asked Mavis, 'I'm sure he almost smiled then. He hasn't won the pools or clicked with one of the cleaners, has he?'

'You've seen nothing yet,' Mavis replied. 'Just wait 'til he starts on the window display - his party piece. You'd think the Queen was comin' the way he ponces about. So my advice to you lads – that's if you don't want to upset him - is to keep out the way an' enjoy the spectacle while it lasts.' She tittered at Eggo as he unfolded one of his many comical expressions to indicate he'd seen it all.

Watching Marmaduke direct operations from the pavement as his assistant scurried backwards and forwards inside the main shop window was a sight worth seeing. Waving his arms like a furious tick-tack man, he scratched his head with his middle finger, stroked his chin through an imaginary beard, yet still found time to prance about as if his feet were on fire. Despite the intense activity, he glowed with satisfaction, whenever the passing shoppers complimented him about the progress of the display.

Mavis was right, this was his big day, and from our lofty position on the first floor we could almost sense his relief that we weren't in the vicinity of the showroom. As Mavis said, Max enjoyed this event more than any other in his calendar, for not only did it give him the opportunity to reveal his percieved hidden talents to his staff, but also allowed him to display the latest crème-de-la-crème bedroom suite, which was always guaranteed to attract an up-market clientele. After fiddling for ages with the curtain nets, he eventually seemed satisfied that everything in the window was in pristine order, and together with Percy he left to enjoy a bite of lunch.

'He's away Eggo,' Chunkie shouted, clambering across the joists on the first floor.

'Right, one of you lads can come with men, but not you, Arnie. You'd be no use on this kind of mission.' Arnie, the same age and height as myself, was slightly bandier and walked swinging one leg in a semi-circle, with the other following in the alternative direction, leaving a barn-door gap between his knees; a phenomenon which was the subject of a number of interesting theories.

Exaggerating as usual, Eggo reckoned when Arnie was a baby and learning to walk down West Derby Road, a small pig escaped from the abattoir and shot through his legs. 'That's the reason he looks over his shoulder and rolls his legs when he walks, just in case lighting happens to strike twice,' he said.

Chunkie therefore volunteered to accompany Eggo on a mission to find and bring back one of the many stray cats living in the shadow of the Central Station. Thirty minutes later they returned, with a flea-ridden ginger moggie, which Eggo was gripping at arms length by its manky neck.

'Is the coast clear?' he whispered, creeping stealthily towards the double doors that led to the showroom.

'Yeah... there's no one around,' we answered simultaneously.

Moving briskly now, he headed inside towards the window display, quickly opening the hatch and gently tossing the straggly cat onto the silk quilt covering the bed. Within seconds we were back upstairs, gingerly making our way across the bare joists and scratching small peepholes in the whitewashed windows, waiting for Marmaduke to arrive.

As Max approached the top of Bold Street and observed the crowded pavement he could hardly control his emotions. In what was a rare moment of affectionate euphoria he placed his arm across Percy's shoulder, and yelled 'we've cracked it old boy, just look at the spectators around my window display.'

Increasing his stride with each step, he galloped breathlessly downhill like a man possessed. Reaching Waring's within seconds, the sound of uproar and raucous laughter stopped him dead in his tracks. Clawing his way through the milling crowd Max finally arrived at the front only to clock the flea-ridden moggie lying on its back with three of its paws pointing upwards. Its head was resting comfortably on the soft feathered pillow, while the fourth paw was scratching away for all it was worth at its hind quarters. Flabbergasted, and with eyes like hot coals, Eggo's antagonist glared up to the first floor, scanning the painted windows for any clue as to our whereabouts. Of course from our secret hideout we could see everything that was unfolding without any possibility of being seen ourselves. Watching Max storm angrily through the doorway of Waring's main entrance into the shop, all we could do was to hope that he wouldn't catch any of his staff enjoying the spectacle.

At that point Eggo suggested it was high time we joined the spectators on the pavement to witness Ginger's evacuation. And so we hurried downstairs, wormed our way to the front of the crowd of window-gazers and nabbed a perfect speck, just in time to see the window hatch swiftly open and the man himself poke his head through. And what a show it was, as Max leaned in with a broom handle, thrashing over and then under the bed, then behind the dressing table and into an open wardrobe as he attempted to remove the swift and reluctant cat from its luxurious new home. Along with the rest of the crowd we cheered every time he failed, with Ginger, dodging the vicious swings for what seemed like an eternity. Finally, though, the hungry moggie was coaxed from 'the good life' with a large saucer of milk.

In all fairness it didn't take Max long to recover from

his ordeal and within hours he was back at his best, his slick salesman's patter easily convincing a string of well-to-do and well-dressed customers that it would be a wise and smart move for them to purchase one of Waring's top-of- the-range beds.

As if summoned by a secret signal directing him to his quarry, Eggo would suddenly amble past as these deals progressed. 'Don't listen to him madam,' he'd mutter, 'the beds are full of bugs.'

Despite looking tired and weary, Max gave every impression of being the happiest man on the planet when our contract was eventually finshed. However, his staff didn't appear to share his new-found elation. Judging by some of their outspoken opinions it seemed they would all miss Eggo's ability for keeping Max on his toes and off their backs.

Mac, on the other hand, seemed delighted with Eggo's contribution.

'He's a character! But he gets the best out of the lads, and, he knows his job,' was how he summed it up.

Church Street drama

Compared to the weekday hustle and bustle, Saturday mornings were usually quiet. Before the jobs were distributed we'd often lounge about in the workshop being entertained by Eggo. One Saturday he was firing some basic questions on the teachings of the trade to those lads who'd assisted him in the recent past. Finding this a welcome change to the usual boring weekday mornings, the rest of the sparks relaxed, supping tea, reading the papers, and smoking cigarettes.

'Reilly! Show these gentlemen how to set a dog-leg in that length of conduit over there,' Eggo said to me. 'Come on don't be bashful lad,' he continued, as I tried to demonstrate using a piece of three-quarter inch tube - a task I subsequently cocked up.

'What's this then, a hockey stick or a shepherds crook?' he demanded, using the bent conduit to pull me playfully round the workshop by my neck.

'Right Chunkie, what size cable do we use on lighting circuits?'

'That's dead easy, the thin red stuff,' Chunks said flippantly.

The sparks laughed as Eggo slipped off his shoe, and then chased Chunkie round the workshop trying to shift the dust from his kecks.

'You're two down already Eggo,' Tom Baines chuckled.

'BONSO...' yelled the maestro. 'Come here lad and redeem my reputation. Just explain to everyone the theory of a star-delta motor. Go on lad show them.'

'Ar hey Eggo, that's not fair,' Bonso moaned. 'I'm only just learnin' that at night school. Go on then, gis a clue,' he pleaded, as Eggo walked towards him ready to grip his substantial sideburns and lead him on tip-toe to the corner of the room.

'What's Eggo's signature tune, Bonso?'

Bonso yelled. 'Whenever you're in doubt, don't forget to shout 'EGGO' and he will sort it out.'

'Well done lad,' he said, leaning over Bonso's shoulder planting a sloppy kiss on the apprentice's cheek, an act that earned the spontaneous applause of an appreciative audience. The exception, of course, was Snypy, who turned to Freddy Focus and muttered, 'he's bloody barmy. No wonder the lads are always messin' about. Mac wants ter get shut of 'im before he has everyone as daft as 'imself.'

Continuing the play-acting, Eggo asked Arnie to fetch the dunce's cap, a cone-shaped hat made from thin cardboard that was used to protect the cable around the drums. Eggo then circled the weary apprentices, clutching the ignominious object in his outstretched hands, and to the delight of almost everyone, he plonked it fairly and squarely on Bonso's head, proclaiming him to be 'Dunce of the Week.'

With the hilarity running at full swing, no one noticed Mac standing by the door, until he coughed. Trembling with fright at this sudden appearance, Snypy scrambled to his feet and in his haste knocked over a billy-can with his elbow, covering young Burkey with the dregs of the cold tea.

'Ah, so we're havin' an assessment of the apprentices, Mister Aigberth. D'yer mind tellin' me how they're goin' on?'

'Very well indeed Mac. Bonso's just trying the hat for size, that's all. Just in case he falls by the wayside before my next examination,' he added quickly.

'Is that so? Well I've got a better idea. He can assist Ted on a nice little job in the abattoir and Ted will make sure he doesn't fall by the wayside, won't you Ted?'

'I certainly will Mac,' Ted grovelled. 'Come with me you big long streak, and get that daft hat off yer head before you smother that pea of a brain altogether,' he ordered.

No one dared look as Bonso trudged from the workshop for fear of laughing.

'Eggo,' Mac turned back to our mentor, 'there's a neon sign needs installing in Church Street, so take the big ladder, an' Reilly and Arnie to foot it. I think they'll just about manage that between them,' he added sarcastically

Like three window cleaners with a ladder and no bucket we set off down Duke Street heading for a town centre, packed with morning shoppers. Forging ahead Eggo cleared all in his wake, trading insults, as only he was capable of, while we trundled behind humping the large ladder.

'Right lads,' he yelled suddenly, 'this'll do. Let's get this show on the road.'

Dropping his toolbox on some office steps, he ambled out into the middle of Church Street waving his arms at the oncoming traffic until he was satisfied all the vehicles were more or less stationary. After checking with us that the base of the ladder was propped against the kerbstone, and that we were footing it properly, he gripped the rung at the top end and slowly walked towards us.

As the Eggo road show began, the waiting passengers at a bus stop, just yards from our new workplace, couldn't have been better positioned.

'Good morning folks, don't walk under the ladder or it's seven years bad luck. You've been warned,' he said, winking at two teenage girls at the front of the queue.

Taking a pair of pliers and a couple of screwdrivers from his toolbox, he bent over and rubbed them across the seat of his pants. Then, slipping off his jacket he rolled up his sleeves, flexed his biceps and completed the warm-up by dropping flat to do a couple of press-ups, before finishing off by leaping up again then touching his toes a half dozen times.

The performance brought a snigger from one of the girls who said, 'the state of 'im an' the price of fish.

Who d'yer reckon he is?' she asked her friend.

'Definitely not Charles Atlas, that's for sure.'

'Maybe he is a Charles - but more like Charlie Chan,' the first one remarked, a typical scouser and quick with the lip.

Discretely ignoring their cheeky comments, Eggo sprang like a monkey up the ladder three rungs at a time, his weight causing it to bow in the middle. At this point, and without warning, he gave it such a violent shake that Arnie and I struggled to stop it crashing to the ground.

As more people joined the bus queue Eggo began acting like a jack-in the-box, bouncing up and down apparently deaf to our cries and yells for him to take it easy.

'He's goin' ter fall off the way 'es carryin' on,' a grey haired pensioner said, fearing the consequences.

I wouldn't go near that for a big clock,' his companion replied. 'Have yer seen the size of those two poor lads havin' ter 'old that big ladder, with 'im prancin' about? It's criminil if yer ask me.'

The passengers waiting at the bus stop were engrossed in the drama unfolding before their eyes and a growing number of curious pedestrians also stopped to stare. Just then Eggo let out a blood curdling scream, startling everyone, including us, so we gripped the ladder for all our worth.

'HELP...HELP...HELP...PLEASE HELP ME,' he bawled at the top of his voice, hanging on to the ladder by an arm and one leg, his face twisted as though tormented and in agony. This had a dramatic effect on the bystanders and within seconds, heavily laden shopping bags were placed on the pavement as complete strangers discussed the mental state of the unfortunate fella stuck in the air; as well as the plight of me and Arnie hanging like grim death to the base of the twisting ladder.

At this point, a slightly built, elderly man, dressed like a teenager in a single breasted Italian suit, winkle picker shoes, gold chain draped across a velvet waistcoat, and with a deaf aid above a reddened ear lobe, approached the scene. Clutching his arm as if the wind would blow him away at any moment was a lady of heavy stature. After observing the drama with mild curiosity for a moment, it seemed the man wasn't at all sure that he was witnessing real or crocodile tears from the bold Eggo. But then for some reason his attention was drawn to the two of us struggling below with the ladder.

It transpired he'd been a man of action, albeit in younger days, and that a flicker of a 'devil-may-care' attitude still remained within, as he swiftly discarded his wife's resting arm and disappeared like a ferret into the mass of crowded bodies, emerging seconds later at the foot of the ladder.

'Move over lads,' he said, leaping onto the bottom rung of the ladder, 'I'll gerr 'im down.'

A young stocky built man passing by jokingly intervened, 'come on dad, get down off there, you're goin' ter strain yer braces an' hurt yourself if you don't watch out.'

'I was in the parra's, so heights don't bother me son,' replied our dapper veteran.

'I didn't know they 'ad aereegogs in the first world war, dad,' the youth continued to taunt him.

'Tell 'im Mary. Tell 'im what mob I was in. Go on, tell 'im,' the action man protested from his perch on the bottom rungs.

But she was not inclined to lend her support. 'Come on Joe, get down off there,' she urged her elderly spouse. 'The lad's right, you're likely to fall an' 'urt yourself. And besides you 'avent changed your John L's.'

Despite what was sound advice, the old man stubbornly refused to move from the second rung. Then Eggo suddenly shrieked out at the top of his voice. 'SOMEBODY'S STOLE ME WIFE.'... SOMEBODY'S STOLE MY WIFE.'

'Ah! It's a bloody shame, no wonder the poor fella's demented,' a red-faced woman commented.

'I know exactly how he feels,' another bystander added. 'Me own lad's wife buggered off with a baldy 'eaded cowboy from the sausage factory, an' he nearly went doo-lal-ly. D'yer know he couldn't even look at a sausage for nearly twelve months without burstin' out cryin'. That's what that cow an' a half did to my poor Timmy. I'd 'ave killed her with me bare 'ands if I could 'ave got 'old of her.'

Italian Joe cocked his good ear towards the crowd. 'What was that?' he asked, looking up at Eggo clinging, some twenty foot above him.

'Someone's stole 'is wife,' the crowd replied in chorus

'An' he's complainin'? If someone stole my judy - and I know there's no chance - but if by some miracle they did, well I wouldn't be hangin' from a ladder. I'd be dancin' on the tables in Yates wine lodge,' he told the crowd, oblivious to the angry stares of his wife. Just then Eggo let out another blood-curdling shriek. 'HELP...HELP...HELP!'

'Somebody should go and fetch a bobby or ring for the fire brigade,' a smartly dressed lady said, looking pointedly at a middle-aged individual who seemed enthralled by the on-going drama.

'No chance missus,' he responded, declining to take the hint. 'I'm not losin' me speck in the queue for 'im. If he wants ter fall, lerr 'im. That's my opinion for what it's worth.'

'Oh my God, don't say that,' cried a sympathetic soul. 'I wunder if he's a Ca'hlic', she added, grasping at a gold crucifix drooping from her neck, and at the same time blessing herself.

At this point all went quiet, as Eggo - still twenty feet from the ground - turned and gazed solemnly at the crowd.

'He's not goin' ter jump is he?' the red-faced woman asked no-one in particular, holding her hand across her mouth.

'Shush,' someone else urged the onlookers. 'He's tryin' to say somethin'.'

'Ladies and gentlemen,' Eggo stammered, 'somebody's stole MY WIFE.'

An eerie atmosphere prevailed. The bystanders stared upwards, some showing the utmost pity for the poor fella stranded on the ladder.

'SOMEBODY'S STOLE MY WIFE,' he yelled, and then bawled even louder. 'THE HORSE THIEF...THE BLOODY HORSE THIEF.'

There was stunned silence for a few seconds before the crowd erupted.

'He's a ruddy crackpot! Fancy him aggravatin' all these people with antics like that. They want ter lock 'im up an' throw away the key,' one irate pensioner ranted.

'It's not right, is it? There's us feelin' sorry fer 'im, an' he's just larkin' about like a soft schoolboy.' a middle age woman complained.

Eventually Italian Joe got the message, stepped off the ladder and glared ferociously up at Eggo. 'Get yourself down 'ere like a man an' I'll knock your bloody block off.'

We tried not to snigger as the crowd drifted away. Those in the bus queue continued to discuss the antics of the looney who created mayhem in a Saturday morning trip to town, until, eventually, a bus arrived. And after it departed, Eggo descended the ladder looking quite pleased with himself.

'I caught that lot dead easily, didn't I? Did you enjoy the performance boys?'

'Yeah, it was a good while it lasted,' we said, laughing loudly now that everyone had gone.

'I think we'll have to consider putting on the show at that little job we've got in Brownlow Hill next week.'

The young fella who earlier had slagged off Italian Joe stepped out from an adjacent doorway. 'Brownlow Hill!' he said. 'You mean the mental home in Rainhill don't yer pal?'

Suspension

The furthest from base and the largest project Pitts had ever been involved in was located in Bootle, just north of the city. It was the kind of job that was completed in stages and at one time or another most of the sparks worked on it. Situated close to the docks, the site provided little or no protection from the Mersey's cruel wind, especially in winter when the blast howled in from the river, tossing clouds of dust and sand into open doorways and the roofless buildings.

Days on end passed slowly, because of the inclement weather, particularly when the main trades - the brickies and joiners - were rained off. Yet, despite these stop-start conditions, Pitts were legally bound by contract to maintain a presence on site. So from early December, Eggo, Ronnie Ching and I had been based there with strict instructions from Mac to stay ahead of the other trades at all costs.

For security reasons a high wire perimeter fence safeguarded the site from intruders, with the main entrance as the only access point. Just inside the gate, a compound housing a cluster of individual cabins contained a labour force of bricklayers, joiners, plumbers, painters, and of course the main offices for the management team. For some unknown reason, the electricians did not merit inclusion amongst their fellow tradesmen, but were treated like some breed of contagious aliens, isolated on the far side of the perimeter fence.

Our cabin, painted a glowing red, was covered with indentations and large muddy blotches on one side, evidence of a primitive alarm system which involved the hurling of mud and stones to warn the inhabitants of impending danger, such as the sudden appearance of the higher management.

Above the roof of our den a battered white ensign borrowed on the QT from an old tramp steamer berthed in the docks, showed the flag for the electricians. Nailed to a rough length of timber this emblem of our presence was always in one of two states - either it flapped like a demented demon, or drooped like one of my old footy socks that had been too long in the wash.

The most significant feature to our shack, however, was a

mahogany cross, a priceless work of art, prominently displayed above the doorway. This unusual artefact had the inscription, *'Here the weary are at rest,'* in Gothic lettering, which had been created by our joinery and painting fraternity.

'Mornin' Eggo, what's up? Have you done your back in again? No, let me guess. You've dropped a thrippeny joey an' its rolled under the cabin.' The site agent was being his usual droll and ironic self as Eggo was caught out again, ducking beneath the timekeeper's window at twenty past eight.

'No Tom, you've got it wrong. I was just checkin' to see if the Crisis Management Team were on their toes for a change, that's all.'

Ignoring Eggo's contemptuous reply, the agent merely continued giving his orders for the day.

'Seein' half the mornin's gone already, you'd better get those lads of yours out on the job…pronto. 'Cos if you're holdin' my brickies up, I'll personally be after your scalp. And I'm a mean bastard if anyone gets up my nostrils, even if I say it myself.'

On his guard as usual, Eggo refused to take the bait and swop insults, or to comment on the size of Tom's nostrils, which the brickies reckoned were similar to the tunnels leading into James Street station. One had described him as the "Mobile nose" or "Pinocchio" - but always behind his back, of course.

'Don't worry Tom, everything's in hand,' Eggo replied calmly, the boys will have my tools dancin' and under starters orders as soon as I open the trap door. And by the end of the mornin' we'll be so far in front of the brickies and chippies, you'll have to throw on the weekends 'til Easter to catch up with us.'

'I've 'eard ducks fart before,' Tom replied bluntly.

The timekeeper, who'd been watching and listening to the conversation, laughed as Eggo waddled away, quacking from the side of his mouth.

'If ever there was a candidate for the loony bin, you're looking at him there, Tom,' he said.

It was a cushy existence for us. We learnt little about the trade but spent hours performing menial tasks, such as making tea by the gallon, running to the Dock Road for bacon butties, reading the newspapers, and dozing off - a subject which was far and away Eggo's favourite pastime.

As time passed by, we drifted into a routine of clambering outside between the showers to do a spot of work, and then returning to the warmth of the cabin and loafing about. The daily pattern of being rained-off and lolling about waiting for the weather to break continued right across January, February and March; and then disaster struck.

One morning after scanning everything of interest in the newspaper, cracking the crossword puzzle, and devouring a bacon buttie dripping with his favourite brown sauce, Eggo - now seemingly content with life - announced, 'it's time for a session of Egyptian P.E. lads. You know the score. I'm just goin' to have a cat nap, so keep your dogs open and don't forget to bark like bull-terriers if the enemy appears.'

Flicking off his shoes he then climbed onto the desk, folded a couple of donkey jackets for a pillow and within seconds was snoring contentedly.

'I'm a bit knackered me'self,' Chingy said, stretching out on the wooden bench beneath the desk. After reading the sports pages and the columns about our local teams he crashed out on the other bench. The rhythmic patter of the rain echoing from the wooden roof and splattering against the window was like a lullaby, and before long I too had drifted off into the land of nod.

I wasn't sure how long I'd been asleep when the unmistakable sound of pebbles rattling against the side of the cabin woke me with a start. Hearing the sounds of shuffling footsteps and chattering voices, I scrambled to my feet as someone rattled on the door with a heavy object. Creeping surreptitiously forwards I bent down, covered one eye with my hand and squinted through the peephole. Apart from the site agent, I clocked four bowler-hatted, black-crombied sombre-looking individuals.

'EGGO, EGGO, wake up, wake up,' I hissed in his ear, shaking him violently by the shoulder.

'What's up? What's all the panic about, Reilly?' he mumbled flinging his long legs from the desk, only just avoiding Chingie's head.

'The gaffers are outside,' I whispered, my voice crackling with fear.

RAT-TAT-TAT. The door shook; the handle turned and failed to lift the latch. Eggo smiled and raised his thumb.

'Come on Eggo, open up. We know you're in there.' Tom yelled.

With sleep in his eyes, his hair standing on end and yawning, Eggo slowly opened the door.

'Good afternoon gentlemen, James Aigberth, Electrical Supervisor at your disposal.'

Before they could move or speak, Eggo took control. Slipping his hand to his trousers he undid his flies, pulled out his plonker and began urinating into a puddle just yards from the cabin step. As if it was the most natural thing in the world he raised the spray angle to waist height, then, like a hosepipe, began swishing in a semi-circle, trying to pee as far as he could, as the entourage shot backwards. Tom stared open-mouthed in disbelief.

Satisfied that his bladder was now empty, Eggo carefully shook off the final drops, then slipped his plonker back into his trousers.

'Come on lads,' he said, turning to us inside the hut. 'Can't you see we've got visitors? Look snappy an' get the brew on.'

The workers on the site and those who'd thrown the pebbles as warning shots, stood around laughing, while Tom and the bowler-hat quartet, their shoulders bowed, trooped off despondently, to the sanctity of the offices. An hour later Mac arrived, seething with anger, his face as black as thunder

'What the bleedin' 'ell's been goin' on?' he demanded. 'Don't you know who those four gentlemen are?'

'Haven't a clue,' Eggo said. 'But I know they weren't sparks lookin' for a bend, 'cos they didn't even bother waitin' for a brew.'

'Christ Eggo! Can't you be serious for once in your life,' Mac replied, calmer now, as if suddenly remembering his high blood pressure. 'Well, I'm sorry to say,' he continued, 'that those four were directors of the firm, and they've told me to finish you up.'

'Can't they take a joke?' Eggo said, showing no signs of alarm at the news. 'Anyway, don't worry about it Mac, I've been sacked by worse firms than Pitts. But not many mind you.'

'I've also been instructed to suspend you two lads for a fortnight,' Mac said, nodding at Chingie and me. 'That's what the powers to be have said, an' I can't do a thing about it, worse luck.' We knew by Mac's doleful expression he was sincere in his sentiments.

After Eggo locked the cabin for the last time, we trudged through the site carrying his toolbox stopping briefly outside the compound. With one hand behind his back and the other raised in a fisted salute, he gestured triumphantly, appreciating the vociferous send off from lads who'd congregated outside their individual cabins.

The Artful Dodger

On the first day of my suspension it felt strange going through the rigmarole of pretending it was a normal Monday morning, which, of course, it wasn't. Taking more interest than usual in dad's movements, I timed my departure to coincide with him swilling his face under the spray of cold water from our one source of supply, the brass tap attached to the lead pipe hanging over the kitchen sink. Stepping outside I instinctively glanced up at the town hall clock. It just was approaching seven fifteen, and within seconds I heard it chime the quarter hour. The next step of my plan was easy. Confident I was in control of matters, I hurried along the street like a fugitive on the run and before you could say Jack Robinson, I'd blended into the shadows of Jenkins factory doorway.

At half seven, as expected, dad shuffled out of our house. From my darkened vantage point in the doorway I followed his movements until he disappeared among the ranks of chattering dockers, their echoing footsteps bringing a touch of life to the otherwise empty streets. Patiently I waited for the tell-tale shrill of the ships' sirens heralding it was now eight o'clock. Then, confident that the last of the stragglers would have reached the dock gates, I dashed through the Court, shot down the jigger and sneaked into the back kitchen. Mam didn't look up; she was flannelling our Tommy's face, while Bernadette, the only other family member present, sat alone at the table munching her cornflakes.

'You should 'ave told your dad son. You know worr he's like if you're not straight with him,' mam said, after the kids were safely off to school.

'Mam, he'd 'ave gone off like a bottle of pop and then blamed me. You know that.'

'Maybe you'd 'ave been better off saying you weren't well then.'

'What? You're kiddin'. There's no way he'd wear that one. You've got to be dying before he'd take any notice.' Without a clear and visible sign of serious injury it was impossible to use such an excuse. Dad was one of those people who classed everyone who took time off with a minor ailment as being a useless malingerer.

Saving my neck thus became a number one priority and keeping out of his way and relying on an element of luck seemed to be the best way of handling the situation. Knowing dad the way that I did, he would have taken my suspension as being slur on his good name; and of course, not showing respect for your elders or your employer, and displaying a lack of discipline, were all actions his authoritative nature would just not tolerate.

Keeping out of his way was easy on the first three days, but on Thursday my lackadaisical attitude almost landed me in hot water when he arrived home at three o'clock instead of half seven, announcing to mam that he was starting night shift that same evening.

After that it became a battle of wits, and I spent most of my time either crossing the river on the ferry, loitering round town, or popping in to visit relatives and friends, keeping one step ahead of dad. Of course I could read him like a book. He only wanted the best for us, with hard work, good time keeping and strict discipline being high on the agenda for success; almost the opposite to my way of thinking and operating.

In complete contrast to my own educational efforts, Our Bridie had done exceptionally well with her exams. She was now studying at a teachers training college, and Dad was delighted and intensely proud of her. He himself had had little or no schooling, and following a near fatal accident on the docks in 1951, he'd been disabled with one leg slightly shorter than the other, a handicap that caused him to limp quite distinctly. And though I knew he was often in pain, he never moaned.

'It's no good complaining,' he'd say 'there's people far worse off than me. And who'd want to listen to you anyway?'

Towards the end of my suspension I sat on a bollard gazing across the river. For some reason or other I was thinking about my twelve months at Pitts, and what I'd learnt during that period. Using the fingers on one hand, I counted every contract I'd worked on, and the type of installation each of these had involved. Most jobs necessitated the bending and threading of conduit, checking for sharp edges, and remembering the size of cables used for lighting and for plugs, all critical points that I'd managed to fix in my mind.

I then began to recall simple things such as how to use a chalk line; how to bore holes with a Rawlplug tool, how to fix saddles properly without forgetting the names of materials or the tools - activities which were all part and parcel of an apprentices first year tasks. But then my mind went blank and I realised that without needing to use the fingers on my other hand, maybe I hadn't learned as much as I should have done about the trade.

Then again, I reasoned, I must have learnt something. Perhaps I was more streetwise now, there was no denying I'd done more enough ear-wigging when the sparks and older lads were deep in conversation, listening to tales of experiences that were often a puzzle and usually way beyond my knowledge. And another thing, to my amazement I'd grown two and a bit inches, which I knew had nothing to do with work. This had been achieved by conscientiously following mam's instructions to keep my legs stretched out full-length in bed at night-time, no easy task with our Tommy kipping at the bottom.

On the Thursday night after dad had gone to work Chunkie called with an urgent message from Eggo. He didn't know why, or so he said, but from what he was led to believe, it seemed it would be in my interest to see Eggo next day at the Pier Head.

Spot on two o'clock, I waited, wondering what was so important to warrant a meeting at such short notice. While I waited for him to arrive, with my attention focused on a crowded ferryboat trying to manoeuvre into position on the landing stage I failed to see or hear Eggo approach.

'REILLY,' he yelled down my ear. I almost jumped into the river in fright. Standing besides the great man was Robbie Ching, laughing his socks off at my reaction. After wandering along the waterfront we eventually found a wooden bench that some old tramp had just vacated.

'Right boys, let's park our arses here an' get straight to the point,' Eggo said. 'First of all, how do you two lads fancy workin' for a proper firm for a change?'

'Where abouts?' I asked.

'Capenhurst,' he said. 'I started last week. It's a good little number, better money, and with knowing the right people I can get you both fixed up on Monday if you fancy it. It's up to you lads, how does it sound?'

- 58 -

We were stunned.

'It's a great opportunity, think about it,' he continued.

I didn't need to give it much thought; I just couldn't believe my luck. It was a perfect opening for me and Dad need never know I'd changed firms. Working at Capenhurst would be just like any other contract to him. My mind was made up at once.

After jotting down transport details on the back of a fag packet, I arranged to meet Eggo on the Capenhurst site at eight o'clock on Monday morning.

Robbie, though, was unusually quiet; as if struggling to make up his mind. With his family having a restaurant business they relied on him to help out at night-time when the café was busy. His job for Pitts was convenient; therefore I wasn't surprised to hear him eventually 'knock back' Eggo's offer.

Pastures new

Over that particular weekend I was like a cat on a hot tin roof, and at one stage felt tempted to tell dad about my decision to move on; but the more I thought of the consequences the less inclined I became. He was still working nightshift, so as far as I was concerned it just wouldn't have been the right time to give him that sort of news. And to be honest this suited me fine.

Monday morning arrived and I was up bright and early, bursting with enthusiasm, relishing the prospects of working for N.G. Bailey, one of the biggest electrical contractors in the country. The site, a nuclear power station was situated in the village of Capenhurst on the outskirts of Chester and was reputed to employ over six hundred contractors.

The underground electric train from Liverpool Central to the other side of the Mersey called at James Street, Hamilton Square, Birkenhead Central, Green Lane and Rock Ferry - the end of the line. Passengers travelling further a field to Hooton, Capenhurst and Chester then had to cross an unmanned bridge to board the steam train waiting on an adjacent line.

I joined the train at Hamilton Square and somehow managed to squeeze into a carriage crammed with contractors and shipyard workers. At Green Lane, the main station for Cammel Laird's, the lads working down the yard disembarked, but this still left a fair number of contractors on board. At Rock Ferry we all left the train and I was virtually carried along with the masses up and over the bridge, and then hustled into a front carriage of the steamer, where as luck would have it I landed a seat by the window. This slice of good fortune not only enabled me to keep an eye on the relevant landmarks for my return trip from this journey into the unknown, but also to enjoy the open countryside during the ten mile ride.

I was sitting dreaming away, happy as Larry, when a strange thing occurred. As we passed through Ledsham, the penultimate station before 'the Cape,' a huge contractor with a Desperate Dan chin, leaned his heavy bulky body across me, slid the window open, then stuck his head out and yelled back into the compartment, 'all clear lads, no coppers this mornin'.'

This message was relayed from carriage to carriage, followed by the sound of the train windows being slammed shut.

Seconds later I heard a couple of sharp piercing hoots, followed by an easing of pressure. The train then chugged slowly into Capenhurst station, eventually stopping beside a bleak looking platform. Although my compartment emptied far quicker than I expected, I didn't join the rush; I remained by the open door instead, fascinated at what I can only describe as being like a football type crowd advancing menacingly on the two ticket collectors manning the barrier.

As the mob approached someone yelled out and suddenly a stampede seemed to take place. Those nearest the front were pushed straight through the checkpoint, as a welter of old tickets, stale butties, empty cigarette packets and other useless bits of cardboard were thrust into the open hands of the unfortunate pair. Out-numbered by the sheer volume of bodies, the two railway employees retreated behind protective railings out of harms way, and only re-appeared to deal with the stragglers, mainly consisting of us new-starts.

Once outside the station I ambled towards a heavily patrolled gate, encircled by a combination of meshed fencing and barbed wire. It reminded me of a prisoner of war film that I'd seen recently called 'Stalag 17.' After collecting my pass from a cheerful sentry guarding the gatehouse, I entered the site feeling no urge to escape from what seemed to be a remarkably similar environment to the one I'd seen at the Gaumont.

Keeping a short distance behind my fellow workers I passed cooling towers on my right, massive tin-clad buildings on the left and open fields surrounding the boundaries. In the distance I could make out a cluster of cabins to which everyone seemed to be heading. At the end of the road I stopped dead, intrigued by the sheer number of shacks and double-decker pre-fabricated offices, wondering where, in this intricate maize, I'd find Eggo.

An old fella balancing a number of steaming hot billy-cans on a piece of pipe dawdled past and asked me which firm I was looking for.

'N.G Bailey's,' I replied.

'Come wi' me lad, an' I'll show you where they 'ang out,' he said, and led me between two large shacks situated on either side of a cable compound. A few yards further on I noticed a clocking-on area where a number of darkened figures swanned around, pushing and jostling each other as they sought to sign in for the day.

'Try that cabin, lad,' my companion said, pointing in the direction of a greyish hut covered with a corrugated roof. As I turned towards it I heard Eggo's unmistakable voice.

'Reilly, where've you been lad?' he bawled. 'I've had Robin Wood, General Custard and old Uncle Tom Cobblers an' all out searching for you. Don't tell me you got lost just walking this far from the station, you young scallywag,' and he grabbed me in a head-lock and frog-marched me towards a small brick building where he rattled the door with the toe-end of his boot.

'This is Jimmy Reilly, the apprentice starting this morning Bill,' he yelled, 'and as you can see he's a real handful, so watch him. You've been warned,' he added, shoving me into a well-illuminated office.

'Leave 'im with me,' a glum looking individual replied, momentarily lifting his head from a daily newspaper, and then dropping it again as if the effort was too much for his oversize neck. He was alone in the office, and I glanced curiously over his shoulder at a plaque on his desk that showed I was standing before 'Bill Wanton, Senior Timekeeper.' Taking even greater liberties, I cast an eye over Bill's profile, noting his long drooping jowls, a heavily burdened belly, and - what I thought most unusual for a man of his enormous size - he was wearing the tiniest pair of pointed shoes. Later I was to learn that certain individuals called him 'prune features' or 'the constipated ballerina.'

It seemed ages waiting for Bill to finish reading his newspaper, but just as I was about to throw in the towel he turned to me, lifted his pen and began taking details of my date of birth, my address, and previous employment. I was then taken into an adjacent office to meet the boss, a red-haired, stockily built Yorkshireman, who let me know in no uncertain terms just what Bailey's expected of their apprentices, emphasising that poor results at night school would not be tolerated under any circumstances. Then, as he glanced at my crumpled application form, I detected a glimmer of a smile playing across what were otherwise seemingly humourless lips.

'So you've been working for The Pitts, eh lad? With a name like that, it's got to be a bloody cowboy outfit. What do you reckon Alf?' he said, turning to his general foreman who was propped on a high stool, sipping tea from a mug almost the size of a chamber pot.

'Never 'eard of 'em. They're a new one on me Red. But one thing's for sure, you can't get much lower than The Pitts, can yer?' he roared, chuckling at his own wit.

'What did they teach you, apart from chasing mice under floorboards lad?' the agent enquired teasingly. 'I hope you didn't get your head down while you were under those floorboards,' he continued, winking at his foreman.

Unsure as to whether he was joking or being serious, I took the easy way out of the situation by glancing at the floor.

'Well, there'll be no kipping or dossing under the deck on this job, will there Alf?'

'Not bloody likely,' Alf replied fiercely, but with a strange look. Later I was told that Red was perhaps hinting at a situation which had occurred just the previous week, when a cockney on nightshift had been discovered fast asleep beneath some checker plates at two o'clock in the morning.

'Have you come here to die?' Red had asked the startled culprit.

'No I came yesterdie,' the cockney had said affably: a reply which had stunned Rod into silence. The agent, caught in something of a dilemma, was not at all sure if this was a case of a smart-arse response from an uppity cockney who needed to be put in his place, or simply the result of a regional dialect misunderstanding.

Shortly after a couple of shop stewards became involved, suggesting all sorts of reasonable excuses as to why their colleague should have been under the deck in the first place, and not at his allocated job. They'd even come up with the far-fetched notion that it was possible some rust had blown into his eyes and, to ease the pain from the glare of the overhead lights, he'd clambered beneath the deck.

'And where did the rust come from?' Red had bellowed at the hapless stewards, 'from scratchin' his head?'

'Be careful Red, no defamation of character,' the senior steward responded swiftly.

'No, you be careful,' Red growled as he moved onto the attack. 'And get all the facts before you come barging in here. Y'see he may've had rust under his exposed big toe nail for all I care, but what I will say, the stench from his socks would've made mustard gas smell like lavender water.'

'Are you sayin' he had his shoes off?' the two champions of the working man had asked, somewhat less sure of themselves because of the revelation.

'Shoes off! He was so cosy all he needed was a pair of striped pyjamas and I'd have tucked him in myself. That's if there'd have been a bloody gas mask available.'

'This is all news to us,' the younger of the pair said, shrugging his shoulders and nudging his comrade towards the door muttering, 'we're onto a loser this time Frank.'

'Some you win. Some you lose. That's the name of the game, lads,' Red had replied, a triumphant gleam lighting his face as the two men scuttled from his office.

My proper trade education began at the Cape where any similarities between the teachings of my last employer and my present could only be described as being poles apart. Bailey's site organisation was enormous with a ranking that ran from Site Agent, General foreman, foremen, chargehands, tradesmen, mates, and finally the apprentices - who, even at this lower level, were in five ranked divisions. For me then there was only one way to go; or so I hoped.

My first task on that first day was to report to the chargehand's cabin. As I waited for instructions as to which squad I'd be delegated, it was suggested that Mervyn Griffiths, an older lad from across the border in North Wales, would show me the ropes by familiarising me with all the places and areas of importance.

'You'll be alright here boyo, there's nowt to worry about on this job,' he confidently predicted; and to be truthful I felt more than reassured by his friendly attitude.

'There's the main stores on your left Jimmy, and see that muddy path?' he pointed towards a track that disappeared over a small hill. 'That's where the bogs are.'

Lifting his sleeve with great deliberation to check the time he revealed an expensive looking watch. When he caught the surprised look on my face, he removed the flashy timepiece to show me the inscription which read 'M.Griffiths, Wales Schoolboys. 1951.'

I was more than impressed, even though Mervyn played down his obvious ability by telling me there were much better players on site than him.

'Come on Jim,' he said moving on, 'I'll show you where we have a good laugh every Monday morning when there's a full house.' He then led me behind a building to a fenced enclosure on the far side of the bogs, where, after lifting the bottom section of mesh, we were able to crawl inside.

Smiling in anticipating of what lay ahead, Mervyn removed a tarpaulin sheet covering a huge half pipe which had running water gushing its way through to the bogs. He then slid his hand under a couple of moss covered scaffolding planks, grabbing a handful of rags which he then dosed with paraffin and thick oil from a couple of cans hidden nearby.

'Watch this,' he said, striking a match on a sandstone block and touching the rags, which immediately burst into flame. Using two pieces of heavy wire he then lifted the blazing balls and dropped them into the flowing torrent in the pipe.

'Quick let's get out of here and watch the fun,' he yelled, taking off like an Olympic sprinter and darting to a position on the far side of the bogs. Although my legs were half the size of his, I was never more than a yard behind during the hundred-yard dash. Reaching a position of safety we watched breathlessly as the doors flew open and the traps discarded the outraged occupants, most with their kecks round their ankles and all screaming obscenities.

'Not bad for this time of the morning,' Mervyn whispered, looking quite pleased with the result.

Needless to say we took the longest route back to the compound to avoid the unfortunate victims, who were mostly rough, tough and uncompromising navvies.

The raid

It didn't take long to attune with an organised regime of clocking on and off, reporting to chargehands for jobs, and going to the stores for materials. Unlike other sites, the apprentices here weren't allowed to make tea, or run for sandwiches to the canteen. These were tasks carried out by older men called 'Peggies,' or in some cases 'Can lads.'

Apart from learning my trade, the most enjoyable time of the day was listening to the banter in cabins, or wherever we managed to find a speck to have our meal breaks. Many of the sarcastic comments aimed at the chargehands calling out 'time up lads,' I found amusing, while the abundance of mickey-takers were something else. From this cavalcade of information coming at me from every quarter I was probably most fond of the tales and blarney pouring from the jokers and storytellers. Fortunately, every cabin seemed to be blessed with a number of these individuals.

Sitting opposite to me in my newly established speck in the cabin one dinner break, a weather-beaten sparks mate called Flatfoot Sam was tucking into his sandwiches. On more than one occasion I'd noticed him travelling in the same carriage as me on the steamer, but I didn't know him well enough to speak to. Now, I decided, was perhaps the time to pick his brains, for despite the opening and closing of the train windows leading to the final rush at the ticket collectors, I still hadn't fathomed out what was to be gained by this sort of manoeuvre.

'Oh, you mean the Jekyll and Hyde's, or I should say the

'snides,' he answered in response to my questions.

'Snides? What d'yer mean like?'

At that moment I was unaware that a number of those sitting at the adjacent tables reading their papers seemed to lose interest in the news, and had suddenly become fascinated by our conversation. Apparently it was rumoured he would occasionally join the ranks of the minority of offenders he was about to defend or condemn, and naturally, they waited for Sam's explanation.

'It's like this Jim,' Sam began to explain, taking the role of Devils advocate. 'Some of the lads startin' here have been out of work for ages, with no dough comin' in at all. So when they get a fix out in the wilds - like this place - they try to get here the cheapest way possible. D'yer see?'

'That's no excuse,' someone shouted from further down the cabin. 'We 'ave to pay our way, so why shouldn't they?'

'Too bloody tight to dip into their pockets, more likely' another commented.

Realising I was still confused and ignoring these challenging remarks, Sam continued.

'What they do lad, is catch the train at Central, or James Street, or even Hamilton Square, and buy a return to the next stop, but then stay on it 'til Rock Ferry. Once they're over the bridge they sit tight on the steamer until it reaches the Cape. Then it's the Charge of the Light Brigade at the ticket collectors, who don't want any hassle, not on the cash they're on; so naturally, they take the easy way out an' throw in the towel. It's as easy as that lad.'

'Well, if it's that easy, why doesn't everyone jump on the band wagon?' I asked.

Some of those waiting to hear Sam's explanation were curious to see if he'd admit to being an occasional 'snide' himself, but he was much too sharp to fall at that hurdle.

'Ah! but there's a catch son. Every now an' again a charra load of cops come up from Ellesmere Port to man the gates. When that 'appens it's like Fred Karno's circus out there, isn't it lads?' he asked, seeking the support of his attentive audience.

'More like the Keystone Cops, as you should know,' one of the mates added hastily.

'But what 'appens then?' I enquired.

'There's no point in me describing it to you son, it's best you see for yourself. But make sure you 'ave a genuine ticket on yer, otherwise you won't be finishing your time here - you'll be doin' it somewhere not half as cushy as this place.'

Having learned about the railway fiddle from Sam, the thought of taking a chance often crossed my mind. Just thinking of the savings I'd make from my expenses meant that temptation was constantly with me. A week or two later on a Monday morning, just as I was about to purchase a 'snide' ticket to Green Lane, for some extraordinary reason I pictured Dad opening our front door to a large, burly policeman. This vision, or premonition, or what ever you could call it, was more than enough to change my mind.

As it was, all went well on the journey to the Cape. It was typical day. Some of the younger contractors played cards, the boozers slept and snored, others read their newspapers, and a hundred and one voices competed with one another, all talking at the same time. Dead on time as the train chugged its way out of Ledsham, the usual crowd stood up ready to drop the windows; when without warning, three sharp blasts instead of the customary two rang out from the vicinity of the engine. This had a devastating effect on those who'd lurched to their feet, and on quite a number of the slumbering passengers. Windows were opened faster than ever, while from the front compartments the cry of 'RAID... RAID...RAID' was bawled by a cacophony of voices.

'Friggin' 'ell, don't tell me the cops are waiting,' one flat capped character groaned. 'Trust my luck! It's the first time I've bunked on the train an' there's a bleedin' raid on.'

'Which platform are we goin' into?' someone yelled.

'Left hand side, left hand side,' a frenzied voice replied.

Before the train slithered to a halt alongside the murky platform, carriage doors were hastily thrust open and the 'snides,' like greyhounds out of traps, were off and away down the tracks, hotly pursued by a posse, with the boys in blue and their quarry all shouting, screaming and swearing as they plunged away into the darkness of an early countryside morning. From where I was standing it was indeed like an episode of the Keystone

Cops. Meanwhile, some of the contractors and those like me who'd never experienced the raids, remained stationary, unsure of which direction to take. There was also a few who tried to bluff their way past the vigilant ticket collectors, who now, with the physical protection necessary for all eventualities, appeared to be greatly enjoying the encounter.

'I didn't 'ave time to gerr a ticket this mornin' la, I just dashed straight through the barriers at Central an' right onter the platform, otherwise I'd 'ave bin late for work,' I heard one stocky fella plead.

'You don't look like a hurdler to me mate. Those barriers at Central are at least six feet high and there's no chance of you gettin' over or under for that matter; not with a belly like that,' the collector bravely replied, glancing at the adjacent coppers in case the recipient of his sarcasm took offence to these below-the-belt comments.

A couple of other 'snides' were going through the rigmarole of emptying their pockets, searching diligently for mythical tickets, then glancing around looking at the deck behind them. Despite their ham fisted attempts at play acting, they didn't find an appreciative audience with those in authority.

One bedraggled character, however, generated smiles all round. Standing in front of two uniformed enforcers he sheepishly explained that he'd slept throughout the journey, so that instead of getting off the train at Green Lane for Laird's shipyard he'd ended up at Capenhurst.

'Tell us how you managed to cross the bridge from the underground to the steamer, unless you were sleep walkin?' the collector sneered.

'Well, I'm 'ere so I must 'ave done,' Rip Van Winkle replied innocently.

As this drama was unfolding, those of us with genuine tickets were enjoying the novelty of queuing in an orderly fashion, instead of following the usual dramatic fiasco of having to scramble through barriers, ducking missiles thrown by the tricksters.

The main topic at work that day concerned the number of reprobates who'd been captured by the police, and in particular the plight of a new African recruit. Unfortunately, he'd travelled in the same carriage as a majority of the 'snides' who legged it down the line as soon as the train stopped. Without a second thought, our man had also taken off like a rocket, but was pursued by two young and fit policemen who eventually caught him just outside Ledsham Station. Apprehended and questioned about not paying his fare, the young man then produced a genuine return ticket. Surprised, and not a little perplexed by this turn of events, the coppers then asked why, if he had a ticket, was he running down the lines like the clappers? Breathlessly he'd replied, 'white man run, I run.'

The following Thursday he appeared with the others, at Ellesmere Port Magistrate Court and was duly fined ten bob for trespassing on railway property. Rough justice was a general verdict on the site.

These random police raids inevitably resulted in a union meeting being hastily convened and this time and occasion was no exception. At this particular gathering the discussion and recommendations centred on three specific topics; loss of time; police brutality and racial discrimination. The fifteen minutes lost due to police presence at the station was deemed negotiable with management, the committee members reiterating their confidence that the stewards were sufficiently capable of twisting the agent's arm for him to concede to a 'genuine error and raw injustice.'

The police brutality was graphically described to members of the shop floor by one of the convicted 'snides,' a witness to the injuries that a fellow rogue (who happened to be his brother) had received. The bruises to his buttocks, it was said, were caused by a massive pair of highly polished black boots, which had been applied when the recipient had slipped on the tracks as he ran off. However, a proposal that the chief constable be approached with a request to consider the possibility of compensation was unanimously defeated. Someone then suggested the injured party shouldn't have been 'arsing about on the railway lines in the first place,' a comment wholeheartedly approved by 99.9 per cent of the shop floor.

A lengthy discussion concerning the treatment of our colonial brother then followed. But when a proposal was made that his fine should be paid out of the stewards fund, it quickly came down to a case of brass tacks, with someone crucially and discretely suggesting a precedent could not be created. Their argument - that there were a number of dubious characters who excelled in manipulating the truth to their own ends, and a practice of paying fines was liable to bankrupt the stewards fighting fund - seemed an acceptable explanation to the majority of the shop. It was pointed out for the benefit of newcomers, that this particular fund had been diligently collected to finance anticipated conflicts on site. A few of the older hands remained suspicious though, fuelled by rumour that the stewards fighting fund occasionally had a curious habit of disappearing without trace at the end of a contract.

This was the first union meeting I'd attended and although my understanding and actual view of what was going on was restricted, I nevertheless enjoyed the proposals, the comments and especially the cross accusations between those who were less radical but still as honest as a day was long, and the militant fraternity who demanded justice at any price from every one of the custodians of authority.

Leisure

When you're sixteen and a half and feeling your feet for the first time and have to pay digs from a wage of just over thirty bob a week, there's not much you can do about painting the town red.

I was lucky in a way for Baileys, unlike most firms, paid travelling expenses, which was enough to cover my daily train fares. Of course, at that age money wasn't quite as important as it would be later on, when beer, girls and the Teddy boy syndrome slipped into the equation.

Chunkie always seemed to call on me at the wrong time on Friday nights. I often thought he did it on purpose. There wasn't much room in our house at the best of times, but nine times out of ten you could guarantee he'd knock when everyone was crammed into the front room, while I was sitting comfortably on the lavvie, enjoying a rare moment of peace before dad came in from work.

'Jimmy,' our Tommy yelled. 'Chunkie's at the front door. He want's ter know if you're goin' out; oh an' Dick Barton's just startin' on the wireless.'

'Tell 'im ter come in, and wait in the kitchen for me.'

Gripping the heavy cistern chain, I yanked it, releasing the deluge that could be heard half-way along the street. Before extinguishing the flame from the candle that would plunge the lavatory into darkness, I sat for a minute recalling the numerous times I'd been scared stiff to go to the lavvie at night time. It wasn't that long since the slightest sound would be enough to send me flying back up the yard pulling my trousers up as I ran. Then again, I could well recall holding a flickering candle, the wick down on its last thread, as an occasional rat with a moggy in pursuit, scurried behind ma's mangle, while one of the kids standing by the open door moaned or whistled into the cold night air. No wonder we were traumatised every time we ventured to the lavatory.

But now that I was a wage earner, neither the demons of the past or indeed the presence of a full moon casting its intangible beams under the bottom of the lavvie door bothered me.

With finger and thumb I snuffed out the warmth and glow that the wick had provided during the few minutes I'd spent in my retreat, and swaggered back into the yard.

Passing the doorless air raid shelter I paused. For some reason or other I had a vivid memory flash of the sirens wailing, and of us clinging to mam for dear life as we huddled beneath a thick grey woollen blanket. In my mind I could hear the strange but inevitable sound of the ear-piercing incendiary bombs as they whistled down, followed by the deafening explosions as they tore into the Mersey Docks at the bottom of our street.

Out of curiosity, or maybe instinct - I couldn't say which - I felt somehow compelled to poke my head into the darkened shelter now used as a coal hole.

And there they were, still before my eyes just as if it was yesterday. Unchanged and still in charge, the massive hairy spiders and the daddy longlegs that had frightened the life out of mam and the girls. But not me though - I'd capture them with my bare hands, no bother.

Smiling at these childhood memories I opened the back door and entered the kitchen to find Chunkie sitting alone. He seemed happy enough tucking into a plate of mam's speciality bread pudding, while the rest of the family sat in the front room listening to the latest episode of Dick Barton, Special agent.

The kettle had long since boiled but the water was still warm, so I topped up the bowl, stripped to the waist, and, after whisking the bum-fluff from my pimpled chin with one of dad's old Seven O'clock blades, I began washing the top part of my body. Stretching to the tips of my toes I removed a clean shirt from the clothes pulley and slipped it on. Then I attacked my hair with a comb, dripping with a good dose of the old 'Corporation Oil,' and parted it down the left hand side of my head.

'That's me done and dusted,' I said to Chunkie, who, between mouthfuls of bread pudding, began telling me the latest news from Pitts as the custard and raisins dribbled down his chin.

'You'll never believe it, but Mac's gone off sick with high blood pressure, and old Snypy's took over running the job,' he spluttered. 'Half the sparks have wrapped in already, an' poor Bonso's rushed off his feet. As for Arnie, well he's right in the shit.'

'How come?'

'He slashed through one of the power cables in the workshop an' put everything in darkness. Snypy came tumbling down the stairs from the office an' called him a bandy-legged nitwit.'

'What 'appened then?' I asked, keen to hear the details.

'He told Snypy he was an old gob shite and threatened to stick one on him.'

At a time when discipline was tight and deference to seniority was a matter of great importance, this outburst from Arnie was indeed heavy stuff. It took some bottle to muster up the courage to answer your elders back.

'Bloody 'ell,' I gasped, 'it's a wonder he didn't sack 'im on the spot.'

'He didn't 'ave the nerve, but it's not the end of the matter. He's goin' to see Mac about getting Arnie suspended, and Arnie said he can please his uncle, 'cos things will only get worse while he's in charge.'

I had to laugh. Snypy was little more than a bully, and ready for the knackers yard as far as I was concerned. Yet here he was, acting like a tyrant; ready to blow his last opportunity of making a mark, and now likely to be remembered for all the wrong things.

I thanked my lucky stars I was fortunate to have been given the chance of leaving Pitts when I did. Working with Snypy had been bad enough, but to have him in charge of all contracts would test the patience and determination of a hundred saints... and sinners...and their apprentices.

'Where are we off to?' I said to Chunkie, throwing an old lumber jacket that was at least two sizes too big over my tiny shoulders. Without thinking he slipped his right hand into his trouser pocket, rattled a few coins between his sticky fingers and produced two half crowns, a threepenny bit and a sixpence.

'Five an' nine.' he said. Not bad seein' I've paid me digs

and me club money. What d'yer reckon. Shall we give Fabri's the once over?'

We left our house just before the half-seven hooter at the docks heralded the end of a working shift, and by the time we reached the gas lamp light at the end of Brookie the sound of tramping feet could be heard closing in on us.

Fabri's ice cream parlour wasn't too far, about a fifteen minute walk, but by kicking a tennis ball to each other then dribbling rings round passing lamp posts and the occasional imaginary centre half or full back, it only seemed like five. Chunkie ordered the first round.

'The usual, without straws,' he said to the dark haired lady who served us every Friday at roughly the same time.

Raising our glasses of Vimto, we clinked them together. 'To all the lads at Pitts, 'I said.

'To Snypys early retirement and Mac's quick return,' Chunkie added quickly.

Sometimes we'd nurse a glass for an hour or more depending on how much cash we had left in the kitty. On other occasions we'd go overboard and spoil ourselves with a knickerbocker glory.

But, of course, there was nothing in our book to compare with Sunday afternoons when we'd gallop round the footie pitch for hours on end, hoofing a leather casie all over the place before collapsing in a sweaty heap gasping for a drink. This was definitely the highlight of our week. We'd then mosey past the Queens Hotel to Bob Martins drinking parlour on the next block up Conway Street joining the rest of the lads from school, to sup ale - full pints of Ginger beer or pint glasses of Sarsaparilla. This, we'd kid ourselves was proper ale, the real thing to us budding boozers. But then after the extravagance of the Friday night Vimto and knickerbocker glories, and these Sunday thirst quenching pints, I was usually skint for the rest of the week.

'Are you still working with Eggo?' Chunkie asked, as Tucker Griffiths popped his head into Fabri's door looking for us.

'No, he's working in another part of the job,' I explained, 'but I see him everyday on the train and he hasn't changed.

He's still nuts, shoutin' an' screamin.' Mind you he's not on his own, there's loads of head bangers on our job.'

'There's no crack at all in our place,' Tucker said mournfully, sitting down beside us, joining the conversation.

The waitress came from behind the counter and after removing a couple of empty glasses from the next table, half - heartedly swept the surface using a damp cloth. Taking the hint, we ordered a further round of drinks and began talking about football, which was our passion; with Everton our team and Goodison Park our shrine. Over the Vimto I described to Tucker what went on at the Cape where all the football-mad workers were either devotees of the reds or the blues. During the hour-long dinner break fiercely competitive football matches were played on the vast concrete pitches stretching behind the main building. As in all the hard fought local derby games between Everton and Liverpool, it was always a case of no prisoners taken.

Sometimes there would be as many as twenty players slugging it out on each side until five to one, when the spectators would begin drifting back to work while we'd wait for someone to shout 'next goal's the winner.' In those last few minutes frenzied bodies would clash head on, as they attempted to score that vital goal which meant so much to both teams.

Changing the subject from the intensity of idolising the blues to the more mundane but ever-pressing subject of finance, Chunkie asked when I'd be getting my next pay rise.

'On me seventeenth birthday,' I told him. 'I'll be on one and ten an hour then, so if all goes well I might get me'self fixed up with a new suit, an' some clobber.'

'Seein' you'll be loaded, p'raps we can go over to the Pool and meet the lads for a night out,' Chunkie said. 'I suppose you know Bonso's got 'imself a judy, an' he's out on the pop every weekend now,' he added.

'Good on 'im, if he can afford it,' I replied.

'Bonso might be movin' out to Kirby, now there's talk of knockin' part of Scottie Road down,' Chunkie said, keeping the conversation going. 'With Snypy in charge, he'll 'ave to be on his guard if he's late gettin' to work from out there though.'

'He's not in his own,' I told them, 'my old man's been tryin' for ages to get us a new house, on the Mount or the Woodchurch estate.'

'The Woody! Bloody 'ell, that's way out in the sticks. You'll 'ave to be up at five in the mornin' to get to the Cape from there,' Tucker said.

'Ah well, there's one thing I can say about me old fella,' I replied, 'you'll never get chance to sleep in as long as you're workin', no matter where it is.'

Chunkie then launched into a story he'd heard from his mate, Daggy, about his older brother, Billy, visiting the Council-housing manager one recent Friday afternoon.

'I've come to let you know I'm now in a position to buy me own house, so I'll be handing the keys back on Monday for the terrace one I've been renting for the past three years,' Billy announced.

'Fair enough' the manager said. 'But don't forget to leave the property in the same condition that you found it when you first moved in,' he added sharply.

'That could be a problem mate' Billy fired back.

'Why's that?' said the manager, warily.

'Just where d'yer think I'm going to get a thousand cockroaches and bugs from before Monday morning,' Billy replied.

Tucker and I laughed at the way Chunkie told the tale; there was no denying he had great gift for imitating or creating voices.

As we stood up to leave Fabri's, having almost exhausted our meagre pocket money, Chunkie, blimped a girl who lived in the next street to him entering the cafe. Without any prompting he wolf-whistled and clucked like a hen. At first she ignored him, but then after fiddling with her hair we caught her taking a sneaky look towards were we were standing at our table. Clocking Chunkie grinning like a hyena and winking as if he had a permanent twitch in his eye, she went straight for the jugular.

'What's up with your eye, fatso?' she growled like an angry bear. Then turning on me, she let go with both barrels, full of venom. 'And you've got nothin' to laugh about, with your patched up kecks and spuds in your socks.'

I may have been small, Chunkie may've been a bit mouthy and Tucker was no oil painting, but we weren't slow off the mark, and with living down town we'd had plenty of practice.

'It's better than havin' spuds in your drawers,' I answered sharply.

'That's if she's gorr any on,' Tucker added.

Our antagonist retaliated in a flash. 'I 'ave and they're clean an' well paid for,' she yelled, lifting her frock a couple of inches above her knees to reveal a tight fitting elasticated pair of passion killers.

'Bloody 'ell, I hope your ma's got plenty of tin openers to get them off,' Tucker grinned. 'Or a couple of pairs of your ould fella's tin snips.'

Not to be out-done by her tormentors, she had the last word.

'You'll be laughin' the other side of your faces when our Tommy gets yer,' she replied, casting a couple of reversible Churchill V signs in our direction as we swaggered from the café, our egos firmly in place and still intact.

It was all just good fun as far as we were concerned - at that point we didn't bother with girls - we were happy enough without them. With footy everyday, ginger ale and Sarsaparilla on a Sunday, a couple of hours in the boys club, and mooching about in Fabri's, well, what more could you ask for, or receive for that matter. And all on ten bob (50p) a week pocket money. In my case, who'd be interested in us anyway, with our spotty chins, our squeaky voices that hadn't quite broken properly, our hand-me-down clobber and being unable to afford a couple of cheapies - even without popcorn - in the local flea pit.

So for the time being we were happy with our lot.

'But just wait 'til we're seventeen, Chunks,' I said. 'There'll be no stoppin' us then.'

Harry's domain

The corrugated building at Capenhurst not only housed the site offices but also contained a workshop and a segregated main store, which was accepted by all and sundry as being Harry's domain.

Harry was a rare character on a building site. Unlike everyone else he never succumbed to using four letter Anglo Saxon expletives as a means of enhancing, flowering or even defiling a conversation, formal or informal. Instead he preferred to use a similar sounding nautical expression which though not as blunt or as final, always seemed fitting and in keeping with his strong local accent.

Every morning, a dozen or so of the mates, together with the apprentices and an occasional journeymen, would gather on the other side of the wired mesh partition waiting for the store to open; and without fail Harry would listen to the gossip as he prepared the drilling machines, the grinders, extension leads and the other plant items, prior to their distribution. And as he listened, he knew he could be relied on to be a willing participant for the wind-up merchants, as they set about teasing the young lads.

Depending on age and experience, and the time you'd spent on the job, apprentices would quickly learn the ropes, or like me would be slow to catch on to such teasing. To become classed as streetwise, believe me, was always something that was earned the hard way, and I was never a quick learner. Dad always said, 'Jimmy, your too slow to catch a cold,' and he worried I was never as worldly-wise as he might have wished, even though he'd taken endless trouble to ensure I never became one of those scallies he'd describe as being 'too smart for their own good.'

One morning, during my early days at the Cape, I arrived at the stores carrying a note from my journeyman requesting a half a dozen underground sky hooks and a long stand.

'Wait over there lad 'til I serve these other customers, then I'll nip to the compound for the sky hooks,' Harry told me.

A few lads were grinning, but I didn't take much notice, my attention being centred on the appearance of a huge black cat walking towards me. It stopped by my feet, looked up and stretched out on its two back legs, just like a dog. As I bent down to stroke its head, it jumped on my shoulder, licked my ear, then, after feeding on the debris caked inside, it sprang to the floor and ambled off towards the stores.

'It's your lucky day, lad. You know what they say about a black cat walkin' in front of yer,' one of the mates remarked, moving quickly as the moggie ran straight at him before leaping over the counter and disappearing into the stores.

My lucky day didn't last long. It was doomed from the moment my foreman, 'Flapper' Forshaw, appeared from the direction of the workshop.

'Worra are you skiving at lad,' he bawled, watching me lounge near the far end of the stores, gawping at a configuration of light fittings and wondering how they'd been wired to produce such power.

'I'm not skiving. Me mate's sent me to get some sky hooks an' a long stand, and 'arry's gone to get them from the compound,' I replied indignantly.

'Flapper' was reputed to smile only when he got an acute dose of the wind or when some senior gaffer was cracking jokes. Then he'd emit a unique 'hee-haw, haw' reverberation, a tell-tale signal to those working nearby that someone from higher management was in the vicinity. Now he turned on me, fearing I was deliberately setting out to undermine his authority; and what's more, doing it in front of the mates and sparks coming and going from the site offices.

'Listen son,' he snarled, 'go an' tell ball-bag, who, incidentally you're supposed to be workin' with, that you're here to serve your time, not waste it. Now move your arse pronto.'

Later that same afternoon I was sent to the store for the second time. After serving me, Harry enquired whether I'd passed 'Flapper's message on to my mate.

'Yeah, I told ball-bag what he said, an' also that he'd be on the next Pump List if he wasn't careful.'

'Friggin 'ell what did he say to that?'

'That the bloody mingebag's got no sense of humour,' I repeated.

In an attempt to keep their travelling clothes clean, a number of tradesmen bought re-conditioned boiler suits from the Army & Navy stores. A few of the older apprentices followed their example, but the younger ones - probably because the outfit looked old fashioned - didn't seem too keen. After listening to the sparks I was working with arguing the toss, I decided to set a trend by investing in a pair. The problem for me was my size; with even the smallest set available sitting massively on my tiny frame. Undeterred by this complication and confident I'd eventually grow into them, I arrived at work on Monday morning as proud as punch with my new possession.

Feeling no embarrassment whatsoever about wearing an oversize boiler suit, I slipped my feet down the huge long legs and fed my arms into the giant sleeves, managing to pull each hand through the bulky material without much difficulty. In order to reveal my size five shoes I then rolled up the bottoms of the legs, a manoeuvre which left the crutch perilously close to the floor. This didn't bother me in the least, nor the feeling of being inflated to twice my normal size. On the whole, I was quite pleased with the ultimate result. Unknown to me, though, my loose-fitting, over-size overalls had caused quite a stir among certain comrades, particular with that group who loved to voice their opinions and prejudices during the early morning chin-wag session at the main stores. Harry, the storekeeper, was stationed as usual in his 'mind-your-own-business-seat,' just out of sight of the gossip-mongers, but still within earshot.

'I see young Reilly's taken up ballroom dancin,' chuckled one of the hidden faces.

'Did yer hear what old Charlie said when he put those ovies on?'

'No what was that?'

'Don't go down the mine lad, you've got enough slack in your pants.'

Hearty guffaws drifted into the stores, as big Tom Simpson - considered by many to have the loudest voice on the job - bawled, 'he must have five of 'is old fella's jumpers on. Did you 'ave a decko at 'is arse end? It looks like the back of a double decker bus.'

Hearing this, Harry had eased his tall frame from the secret speck in the stores, peeping through a crack half-way down the wooden partition to see who, besides Tom and Charlie, was blackening my name. Of course I wasn't aware of all the shenanigans going on behind my back.

'What the friggin 'ell's Reilly been up to now?' Harry had muttered to himself, before entering the serving area to address the waiting mob with his usual morning greeting.

'Mornin' youse lot. Same old friggin faces every day. Now, you know the score, so don't be askin' for something I 'aven't friggin well got, or wastin' me time like you usually do,' he said, scanning the motley crew before him, most of whom were well known for pinching a quarter of an hour every morning by hanging around the stores.

On more than one occasion Harry had been reprimanded by the shop stewards for calling the early morning regulars, 'friggin deadbeats.' But if he was bothered by their disapproval of his lack of respect for their fellow trade unionists, he wasn't one to show it. It was all water off a ducks back to Harry, who would just remind you that 'you can't kid someone who's kidded thousands;' a philosophical quote he'd repeat to anyone prepared to listen.

After the queue dispersed in the direction of the work place; or, in some cases, as Harry observed, into the bogs to kill yet a few more minutes before the brew, his mind drifted back to what he'd just heard. He must have been contemplating this when I waddled into the stores in my new outfit. I didn't see him at first, but for some reason I felt he was watching me from the shadows at the back of the store until suddenly he appeared from behind me. I thought he had taken ill, as I watched him double up, keel over and grasp the pit of his stomach; but then he began laughing uncontrollably.

'Oh Reilly! Friggin 'ell. I've seen the lot now,' he chortled, before straightening up to resume his position behind the counter.

Almost immediately he seemed to recover his composure and called for me to join him.

'You've put some friggin weight on over the weekend lad,' he said, stretching across the counter to feel my biceps under the heavy layers of padded insulation.

'Worr 'ave you done, given your old lady some extra digs money?'

'No,' I replied, 'it's just that the ovies were a bit too big that's all, so I've put a couple of our kid's jumpers on underneath.'

'Oh I see,' he said, as if this was the end to it, but then wandered away stopping in front of a couple of shelves, where seemingly, lost in thought, he began emptying boxes of nuts and bolts into plastic containers.

'I've been thinkin,' he said, after pondering for a few moments. 'How do you fancy earnin' a few extra bob on the side, Jim?'

The thought of overtime and ten bob notes flashed momentarily before my eyes.

'No problem, what d'yer want me to do 'arry?' I asked eagerly.

'Come over 'ere at four o'clock every afternoon, an' it will be worth a tanner an hour if you'll walk twice round the stores and brush the friggin floor with your arse.'

That night, after devouring my dinner, I began reflecting on the day's events, finally reaching the conclusion that there wasn't much chance of me growing into the reconditioned ovies.

Ditching them was an alternative, but there was no way could I afford to lose seven and a tanner, not on my wages. Without a second thought I nipped upstairs, slipped the ovies on and paraded myself in front of the full size mirror. 'No wonder they took the piss out of me,' I muttered, laughing at the reflective image before me.

'Mam,' I yelled. 'Will you do me a favour please?'

'Yeah, what is it son?'

'Will you chop the middle off me boiler suit an' sew it back together again. And you can dock half a dollar out of next week's pocket money.'

'Rock Ferry' Frank and the lost brew

As time passed I found going to work was more of a pleasure than a drag, particularly when I was assisting those tradesmen or mates who made the best of the long days by introducing a touch of humour to the work. Quite often I was the only apprentice in a gang, and not surprisingly became the butt of many a crack. However, now that I'd turned seventeen I felt there were times when I gave the jokers a good run for their money

During my spell with Bailey's I'd worked for quite a number of foremen. Now, for the second time round I was back in 'Flappers' gang, assisting a spark called Arthur Foster, and his mate, 'Rock Ferry' Frank, wiring and installing some high-bay light fittings. To gain access to the job a scaffolding platform had been erected just beneath the roof area, with a fairly long ladder as our only means of approach.

The start of a day usually began with my early morning visit to the stores to get the materials for the job, and to collect a drilling machine and extension lead. One morning, feeling full of the joys of spring I left Harry's place and took the longest route back to the job, entering the building through a side door. As I approached our working area something strange caught my eye - the scaffold boards were shaking and clanging at an alarming rate.

Suddenly, Frank came hurtling down the ladder, shouting for all to hear 'quick gerr out the way the Penguin's thrown a cobbly wobbler.'

Frank's panic-stricken face was enough to show that this was a case of 'every man for himself,' so I dropped the drill and extension lead in a heap and legged it, keeping a yard or so in front of 'Rock Ferry' until we'd reached the adjacent building.

Now Frank was the sort of character who generally spoke with a hand cupped across his mouth, which had somehow contorted the side of his face. Added to this he rattled his words out in short sharp bursts, and was a somewhat highly-strung individual, prone to making military style gestures. What's more he didn't walk, but marched with his shoulders straight back, his arms swinging in perfect unison, and his feet stamping in a rat-tat fashion. Another quirk or peculiarity was his habit of saluting anyone in authority, from chargehand upwards.

'What's up Frank?' I asked as soon as he'd got his breath back.

'The Penguin's thrown a cobbly wobbler, son.'

'What! What's that then?'

'A thripenny bit lad, a thripenny bit.'

'I don't get yer. What d'yer mean, like?'

'A fit lad. He's thrown a bloody fit an' caught me cold stone,' he raved. 'I was about to get me brew out of me 'aversack when he let out a blood-curdlin' scream. Christ, I nearly bleedin shit me'self lad. I turned round and there he was frothing at the mouth an' waving his arms like a traffic cop. And yours truly wasn't waitin' around for any glory medals, no sir..ee. He's a bloody big fella, you know, an' if he happens to clip you one it's good night San Francisco, that's for sure. So he's best left alone bouncin' up there out of 'arms way.'

And he was right, Arthur was a big fella. Tall, and broad with it, like an oak tree and with a trunk that was only matched by his solid legs. Oddly, at the base of his massive legs he had two flat and totally useless feet that seemed somehow unlikely to be able to support the bulk that loomed above. What's more, these small and narrow appendages tended to stick out at right angles to his legs, so that dubbing him with the nickname 'The Penguin' had been almost an inevitability.

After rolling a ciggie not much thicker than a match stalk and inhaling a few swift drags which seemed to calm his shattered nerves, Frank decided to check up on Arthur.

'Right lad, we'd better go an' see if the coast's clear, otherwise we'll miss out on our brew,' he announced, checking his watch. Of course, we'd no sooner got back to the job than a whistle blasted from somewhere at the bottom of the bays, signalling break-time; and the building suddenly came to life. From various nooks and crannies shadowy figures appeared, swinging their billy-cans and dried milk tins over their shoulders, windmill fashion, to ensure the tea was well and truly stirred.

Meanwhile, Frank slowly climbed the ladder, stopping at

every other step to listen. Moving on up he beckoned with tic-tac gestures for me to keep quiet and remain where I was standing. From my position I watched as he reached the platform level, peering from under the peak of his cap glancing left and right. He then looked down and gave me the familiar thumbs-up signal to join him. Confident all was now well, he then climbed the few remaining rungs and stepped onto the platform.

Within seconds I'd scaled the ladder and was shocked to find Arthur still lying flat on his back, on the boards, his feet pointing in the ten-to-two position, and Frank creeping slowly towards him whispering words of comfort and encouragement. It was enough to stop me dead in my tracks.

'It's okay lad, it's okay. Take it easy,' Frank murmured.

Without warning Arthur sat up, howling like a banshee and Frank retreated backwards, quicker and lighter on his feet than Fred Astaire. I was even faster, shimmering down the ladder runners, hands and feet, fireman style. When I hit the floor I looked back up at Frank standing at the top of the ladder, one foot on the rung and the other on the boards, all the while still reassuring Arthur to get a grip and keep calm. After a few minutes he seemed satisfied it was safe to proceed and once again gave me the thumbs up to join him.

Arthur was sitting up when I reached the top and poked my head over the boards, but Frank appeared now to be in a quite different mood, and for some reason had become agitated. For a good minute or more I stood wondering what was going on and why it was that he kept muttering to himself, until suddenly I heard him speak out quite plainly.

'Where the bleedin' 'ell's me brew gone, it was there half an hour ago,' he blurted, pointing to where Arthur was now parked beside the pipe bender.

Frank eventually came across to where I was standing, cupped his hand to his mouth in his usual fashion, and whispered. 'The Penguin must 'ave swallered it Jim.'

After a further search for the folded newspaper packet which had contained his brew - a mixture of tea and sugar - Frank again peered at his watch. 'Bloody 'ell, the way we're shapin' we're not goin' to 'ave time for our brew.'

'Jimmy,' he ordered, 'get yourself down to the bottom of

the building and bum a drop of tea from the woolie backs.'

'What, you've lost your brew again, who d'yer think you're kiddin' lad?' A ruddy - faced mate called Shifty Jones was less than happy when I asked for a midges of tea. His companions were equally aggressive, and their dismissive replies left me in no doubt Frank must have felt his ears burning. Undeterred by the obscenities showered on me, I carried on, determined I would spoil their tea break until they gave way to my reasonable demands.

'How about a few drops left in the can over there then?' I asked, pointing to a blackened old dried milk tin that had been shoved to the end of the planks. The owner of this concoction sighed, folded his newspaper and picked up the can. Peering affectionately into the remains of his heavy - duty brew he seemed to ponder as to whether it would be an act of kindness to allow me the opportunity of tasting his genuine Typhoo tea, or if he should discourage an act of begging. After a few moments of quiet deliberation he made his mind up.

'This 'ill put lead in your pencil lad. An' tell yer bloody mates this is the first and the last time you'll cadge off us. We're not in the habit of encouragin' bums on this job. Oh! And don't forget where this little fella's 'ome is,' he added, holding the tin up as if it was a family heirloom.

Thanking him, I nodded to the rest of his companions and then headed back towards the job, swinging the can backwards and forwards over each shoulder in turn. Frank was munging into his butties when I arrived, and three tin mugs had been laid out on the boards, ready to be topped up. Careful not to spill any, I tipped the can slightly and poured the tea, making sure each mug had an equal amount.

'What the friggin' 'ell's that?' Frank muttered through his cupped hand glaring at the muddy coloured fluid as it dribbled out of the can containing bits of dark tea leaves and black unrecognisable lumps. Picking up the nearest mug, he sipped the contents and then spat it out contemptuously.

'Who gave you that lad? It's like bloody gnat's piss,' he growled, staring in the direction of the shadowed part of the building.

'The thin Welsh fella with the big conk. He said we'd gerr

a decent brew out of the dregs,' I answered; and to be honest I couldn't understand what all the fuss was about, seeing as it cost nothing and was warm and wet.

'The bloody mingebag must 'ave been using that brew for a week at least,' Rock Ferry grumbled, inspecting the taddies floating on top of the remains of his brew.

Meanwhile, Arthur had totally recovered from his 'eppy' fit and was tucking into his butties, gulping down the tea, dregs and all; totally oblivious to Frank's criticism of the offending liquid. Nor was he showing any signs of his recent blackout; which was just as well, for Frank's attention was now directed solely at the crowd still huddled together down at the bottom of the building.

'See that lot, lad?' Frank said finally. 'To think that I fought for the likes of them in the last war. An' just look at them, they wouldn't give yer the sweat off their brows. D'yer know what son, I'll tell yer a tale 'ere, an' it's the truth, believe me. I remember crossin' the desert with the Eighth army, an' my platoon stumbled across a Bedouin tribe, I can see them now sitting crossed - legged inside a great big tent, all in fine robes and drinkin' tea outa these little posh cups.'

He smiled at the recollection, then continued. 'Well, we were gaspin', honest lad; so I sez to this fella with a big black beard, who only 'appened to be the chief, didn't he? How are we fixed for a drop of yer Rosy Lee, la? You wouldn't believe it son, but 'e spoke even better English than me.

'Sit down, sit down' he said. 'So we all sat down. An' I'll tell yer what kid, talk about welcome. They not only gave us the last dregs of their tea, but all their little fancy cakes as well. And we were total strangers. Now that's worr I call genuine. Not like those minges over there who are supposed to be yer workmates. It's a bloody good job Hitler never won the war, 'cos that lot would 'ave 'ad us veterans put down. And him as well,' he added, nodding towards big Arthur who was rising to his feet and stretching out his arms as if he'd just left his bed.

'Pass me a length of that conduit, Frank,' he said, 'an' I'll show the young lad here one of the tricks of the trade. Like how to bend tubin' properly, for starters.' Then he slipped his hand into the pocket of his brown overalls to remove a handkerchief.

As he tugged at the blue spotted hankie, a small newspaper wrap fell and drifted to the floor, almost tumbling over the edge of the boards. That's until Frank leapt across with an amazing agility and stamped on it.

'What's that?' Arthur asked.

'Only me friggin' brew. That's worr it is. No wonder we couldn't bloody well find it, hidden in that ould brown dungeon of yours. An' next time you throw a cobbly wobbler lad, make sure it's after tea break,' he added, slipping the elusive brew inside his shirt pocket.

'On Guard'

Security was always of the utmost importance at the Cape. As one would expect on a nuclear power station site, the guards on the gate had to be extra vigilant to deter a range of enemies - Soviet spies, assorted peacemakers, anti-nuclear demonstrators or even fox hunt saboteurs; and not forgetting a few die-hard individuals seeking work who'd occasionally attempt to penetrate the barbed wire enclosures surrounding the site in an effort to short-cut the official approach.

Naturally, The M.O.D prided itself on its impregnability. So any bid to breach the triple wired fencing or the Fort Knox entrance, was viewed with extreme concern by those employees of the faceless ones residing in Whitehall, or in similar secret establishments dotted round the country

But of course one day the inevitable happened, and as a consequence the alarm bells rang from all the way up the old A41 to the capital. The event took place one bright Monday morning, when the guards, having enjoyed a peaceful weekend, were not quite as alert had it been a Friday, the day they received their little brown perforated pay packets. On this occasion an old black Standard Vanguard clattered towards the gate driven by a trusty. Now a trusty was one of the characters who earned a living by furnishing the management fraternity with all sorts of unobtainable goodies and was rewarded accordingly. This time, however, the boot of the car not only held the inevitable boxes of loot, but also contained the cramped and hidden figure of a charismatic opportunist who hailed from the Scottie Road area of Liverpool.

The jalopy was allowed through the barrier by an obese individual, who somehow managed the feat of checking out the vehicle without removing his podgy hands from his pockets; a curt nod of the head and a wink being sufficient for entry. After parking at the rear of the offices, Joss, the opportunist visitor, nipped smartly out of the boot, slipped his collaborator a shilling piece, and within minutes had disappeared among the army of workers heading down the site towards the cabins.

Joss was a popular man who everyone seemed to know. And

even before the cabin was half full, his personality and immense sense of humour brought the place to life with his latest ale-house jokes, hot off the press being passed around. But just as everyone was settling to enjoy the atmosphere, the chargehands appeared. Now they had the unenviable task of emptying the huts in record time, and of motivating a reluctant workforce to head in the direction of a bleak and unpleasant site; and all for the sake of an extra sixpence an hour.

At five past eight we reluctantly left the comfort of the cabin. Joss, confident now that the offices would be up and running, made his way to the compound, hoping his enterprising initiative in gaining entry to the site would be sufficient to persuade someone responsible that he was a worthy candidate for a position as a fitters mate.

Unknown to Joss, however, the Clerk of Works cabin happened to be located alongside the contractors offices, and the owner of this particular title ruled the site like a brigadier on active service. Dai Lewis Jones could always be easily identified by a mode of dress which rarely changed, and could be seen a mile away in his green Shetland tweed suit, matching cap, lily white shirt and red-spotted dickie bow. These fashion traits were apparently inspired by an illustrious past and were rumoured to be the result of his having served as a colonel in the Coldstream Guards. Others were not so generous in their assessment, reckoning he'd only commanded a section of the Home Guard - and had not made much of a success at that!

Few contractors had a good word for Dai. According to 'Flapper' he was a tactless, pompous and an interfering old tyrant who never missed a trick, and he'd not missed this one; his attention, it seemed, was now focused on Joss, who was nipping in and out of various cabins and offices.

'Hey you, who do you work for?' he yelled out in sing-song fashion.

'Me?' said Joss, holding his hands out and spreading his palms upwards, as if caught in an uncompromising position and protesting his innocence.

'Yes you,' Dai replied, coming face to face with Joss. 'I asked you a question. Who do you work for?'

'Me wife an' kids, of course.' Joss replied.

Dai wasn't in the least impressed by the smart-arse reply and to assert his authority raised the decibel level by a hundred per cent.

'DO YOU KNOW WHO I AM?' he yelled.

Before Joss could commiserate with him for not knowing who he was, the Clerk of Works continued. 'I am Mister Dai Jones, and for your information, I'M...THE...CLERK... OF... WORKS.'

But Joss didn't appear to be impressed by this revelation. 'Go way. Yer kiddin' me. You're tellin' me you're the clerk of works for the whole of this big site, an' all on your own?'

Jonesy glared contemptuously. 'You heard me, now what have you got to say for yourself?'

'Well pal, all I can say is you've gorr a bloody good job there, so look after it.'

No transport was used for Joss's eviction. He was physically thrown out and returned to the Pool, courtesy of a snides ticket. Meanwhile, Dai Jones adjourned to his office to complete the safety forms in triplicate, necessary for the M.O.D, in Whitehall. These, we heard, were to ensure that if Joss was indeed employed by Stalin, Molotov, Bulgahvin or Malekov, then the powers that be were fully alerted to the dangers.

Mind you, no one had ever bothered to check out whether Eggo was a Soviet plant or card carrying member of the Communist Party. And what about me? I could well have been a mole, planted by any of those tyrannical Eastern - bloc republics.

Time served, or tool-wise

In my early days at the Cape I was often surprised at the resentment shown by certain tradesmen towards the electrician's mates, who were derogatorily referred to as dilutees (dilettantes). This derisory attitude, I learned, was their way of protesting about those mates who'd been promoted to tradesmen status by gaining their experience 'on the tools,' instead of in the traditional manner of serving a five year apprenticeship. Some journeymen became so incensed at seeing a mate handling the tools that it wasn't uncommon for the subject to be brought up at union meetings. From what I could gather, the situation had come to a head during the war when everyone contributed to the task of finishing a job, regardless as to whether they were timed-served. In fairness, these 'mate baiters' seemed to be in a minority. The main body of tradesmen and the younger generation of workers were far more realistic, allowing their counterparts the opportunity to use the tools and thus gain the experience needed to enhance their prospects. Yet, the mate problem did not affect just the electrical trades; pipe-fitters, welders and the mechanical trades also faced the dilemma. Indeed, Rod Bush, a friend of Tucker's told us of similar incidents at the site where he was working.

Rod, an apprenticeship welder, worked with Charlie Swan, a tradesman openly hostile to the idea that 'made-up mates' could be given full union cards as artisans. As soon as a new-start arrived on his particular job, Charlie would quickly offer his opinion on this, his pet subject. On one occasion during a meal break he was again on his soapbox, blasting everyone within earshot with his peculiarly biased point of view. After a few minutes, as the tirade rattled on, Tim Roberts, a mild mannered character who'd been working alongside him for months, quietly folded his newspaper.

'Charlie,' he said in a calm but decisive manner, 'I'm not a time-served welder me'self you know;' but he added quickly, 'I am a fully qualified tradesman.'

Charlie's mouth fell open. He was lost for words - stunned - as if his hearing had failed or wasn't quite right.

Staring over a pair of half-moon reading glasses he weighed up his boiler-suited colleague. Then the penny dropped as he realised Tim was admitting in front of the squad that he wasn't a bona-fide welder. Such an admission seemed almost a matter of bragging, and was far too much for Charlie to bear, regardless as to how quietly and placidly it had been made.

'So you're not a qualified welder. Well what the bloody 'ell are yer qualified at then?' he growled.

'I'm a master baker,' replied Tim, almost apprehensively glancing at his silent colleagues.

'YER A WHAT! A MASTER BAKER?' roared Charlie, his mouth opening significantly, his eyes rolling in disbelief. Recovering his poise slightly, but still trembling with rage, he glared at Tim. Then in a voice which cut the atmosphere like a knife, he declared, 'listen ter me lad an' listen properly. If any of us drop a bollock in our game, someone out there is likely ter get hurt or maybe killed, an' that's a fact of life; get me? Now with regards to your trade, if any of youse lot drop a bollock, all you've gorra do is bend down, pick it up an' eat it.'

Tim said nothing for a moment, then leaned forward as Charlie stepped back as if fearing he was about to be attacked.

'You know that sarnie you scrounged off me earlier, at break-time Charlie?'

Charlie said nothing, but nodded his head in agreement.

'Well I hope for your sake my Master Baker's training was okay, don't you? Because I made that sarnie Charlie. And no, I didn't drop it on the floor. But I may have made it with some duff mayonnaise, Charlie. And in an hour or so - if that's the case - then you're in for a nice dose of food poisoning - and more than a fair percent of them are fatal, Charlie.'

'What yer trying to say?' Charlie had gone quiet.

'It's not just welders and electricians who have the matter of life and death in their hands. Cooks and Bakers are just as important in the order of things,' Tim said firmly.

'In fact, there's far more put into hospital through eating duff food than from getting an electric shock or a bracket falling on their head. So let's hope I had good training, eh, Charlie?'

I don't suppose it made any change to Charlie's fanatical

belief in the position of 'made-up' mates, but after that incident there was a definite reduction in his readiness to leap onto his soap-box at every opportunity.

In my first twelve months at the Cape so much happened that I found it difficult to keep up with events. As every day passed I became more knowledgeable, not only about my trade but also about the harsher facts of life and about my compatriots expectations, their aspirations, and what made certain people tick. During this same period our family moved to the Woodchurch, a council estate some six miles out of town. I don't know who slipped up, but somehow dad soon learnt that I'd changed firms and was no longer at Pitts. To my surprise, he didn't kick up a fuss or dwell on the matter, and if the truth be known, he seemed quite pleased I was going to Tech College. I suppose the fact that I was working for a well-established firm such as Bailey's gave him peace of mind, with a reassurance that eventually I would finish my apprenticeship.

One downside living out in the sticks, meant that we had a longer day because of the travelling time. Nevertheless, Dad enjoyed the pleasure of having hot water without having to boil a kettle, the luxury of a bathroom, and the un-dreamt novelty of an inside lavvie. The gardens to front and back were a challenge, and as we predicted, he tackled their cultivation like a bull at a gate. Incredibly, he soon created a very reasonable lawn, which I felt wasn't bad for a docker without any history of gardening or the slightest knowledge of rural activities.

Mam adjusted well, as did Tommy and Bernadette. Bridie remained at college, but what I missed most was the convenience of popping around the corner to chat with my old school mates.

Last in first out

The Cape, probably the largest construction site in the area, absorbed a massive workforce of all disciplines. It was therefore inevitable, as time went by, that large scale redundancies would take place. A 'first in last out' policy proposed by the shop stewards was rejected by the management, which gave Bailey's an overall victory on this site. As a result I witnessed the dreaded 'black spot' given to many of the sparks I'd worked with, including Orange Billy, the Jones brothers from Wrexham, and the bold Eggo.

There was no chance of the latter leaving without seeking me out, and true to form, as soon as I turned my back he sneaked up behind me, gripped the backside of my ovies, and hauled them up almost strangling my ollies. Grabbing my hand, he shook it vigorously and said, 'now listen young Reilly, take a tip from me. You spend most of your life at work, so wherever you are or whatever you may be doing, always have a good laugh and remember me. And that's without piss-balling about, like I do.'

'D'yer mean like you did at Pitts when we got suspended?' I replied quickly.

'You've got it in one son. Take care, Jimmy. See you round, like a doughnut.' Then off he went, toolbox on his shoulder, singing his own version of the well-known song from Snow White; 'Hi-ho-Hi-ho, it's down the road we go. We work all day for sweet F.A. Hi-ho-Hi-ho.'

Eggo wouldn't be out of work for long, not with building sites springing up like mushrooms, and it was generally accepted that most tradesmen would walk out of one job and go straight onto another.

Not unexpectedly as the rumours persisted that another list was an inevitability, the news seemed to have a devastating effect on certain individuals who'd leave no stone un-turned to avoid redundancy. 'Look at that 'snide' graftin' away 'cos he's 'eard about Friday's pump list, Eddie May remarked as we made our way to the canteen. 'The lazy bastard's not lifted a screwdriver since he's bin here.'

I'd been working with Eddie for a few weeks, and knew by now that like many of his generation he held strong views based on the principle that if you're paid for eight hours, eight hours graft is what should be given in return.

Of course, now that I was approaching seventeen and a half it was imperative that for the next six months, at least, I keep my nose clean and obtain good results at the Tech College. Everyone knew that as soon as a lad reached eighteen there was no escape for those without a trade, and apprentices whose company failed to sign their deferment papers would be quickly nabbed by H.M. FORCES. .

'Jimmy, to save you worrying about getting called up for the army, why don't you join the union?' Kenny Robbo said to me one dinner hour. 'I've seen lads paid off many a time by some of those cowboy outfits knockin' around. At least with the union behind you you'll get some sort of protection, which is more than you've got now,' he continued.

Robbo was just one of many sparks who'd advised me to join the union since I'd begun working at the Cape, though there were as many anti-union individuals who advised the opposite. Classed by many workers as 'snides,' such men dismissed Robbo's arguement that joining the union would be a benefit to me.

Although recognising the vast differences of opinion, I nevertheless found that some tradesmen were inspirational, as well as being educational. Mickey Blandford, for instance, was a perfect example, being a fully committed trade unionist if ever there was one. He knew the rule book inside out, often referring to it as his bible, and though he conscientiously worked without skiving, his main train of thought seemed to be focused on my education into trade union policies and principles. He even lent me his most treasured literary possession, a tattered copy of 'The Ragged Trousered Philanthropist,' which he called 'A working class masterpiece.' 'Read and absorb this lad, an' learn about the real life on the terraces - the battle between us an' them.'

Although I was grateful for his gesture, I found it difficult enough ploughing my way through the electrical manuals for college, never mind reading a book that was thick enough to choke a donkey. Besides, there were distractions away from work which were taking up all my spare time.

Mickey gave the impression to those who didn't know him well that he was a reserved individual, principally interested in his own thoughts, and not aware of what went on around him. But little escaped his attention, even though he peered at the world through thick-lensed glasses. Indeed, I lost count the number of times he'd point out what he called 'the enemies of the workers,' with 'fence hoppers' being especially high on his list of a scathingly derided low-life.

'They're worse than the genuine snides Jim. Just watch them at the next meetin', duckin' an' diving, an' hiding in corners, shit scared in case the chargehand's clock them votin' for the stewards recommendations.'

'Workin' men are their own worse enemies,' he said. 'An' that's a fact lad. Instead of bein' united an' fightin' as one, some of 'em would lick the bosses arses from here to the Pier head, believe me,' he continued. 'It's only when they get the bullet that they suddenly become militant. That's what makes me spew.'

'But all the chargehands are in the union, aren't they?' I added, keen to let Mick know that I was listening to his points of view and taking in the lessons they contained.

'They are. But some are only in for the benefits they can get out of it. Never trust anyone who sells his principles for a tanner an hour lad. That's always been my yardstick. And I'm never far wrong, even if I've got ter say it me'self.'

'But your kid's a chargehand, isn't he?' I asked.

'Yeah, unfortunately. Self-first, self last, that's him. He's never been any different Jim. I can remember him blowin' in me ould fella to the bizzies when they were searchin' houses for knock-off gear; an' he was only ten years old then. So once a snide, always a snide as far as I'm concerned.'

Despite Eggo's departure there remained a number of eccentric characters fit to carry his illustrious banner; though as everyone agreed, his would be a hard act to follow. During spells in different gangs I came across many unusual and very odd individuals. One spark was a guy who'd reverently been nicknamed the Pope. A dead ringer for Pope Pius X1, he resembled him in every possible way, except that he happened to be a fire and brimstone breathing Welsh Baptist.

Being a look alike was only part of his make-up; he really seemed to think he had the religious authority of the Papal Father, which not only caused great difficulties, but lots of fun and laughter for the apprentices placed in his charge. Grasping the slightest opportunity, the 'Pope' would continuously preach and moralise to his young trainees; and, indeed, to anyone else working in close proximity to where he was laying down the law. He would chastise us for swearing, or for telling dirty jokes, yet always seemed to be within earshot when an adventure or youthful conquest with someone from the opposite sex was being discussed. Of course, it didn't take long for us to become aware of his secret weakness in this department, so each and every ordinary encounter we'd had with some fair maiden would be greatly exaggerated, with lurid detail. And as he listened intently, we'd tease him by asking if he'd like to hear our confessions.

Then there was Billy the Minge, a mate working in our squad, who was rumoured to be so tight that he'd once been put on probation for breaking into a ten bob note.

'Money's made round to go round Billy,' was a phrase put to him on those occasions when he refused to contribute to a stewards collection, or to some other worthy cause.

'Yeah an' it's made flat to stay flat,' he'd reply bluntly.

His ultimate put-down happened one day, when, from somewhere deep down the bottom of his long pockets he extracted a ten-bob note, with his very short arms   Before the moths had a chance to wake from the darkness, one of the sparks grabbed the note as the King blinked in the unexpected daylight.

'It's a pre - war one, brand spanking new,' he yelled, running around the cabin waving the note in the air, 'and its still got the bloody resin on it.'

'Tater Gob' was another character, a jovial thirty-year-old spark, who thought he was still serving his time. During meal breaks he'd often join the apprentices, getting involved with whatever we were doing at the time. Even if we were messing about, Tater would be first to grab a piece of the action. His most prominent feature was a mousey coloured moustache-cum-beard which curled to either side of his mouth, ending about a half inch under his chin. From close range, with his mouth closed, he looked the ringer of a King Edward spud - hence his nick-name.

'What's this Tater? Are you tryin' to grow a goatee or are you only kiddin?' we'd say, grabbing the straggly strands of hair beneath his chin. And though he took our play acting in his stride, inevitably it would end up as a sparring contest. Everyone knew that'Tater' just loved the art of shadow boxing and that Sugar Ray Robinson, the then world champion, was his idol. Unlike the champ though, 'Tater' often forgot to duck, taking many a mandatory count from a stray uppercut dealt by an apprentice half his size - occasions that would bring bursts of spontaneous applause from the watching audience.

Naturally, all this ribbing of the Pope, Billy the Minge and Tater Gob, didn't go down well with everyone. Some of the older tradesmen saw it as a serious threat to their own status and place in the hierarchy of things and consequently they chastised us 'for not taking the job seriously enough.'

The Quisling

Following the political indoctrination I'd received from Mickey Blandford, the union meetings seemed more intriguing than the past. Despite always standing with a group of apprentices who were known to mess about, I revelled in the set up and the traditions that were about to unfold.

The shop steward and chairman sat behind one of the fold-away tables used for meal breaks, while the committee members mingling nearby appeared to be scrutinising everyone entering the cabin. I often wondered if they could read our minds and identify those who were likely to vote against the steward's recommendation.

Easing his long, gangling frame from a comfortable chair borrowed from the time-office, the Chairman would begin the meeting with a headcount and a piece of typical trade-union protocol.

'Can we 'ave a bit of hush brothers an' get this meetin' under way,' he'd demand, after reprimanding a few noisy latecomers. 'I now declare this meetin' open,' he would intone, 'so I'll hand you over to your elected leader, George, to start the proceedings,' , and then fold himself back into the comfortable chair.

George, the shop steward stood up, cleared his throat, then glanced swiftly at the bundle of hand-written notes he always held close to his chest. This was in case any of those standing at the front tried to read them before he'd had the chance to report in detail on battles with management they'd won and those they'd lost since the last meeting.

During the next ten minutes or so, points would be made, heated discussions take place and accusations for and against each item be contested - back and forwards - by rival groups, until, finally all arguments were exhausted. Only then was a vote taken to accept the steward's recommendations.

At one meeting things got very contentious. 'Brothers, I'll move on to further business,' George said, as the white-heat of the fray over some matter died down and the rumblings of discontent or agreement drifted away. When the cabin was quiet

George pulled his notes in close to his chest, squinting briefly at them as if to confirm what he'd already written and probably knew by heart. Looking out on the now silent gathering, he then spoke out harshly and with unusual emphasis.

'I'm sorry ter say lads, but we've gorr a quisling amongst us.'

Not a sound could be heard following this startling revelation. Everyone seemed to be trying to take in and digest the seriousness of this unexpected allegation.

'This sort of scum is the lowest specimen on this planet, and it's something we won't tolerate,' George continued angrily.

'What the friggin'ell's a quislin?' Arthur Foster asked his mate Frank, who was a world traveller and expert solver of crossword puzzles.

'Yes, what's a quisling, Frank,' I whispered. 'Someone whose nosy, always quizzin'. Y'know, the inquisitive type?'

'Nice try, Jim,' Frank answered. 'Sounds as if it should be. But no - it's Quisling - from Vikund Quisling, Norwegian of recent times.'

'I didn't know we had any Norwegians on the site,' I said.

'We don't, just Irish an' Welsh an' Jocks an' loads of Scousers. No Jim, Vikund Quisling was Hitler's stooge in Norway, puppet prime minister from 1940 till 1945, when he was taken out and shot.'

'He was a snide, then,' Arthur Foster said. 'Like Lord Haw Haw.'

'That's it,' said Frank. 'Backed the wrong side and lost.'

George continued his onslaught against this creature. 'The rat-bag's bin listenin' to our private meetin's, an' worse still reportin' major tit-bits of our conversation to the enemy. So now the bleedin' queer fella knows what's on the agenda even before you'se lot do.'

'How can you be sure it's not one of your elite crew up there that's the grass?' interrupted a snide - one of those Mickey Blandford had identified as being an enemy of the working class.

'Because I can guarantee that all these lads are dedicated trade unionists, that's why.'

'Then how come one of your committee members was seen bevvyin' with the gaffer in the Ledsham Hotel last week? How d'yer know it wasn't 'im like?' the snide retaliated, throwing in the allegation like a hand grenade in a crowded room.

It was like a bomb had gone off, as the place erupted into chaos, with the militants - by far the majority - demanding proof of the accusation, even as others pressed for the instant removal of whoever was the snake-in-the grass culprit.

With everyone wanting to speak at the same time, the noise in the cabin became almost unbearable.

'ORDER, ORDER! THROUGH THE CHAIR BROTHERS! THROUGH THE CHAIR,' the steward yelled.

Eventually, a semblance of normality returned and the meeting got under way.

'You. Yes, you at the back,' the chairman declared pointing to a sallow face loner, known for his anti-union, anti-management and anti-everything tendencies, Billy Ray, an obvious nark in everyone's eyes, rose to his feet

'What was he doin' bevvyin' with that red headed bastard in the first place, that's worr I wanna know?' Billy growled from the rear of the cabin.

'Language, brother! Language!' The Pope cried, his bald crown diverting the soft luminous rays of a sixty-watt bulb hovering above his head straight into the eyes of the taller Tommy Mathews who was standing directly behind.

Once again voices were raised and for the second time the steward had to intervene to restore order. Exasperated by the continuing disruption, eventually he called out, 'come on lads, this is gettin' us nowhere, I think it's time we moved on to further business. We can discuss the last question later, in private, with the full committee. And believe me brothers, we'll get to the truth in the end.'

His attempt to appease the agitators seemed doomed, however, for further unsubstantiated derisory comments and a welter of insults were brought to everyone's attention by certain members of the shop floor - dubbed the 'snide brigade.' Eventually a few outspoken militants tore these malicious accusations to shreds and a semblance of democracy again ruled the day. Not to be outdone by the rabble rousers, the chairman, at this point, rose from his comfortable chair to give his considered and irrefutable opinion on the matter.

'Look brothers we're playin' right into the management's hands fightin' amongst ourselves. That's what they want us to do. So I propose we leave it in abeyance as suggested by your democratically elected steward and let the cool heads of the committee sort this one out.'

As the clock ticked perilously close to knocking-off time, the debate ended. Hardly anyone wanted the hour-long meeting to run into extra time; missing the train meant a bitterly cold wait for the next one, and the only thing that might achieve would be a dose of flu.

Bonso's misfortune

'Jimmy, in a few months time you'll be eighteen, so don't you think it's about time you got yourself rigged out properly.'

George Burnett, perhaps the smartest man at the Cape, shook his head sadly as he looked at my trousers which were at least two inches above my shoes.

'No wonder the lads are always asking when the China boat's coming in,' he added. 'Take a tip from me lad and invest in a decent suit, because no judy will give you the time of day dressed like a paraffin lamp.'

His advice surprised me; as far as I was concerned my grey longies were no better or worse than Tuckers or Chunkie's, and theirs looked all right to me.

George, who worked as a sparks mate with Trunkie Davies, was never seen without a sharp collar and smart tie and resembled Errol Flynn, having many of the film star's swarthy but handsome features. To cap it all, he was rumoured, like Flynn, to be hung like a Southport donkey, and the general consensus of quite a few of his envious colleagues was that he must have been born with more than one silver spoon in his mouth..

It was thanks to George's intervention that six weeks later I was the proud owner of a midnight blue, half-drape, finger-tip length suit, purchased on the knocker from Abe Black, the Cole Street tailor, for seven and six a week. Not long afterwards, Chunkie, Arnie and the rest of the lads followed my example and spent a few bob on similar outfits, with ambitions to take the world by storm. Feeling like the real McCoy, we teamed up with Bonso who was generally acknowledged to be streets ahead of us in fashion and know how. This wasn't surprising considering he'd been drinking and courting since he was sixteen. With his wealth of experience and being older than us, he automatically became known as the Godfather.

'Next Saturday we'll meet at Ma Egertons, 'ave a few bevvies, then we'll mosey on to the Grafton,' he suggested.

Now, that might seem to be nothing much, but the trouble

was I had never been in a dance hall before. In fact, it was only a couple of weeks previous that I'd sampled my first pint in the Observatory pub with Robbo, on the way home from work. Robbo, an ardent bitter drinker, had ridiculed the Birkenhead Brewery ale, calling it 'boys beer'; though I soon discovered that two pints was more than enough for me. At the first hint of fresh air my legs wobbled like jelly, and my voice developed a speech impediment. Fortunately, I managed to stagger home and up the dancers without bumping into my old man. I knew quite well he'd have given me 'Birkenhead' ale in buckets if he'd caught me.

On a Monday morning, at break-time, the main topics the lads settled on were football, dancing, the weekend happenings - and of course, girls. It's no exaggerating to say that the opposite sex was the one subject which could always attract everyone's attention, including those seemingly ancient sparks who teased us endlessly about our amateur exploits; which, according to them were nothing when compared to their own illustrious ventures.

'Listen to the crap from this lot. All pimples an' bum fluff. None of you'se would know a good thing if yer fell over it,' said Dicky Malone. He was a tall gangly mate, who, apart from suffering from acute acne, had a large and unsightly wart on either side of his nose. Despite being the butt of many a tasteless comment, to give him his due he gave as good as he got. He'd even accepted the unkindly remark from the manager of the 'Wizards Den,' a local joke shop which sold Halloween masks when he'd said, 'I'm not swapping that one lad, you never got that from here.'

By the time Chunkie and I landed at Ma Edgies that next Saturday evening, Bonso, Arnie and Harry Burkey were supping their third pint. Bonso, who was showing off on the far side of the bar, demonstrating a few jive routines, was annoying a couple of elderly Evertonians, deep in the middle of consoling each other after yet another devastating home defeat.

'Bugger off outside if yer wanna arse around. We're 'ere to drink, not to piss-ball about,' one of them muttered, nudging Bonso against the juke box just as he was about to go down on one leg.

The next minute he'd tumbled to the floor, pulling Arnie with him.

'There's no need for that, grandad,' Bonso moaned, brushing white dust from his slick black crombie jacket, but the old men ignored him and carried on discussing the match.

'Right lads let's gerr out of 'ere. It's like friggin mortuary anyway, full of zombies - and Evertonian ones at that,' Bonso said, glaring in the direction of the old fellas still deep in conversation. The proprietess perched at the end of the bar didn't raise an eyelid. She knew there was no likelihood of these novices raising the coffers in her till to record breaking levels.

Leaving Ma Edgies we traipsed to Lime Street then boarded a bus out to West Derby Road. After sampling four more pints in a couple of the abundance of lively pubs in the locality, we finally converged on the Grafton Ballroom. Bonso led the way forward with us trailing behind. On his orders we swaggered confidently past the bouncers who were greeting their patrons with grim, thin-lipped smiles; and reminding everyone, especially us it seemed, that if any trouble occurred, then even the draught from a missed punch would be enough to knock any of our team clean out.

Once inside the ballroom it took a few minutes for my eyes to focus in the dark. I gazed around at the scene and the brilliant surroundings, somewhat surprised to find that the girls were dancing together, as groups of lads stood nearby laughing and joking. Occasionally a few of the brave ones darted across the floor to try to join the boppers, but then, if rejected, would slink back into the shadows.

'See them tarts over there?' Bonso said, pointing towards a blonde dancing with a short, dark haired girl in front of the band. 'I copped off' with the dark 'aired one last week an' took 'er 'ome on the last bus. But I didn't know until I paid 'er fare that she lived right out in the wilds, only on the other side of Knowsley if you like.'

'How d'yer gerr on?' Arnie asked ogling the blonde who was twisting provocatively.

'A waste of good leather. Bloody 'alf two in the mornin' I gorr 'ome. Me bleedin' feet were red raw. Then me ould lady bubbled me to Molly, so now she's talkin' about packin' me in an' breakin' off our engagement. An' after all that I got nowt.'

'How come yer got nowt?'

'D'yer wanna know why? 'Well listen an' I'll tell yer. It was pitch black when we gorr out there, an' when I found this nice cosy bus shelter with no one in, I thought me luck was in for a change. Anyway we'd just started neckin' when this gorilla appeared from nowhere. Honest ter God, I nearly shit a pan of pink sparks. It was only 'er ould fella wasn't it.'

'What time d'yer call this?' he bawled, and stuck an alarm clock in 'er face. 'Go on gerr 'ome before I break your bloody neck,' he yelled, an' she was off before I had chance to blink. Then he called me a long streak of paralysed piss an' told me to beat it before he put 'is foot up me arse. Christ he was a mean lookin' bastard. I didn't need tellin' twice and I was off like grease lightnin'. Never stopped runnin' for at least two miles in case he changed 'is mind an' friggin well came after me.'

Listening to Bonso's tale of woe we were stunned into silence for a minute, until Arnie broke our train of thought.

'How about splittin' them up then?' he suggested.

'You're kiddin' aren't yer. After what Bonso's just told us,' I said.

'Give 'em a wide berth,' said Chunkie 'they only want someone to pay their bus fare 'ome, an' then you'll be lucky to gerr a peck on the cheek.'

'I've gorra agree with yer there la, you're dead right. Steer clear,' Harry Burkey muttered.

'Let's make a move,' said the Godfather, so we trailed behind as he weaved his way through the chaos of acrobatic jivers executing their skills under a barrage of flashing lights across to the other side of the dance floor. Finally, he stopped a few yards from what well might be described as a couple of larger than average peroxide blondes.

'How about these two?' he said. We didn't share his enthusiasm though, nor were we brave enough to take them on. Unperturbed at our reluctance he wandered over.

'Are yer dancin'?' he asked the more attractive of the two girls.

'Dance with our kid, I'm sweatin'', she replied - lady-like - and so Bonso somewhat hesitantly obliged.

After performing a couple of his most spectacular and popular jive routines - largely for our benefit - he swaggered back to our little group.

'A pair of 'ard cases them two,' he whispered. 'One of 'em takes ugly tablets, an' 'er sister chews 'er ould fella's razor blades.

By this time the action seemed to have shifted towards the stage, so we strutted across, determined to grab a slice of whatever was happening. It was then that Arnie caught sight of a tall attractive girl we all recognised as being a member of a local vocal group who'd appeared occasionally on television. When he announced he was going to make his debut by asking her up for a dance we could hardly believe our ears, even though Bonso, who seemed to know everyone, tried to change his mind by telling him she was a big headed cow. However, this failed to deter Arnie who was even more determined to try his hand, no matter what anyone said.

'I'll bet you a tanner she back heels yer,' Bonso remarked to him..

'You're on,' said Arnie, 'shake on it.'

We stood around watching as Arnie, all five foot five of skin and bone stagger towards the six foot celebrity; knowing for a fact that not only was he half-pissed, but was totally clueless when it came to dancing.

'Are yer getting' up or what like?' Arnie asked the girl, using what he considered to be an appropriate form of invitation - the standard approach used by our mentor, Bonso.

'Go away you horrible little man,' she answered, looking furious and extremely embarrassed.

'You're not knockin' me back are yer?' spluttered Arnie.

'Get lost you drunken lout.'

Having endured Snypy for almost three years, Arnie was resilient and never short of an answer. 'What's the marrer with yer? Beggars can't be choosers,' he replied, staring up the nostrils of the stage-struck celebrity.

'Well this beggar can, and I wouldn't choose you - even if I won you in a raffle,' she replied, striding from the stage and making for the ladies room.

We laughed as Arnie scratched his head, then looked round furtively to see if anyone was watching, like most fella's did when they were knocked back. He then traipsed towards us, shrugging to show us it was her loss.

'The snooty mare's back-heeled me,' he said. 'And that's the last time I'll be askin' 'er up. Anyway she doesn't know what she's missin'.'

'You're dead right there Arnie,' we replied.

'An' don't forget the tanner you owe me,' said Bonso.

During the following months the visit to the Saturday night dance became a ritual. Dressed up in the latest fashions, which in my case meant a jacket almost down to my knees, sixteen inch bottoms and no turn-ups to my trousers, as well as a fair lathering of Brylcreme dolloped on my swept-back Tony Curtis, we'd set off to aggravate the floors of our regular haunts - the Grafton, the Locarno, the Tower ballroom and the Kingsland. As time went by we became skilled connoisseurs of the bop and the jive, and when the four saxophones turned in unison to honk their semi-quavers behind the girl vocalist, we'd gyrate in front of her hoping to catch her eye.

And that was just fine, until on one memorable occasion we decided to go a bit up-market - well Bonso did - and under his leadership and as a result of his cajoling us, we ventured into Reece's during the time we were enjoying the fortnight break of our summer holidays.

Now Reece's was not somewhere we'd previously thought of going, but Bonso had heard on the grapevine that a large number of local shop assistants spent the half-day-closing-break learning to dance at this particular venue. Rumour had it and the crack also suggested, that Reece's was a bit up-market, a bit pricey, and with a clientele who would probably look down their noses at the blue half-drape, the sixteen inch bottoms and the crepe soled brothel-creepers. But nothing gained, as the saying goes, so we agreed we were up for it if the leader was, and as Bonso thought it was about time we expanded our horizons it was decided to give Reece's the benefit of our presence

And so one Thursday afternoon, with a couple of pints of best bitter under our belts, we slipped passed the restaurant and up the stairs to the dance hall. Before we barged through the door though, we were stopped abruptly, stunned by a large photograph of two ballroom dancers on a colourful display with the words 'Welcome to Reece's afternoon Tea Dance,' highlighted in large capital letters.

'What's this crap. A bloody Tea dance?' Bonso said, scratching his head in disbelief.

Never one known in our eyes to make a bad decision we gathered round him waiting for his next move.

'Well, as we've come this far we may as well give it a whirl,' he muttered, leading the way into a foyer littered with palms and plant pots containing exotic bushes and flowers. Music, from what sounded like a symphony orchestra on a bad day when only half the players had turned up, drifted down as we preened in front of the mirrors in the gents, combing our locks and buffing up our looks prior to entering the ballroom. However, the omens weren't looking all that good; for the other guys in the bogs were all old men, and one or two even had monkey suits on.

'Bad move all round,' Chunkie whispered, as we turned in through the doors to where the action was. We could see at a glance that it was dead posh, with candlesticks adorning ornate tables and fancy braid chairs placed strategically around the perimeter of the dance floor.

'Look at all the ould girls,' Arnie said, nudging me in the side.

The place was full of older women, most of who must have been at least thirty-five, perhaps even forty. And they were all performing proper dancing - the waltz, the quick- step and the fox trot, or whatever they were called. We drifted to one side, trailing in, trying to fade into the wallpaper and parked at the end of the floor weighing up the talent, just as we would at other venues.

Suddenly, two buxom and elderly women headed straight towards us.

'Watch out lads, 'ere comes old Mother Reilly and her sister to gerra grip of us,' Bonso joked. He'd wrongly assumed they were heading to the ladies toilet, which was behind where we were standing

'Good afternoon gentlemen, it's a pleasure to have some

handsome young men in here for a change,' the taller of the two greeted us, her face caked in powder and her eyes blackened with mascara.

'Look ma,' Bonso replied quickly and defensively, 'were only in 'ere to see worr it's like, that's all.' He glanced over his shoulder, checking to make sure that our escape route remained open.

'Well seeing that you have paid your money, you may as well stay and enjoy a pleasant afternoon of ballroom dancing,' they replied simultaneously. But our godfather was not the type to be swayed by anyone pushing him about, not even with such a bold approach.

'No chance ma. This isn't our scene. We're into boppin' an' jivin' an' all that like. An' besides, none of us can dance anyway.'

'In that case we shall teach you,' they replied, and before Bonso had another chance to intervene me and Arnie found ourselves gripped and whisked out onto the floor.

'One, two three, one, two three!' the lads chanted, laughing and jeering as we began learning the waltz. Worse was to follow when the tempo changed to a quick-step, as Arnie was physically lifted off his feet, his face and glasses stuck between a huge pair of breasts as he was swept along like a rag doll. I fared little better and froze on the spot. For some reason my feet refused to move, so the old girl was obliged to push her tree-trunk legs against my spindles and I ended up being propelled round the floor, looking as if I'd taken short and followed through.

The spectacle was too much for the lads. They jeered an laughed so loud that the noise distracted the regulars. Eventually, a posh fella dressed in an evening suit came across, requesting that either we be quiet or leave the premises: a decision we had no difficulty in deciding on.

I don't know which novice dancer supped the quickest, Arnie or me; but the pints of bitter didn't touch our throats as we recovered in the bar of the 'Legs of Man.'.

'Who told us to go to that joint?' Harry asked.

'Yeah, a bloody waste of five bob, but a friggin good laugh,' Chunkie replied.

'For you'se lot it was,' interrupted Arnie. 'But worr about me an' Jimmy? It was like bein' held in a head lock, an' not bein' able to breath, with me face stuck between a big pair of tits. No bleedin' wonder me glasses steamed up.'

'You were lovin' it,' Bonso said. 'We wuz watchin' yer movin' your face from side ter side, weren't we lads?'

'Only because 'er brooch wuz stickin' in me nose,' Arnie protested.

'Is that why you 'ad a big smile on yer face when she dropped yer down?'

Arnie started to laugh. 'You'se lot would 'ave 'ad smiles on your faces if you'd seen the ould girl tryin' ter throw her lips on Reilly when the dance finished. Isn't that right Jim?'

I laughed, then conveniently changed the subject by ordering another round for the lads.

When Chunkie heard the news he couldn't get round to our house quick enough despite it being a twenty-minute bus ride from town. 'Guess what Jim? You're not goin' ter believe it,' he yelled excitedly even before I had chance to fully open the front door.

'Bonso's stuck Molly in the puddin' club an' he's getting' married in three week's time,' he gasped breathlessly.

'You're jokin', when did he find out?'

'She's almost five months gone, so he must 'ave known for a while. No wonder he's been quiet lately.' He was probably too scared to tell 'is ould fella or ould lady about it.'

Without Bonso's leadership Saturday nights were never quite the same, and naturally, his misfortune became one of the main topics amongst the lads at Pitts. Of course, when I mentioned his dilemma to my mates at the Cape there was sympathy for his parents, but inevitable comments on, and questions about our own moral codes - and their absence - from the sparks. As usual, the older tradesmen always compared our behaviour with that of their generation.

Tommy Taylor, a quiet and benign soul, hailing from the small village of Wem in the north of Shropshire, was happy to give us the benefit of his cautious and undemonstrative life.

'You young fella's can't be too careful dancin' an' a wenchin' in the big cities, there's too much danger and temptation there for you.'

'It's just as bad out there in the sticks' the Seven O'clock Shadow responded vigorously. 'In fact I'd say it's worse, 'cos there's nowt else for the youngsters to do except drink like fishes, play blind man's bluff, an' chase the girls into the woods.' Seven O'clock was a thin-featured spark from Bootle, who always looked in need of a shave.

'Aye, worr about those village dances? Now they were somethin' else,' said Tater Gob. 'I always managed ter score first time round when I was stationed in the countryside durin' me army days.

'What dances did they 'ave in those days Tater, besides the Charleston ?' Young Ned Kelly grinned.

'Let's put it this way lad,' Tater said, taking the bait, 'we had more enjoyment in our days than you can imagine, or will ever 'ave. There was none of these stupid fandangle crazes which all you'se young fella's seem to 'ave latched on to. Twistin' an' throwin' yourselves all over the place, I ask yer.   Tell me, 'ow can you 'ave a proper conversation an' tap up the birds with all that deafening music blurtin' away, that's worr I wanna know?'

'It's dead easy. You wait for a squirrel dance an' then make your move,' explained Monty Monaghan, an ex-apprentice just out of his time and waiting patiently for the army to recognise his talent and send him his papers.

'A squirrel dance? Never 'eard of it,' Tater muttered, looking round the cabin at his comrades for a hint as to what this mystery dance might be. For a change they all looked vacant and said nothing.

'You don't know worra squirrel dance is, then?' teased Monty.

'I wouldn't friggin' well ask if I knew, thick 'ead,' Tater replied angrily.

Monty had a smirk on his face by this time as did all the apprentices. 'If yer wanna know worr it is Tater, then I'll tell yer. It's twice round the floor an' straight outside for your nuts.'

The Pope, lifting his head from his paper, glared his

sanctimonious disapproval and tutted for at least ten seconds flat.

The wedding was something of a hushed up event. As far as both families were concerned there were two main aspects to be taken into account. First there was Bonso's age - he was just eighteen - and secondly there was the fact he was still serving his time. For this reason it was decided that the fewer people who knew about the wedding the better it would be for all concerned. Another worry weighing heavily on the couple, and also the parents, was the problem of how they would manage to get by and bring up a child on Bonso's lowly wage.

To give him credit he pledged to work all available overtime, and to try and obtain 'foreigners' at weekends - even though he had limited experience in the art of 'house bashing' - those re-wiring and domestic electrical jobs that most 'foreigners' consisted of.

To save money the family suggested the couple would be better off staying in Molly's grandmother's spare bedroom; and although she was failing a bit and hard of hearing, it was obvious that Gran looked forward to the prospect of having them living with her for the company.

After a fifteen minute ceremony at St Brougham's, both families trudged through the rain to the Labour club. Clambering two flights of stairs to the top floor, they were pleasantly surprised to find a number of tables laid with a reasonable assortment of sandwiches, sausage rolls, pastries and numerous confectioneries, with a home-made wedding cake taking pride of place in the middle of the centre table. To complete the layout an improvised bar had been hastily constructed for the inevitable session to follow; with the only concern of the ardent drinkers being the fear that the ale might not last out 'til the end of the 'do.'

Bonso, looking uncomfortable in a dark striped suit, silver grey shirt and matching collar and tie, stood next to his bride, his tall, dangling frame towering above both families seated on either side. This was the first time we'd ever seen him wear a tie, and knowing full-well how he normally operated, we could almost feel his deep sense of unease and embarrassment, by the way he kept rubbing his nose with the side of his hand then glancing towards the door as if contemplating making a dash for it.

After reading the traditional 'good wishes' and 'congratulation' cards, the best man told a few tales of Bonso's exploits during his school days, before ending with a familiar endearment, 'and he's always bin a good lad an' all that. Yer know worr a mean like,' a testimony that singularly failed to impress the bride's glum-faced family. Finally, he toasted the bridesmaids - Molly's two older sisters – who made it obvious from their easy and natural responses that this wasn't the first time they'd been chosen for such an honoured position.

'Cheer's our kid, an' good 'ealth to you as well. An' don't forget ter get me up for the first jig,' the larger of the two yelled. For us neutrals watching the event it was difficult to avoid noticing how the bride's father's head sank lower and lower on his chest as his daughter openly flirted with the best man. With three further marriageable wenches to off-load, he no doubt was reflecting that weddings were an expensive commodity.

Next it was Bonso's turn to captivate his guests with a well-rehearsed speech. Rising to his feet he drained the remains of a large whisky, fished a crumpled piece of paper from a jacket pocket, mumbled a couple of inaudible words and that was it; his legs seemed to crumple beneath him and he sprawled back onto his chair. Tony, the best man, professional and as loyal as ever, leapt to his feet and quickly introduced Bonso's dad in an effort to rescue the family pride. Bonso senior, who had settled happily at the far end of the table, seemed to have conjured up a well-thought out and carefully planned strategic response to this invitation to say a few words.

'Thanks for comin' everyone,' he began. 'And Molly, welcome to our family; for worr it's worth.' Then, bending forward and spreading his hands across the crisp-cotton tablecloth he faced Bonso.

'Well son, all I've got ter say to you, is this. I only hope you 'ave better time on your honeymoon than I 'ad on mine.'

And with that he sat down.

If someone had dropped a pin you would surely have heard it in the gap before his words of wisdom penetrated his spouse's sensitive organ of hearing; and then all hell broke loose.

'You baldy, miserable little toss pot,' she cried out. 'Me mam was right, she never effin well liked you in the first place, or yer bleedin' family. Tuppence 'apenny toffs the bloody lorr' of yer.'

Gulping a few hurried breaths she continued her tirade. 'She had you decked alright, you dirty spineless turd, makin' an holy show of us, an' in front of complete strangers as well.'

With fury etched across her face she attempted to rise from her chair, but to her embarrassment found she couldn't move; her husband's bacon being momentarily saved by a new, padded corset.

'Listen to 'er, that's worr I've gorr put with,' he calmly told the listening throng. But, she hadn't finished the onslaught.

'One selfish bastard, that's what you are, d'yer 'ear? Fancy spoilin' our poor Bertram's big day, an' you 'is effin father of all people.'

'Bertram..who's Bertram?' Chunkie whispered. 'Don't tell me Bonso's real name is Bertram an' not Brian.'

'Shush he'll 'ear yer,' Harry Burkey said.

'Shurrup mam, yer makin' a show of me in front of me mates,' Bonso pleaded.

During the fracas Molly's family, had remained silent, like everyone else. Suddenly their whole attitude towards the Bonson's took a dramatic turn - and for the better.

'See, I told you mam, they're no better than us,' Molly whispered to her mother, who, by this time had already decided to intervene. Vacating her chair, she ambled towards Mrs Bonson, placing an arm affectionately around her shoulder.

'Calm down luv, 'es not worth it. They're all the same. Just look at 'im sittin' over there with a bloody kipper on 'im like a smacked arse.' She nodded back towards her own spouse. 'An' all because it's cost 'im a few nicker for a 'do', an' she's only the first. It was all Hunky-Dory when he was givin' me babies an' buggerin' off ter sea enjoyin' himself. But now he's got four daughters to pay for, he doesn't like it one bit.'

Bonso's mother, encouraged by this show of loyalty, was all smiles. Within minutes the prevailing doom and gloom had disappeared as the women swapped experiences and harrowing accounts of their journeys 'through the mill,'while everyone joined in as Michael Holidays crooned 'The Story of My Life' from beneath the lid of a modern radiogram. Shortly afterwards the bar opened and the ale flowed, lubricating parched throats and dry necks; and from that moment on the tensions and feuds simply disappeared as if they'd flown out of the window.

Three weeks after the wedding the devastating news reached us that Bonso had been sacked by Snypy, acting on instructions from the directors. They, in line with many other small companies, were adopting a policy of firing the lads as soon as they'd reached eighteen - or in Bonso's case, quite a few months over - and then employing fifteen year olds on far less money.

Unfortunately, the sparks at Pitts weren't union oriented, nor for that matter were they organised. As a result no action of any kind had been taken against the company, so there was little but heart -felt sympathy for Bonso, and advice to the rest of the lads at Pitts to look for other jobs before their eighteenth birthday.

'Bloody 'ell, what a position to be in. Let's hope the army doesn't capture him before he gets fixed up with another outfit,' Arnie said, after arranging a 'get-together' in Ma Edgies.

But within a few weeks Bonso's misfortunes continued when his call up papers arrived in the post. This really brought home to us just how precarious the situation could be for apprentices coming up to that truly dodgy age of eighteen.

Joining the union

'I told you Jim, join the union while you've still gorra chance,' Robbo advised, as Bonso's dilemma was discussed for the umpteenth time. 'And that goes for you'se lot too' he continued, addressing the rest of the apprentices, all of whom where fast approaching the critical age of eighteen. In all fairness to Bailey's, they did have a reputation for taking care of their apprentices until they completed the statuary five years. But after weighing up the advantages, and taking into account the genuine concern displayed by a number of journeymen regarding my future well-being, I decided to join.

When I mentioned my decision to Chunkie he agreed it could be a move in the right direction and so we arranged to meet at the Park Hotel on the following week, hoping to join the rank and file of The Birkenhead Branch. As soon as the rest of the apprentices at Pitts heard the news they followed a similar course by applying to join Central and other local branches, believing that should they suffer the same fate as Bonso, becoming union members could enhance the prospect of gaining employment with other firms.

At seven o'clock on Monday evening we drifted into the bar at The Park and after sinking a couple of pints of Dutch courage, we climbed the stairs to the first floor and boldly entered a room where the meeting was about to take place. Before we had time to make ourselves comfortable, however, a grey haired, bearded fella whispered discretely to us that non-members had to wait on the landing outside the room until invited into the meeting.

During the next half-hour or so a number of familiar characters who worked at the Cape arrived, including the mate, Shifty Tompkins. We noticed that to gain entry to the meeting, these late arrivals would rattle out the same familiar knock on the door. Within a couple of seconds it would be opened fractionally by a cloth-capped, somewhat surreptitious character, who scrutinised not only those seeking entry, but also those of us waiting outside. As Shifty and his mate stepped inside, the door was immediately closed, severing the mist of smokey fumes that escaped from the room into the coolness of the stairwell. A few minutes later Shifty and his mate emerged, smiling broadly.

'We were bloody lucky there lad, just made it with our subs before the meetin' gorr under way,' Shifty muttered, and tumbled off down the stairs straight back into the bar where he'd left a full pint of bitter beside the pumps.

'Old frosty bollocks didn't look too happy about lettin' us back out,' his companion said, sticking close to Shifty, as if afraid of missing out on a round.

Later we learnt that the regular attendees of the branch frowned on this activity of what was known as 'diving out' before the meeting began. This was considered to be a blatant lack of respect to those members actively engaged in solving the nitty gritty trials and tribulations and problems of their fellow workers.

Just after eight o'clock the door creaked open a few inches and the guardian of the entrance once again confronted us. From beneath the peak of his cloth cap he looked at us without saying a word, relying instead on the action of a fore-finger rising up and down, beckoning us to enter. The official moment to participate in the clandestine haven of the brotherhood had finally arrived.

All heads turned towards us as we were ushered into the crowded, smoke-filled room and I was pleasantly relieved to see there were many familiar faces of my workmates from the Cape present. At the front of the room seated comfortably behind a solid pine table, those branch officials known as the three wise men faced the rows of members eager to get the meeting under way.

Jack, the branch secretary, a well-respected shop steward from Cammel Laird's Shipyard, was perched prominently in the middle of the trio, a ciggie dangling from his lip, with the ash almost touching his chin. Seated to his right was Bob, a jovial looking character and a popular and experienced contractor who held the position of Chairman. On Jack's other side, a pink faced, plump individual was busily scanning the pages of a huge red ledger with the fervour of a Jack Russell about to decapitate a ferret. His name was George Paris and he was the Honorary Branch Treasurer.

Jack rose from his seat, stubbed the ash from his ciggie into an empty matchbox, placed the stump behind his ear, and opened proceedings.

'Right Brothers, these two young lads have been proposed by Brother Roberts of this branch to become union members and seconded by Brother Blandford of Liverpool Central. So if there's no objections or questions regarding their entry, can we have a show of hands and then they can be admitted to the apprentice section.

'Why 'aven't they joined before now?' a miserable looking character interrupted. Robbo leapt to his feet shouting, 'how old where you when yer joined the union arse 'ole.'

'Language brother, language. Remember, he's entitled to have 'is say. After all this is a democratic meeting,' a stern grey-haired chap sitting near the front, observed.

'I'm only askin' 'cos all the apprentices in our firm join the union when they're sixteen, that's all,' said the first speaker. 'Mind you, every one of our lads is indentured and serve their time properly, not like those in the contractin' game, who are always jumpin' from job ter job.'

A couple of contracting sparks did not take kindly to the last speaker's observation, one reacting accordingly and with deep conviction. 'Jumpin' from job ter job, the last speaker hasn't a clue what it's like workin' on the sites an' putting up with some of the conditions we 'ave to endure; and by the state of him, he wouldn't have the bottle or the nouse to tackle site work.'

'Just friggin' jealousy 'cos we chase the cash, that's all. And whatsmore, these lads 'ere 'ave as much rights as any of you'se maintenance cronies to join the union,' a red-faced character standing at the back of the room yelled in support.

Meanwhile, we stood a few yards from the table, like tailors dummies, listening to the flak flying back and forwards and wondering what this all had to do with us.

Order was eventually restored when the chairman intervened, angrily reprimanding those responsible for the outburst for not following trade union discipline. He then recommended that we should be allowed to join the apprentice section of the union. With no further interruptions from dissident members, we were then asked to join him at the front of the room. Rising from his chair, he shook our hands warmly and as he welcomed us into the E.T.U., we were surprised and slightly embarrassed as a ripple of applause rang around the room. George then scribbled our names onto a blank page in his bible, all the while stressing the importance of being up to date with our subs, because, as he warned, all sorts of problems could occur if we were five weeks or more behind. After receiving our temporary cards and thanking him, we turned and headed towards the door.

'Hey, where d'yer think you're goin'?' he yelled. Clarence, the elected doorman, catapulted out of his chair, jammed his back against the thick panelled door and spread his arms as if to prevent a deadly virus from escaping into the outside world.

'Come on lads, let's not start on the wrong foot,' the Hon Sec said with a warning voice. 'There's a meetin' goin' on here, so why not make yourselves comfortable for the next hour or so, an' gerra bit of proper education into those young brains of yours.'

Reluctantly we sat down to suffer in silence, knowing the chance of another pint would have to be postponed for the time being, and all for the privilege of joining the union at the ripe old age of seventeen and three quarters, give or take a week or two.

'Education is a fine asset,' was something dad repeated when he was embarking on one of his many philosophical utterances, but here, in the humble first floor room of the Park Hotel, I discovered a dedication to others that was an even more commendable pursuit. Anyway, that's how I felt on that first night as I listened to these unpaid officials involving themselves in all kinds of problems, many of which had little or nothing whatsoever to do with union business. The issues ranged from writing letters to housing associations, contacting firms regarding claims about unfair dismissals; or simply assisting those who were suffering some social or domestic hardships, such as seeking and obtaining advice on the legalities of matrimonial matters. One of many varied requests, though, had even these ardent stalwarts lost for words, when an irate member asked for guidance regarding a problem which, as he stated, 'had been getting under his skin for months.'

'Through the chair brothers,' he began reverently. 'I wanna know what can be done about the dog shite in Birken'ead Park, if you'll excuse me expression. There's turds all around the football pitch an' I'm pig sick of writin' to the Council, an' all I gerr off them is that they're lookin' into it.'

'You'd get more satisfaction if they were treadin' in it instead of lookin' into it,' a sympathiser said.

'Whereabouts are the dogs supposed ter go? In the streets or what like,' growled a canine owner, who had uncanny features resembling both versions of a boxer.

'Listen brother, my kids can't even play football there. It's like a friggin' Germin minefield, that's worr I'm sayin'. An' I wanna know if the branch can exert pressure, an' get some action at the same time. That's all I'm askin'.'

'Okay brother we've got the gist of your complaint, leave it with us an' we'll see what we can do about it,' the secretary replied, scribbling feverishly on a note pad.

'Exertin' pressure on dog shite, I've 'eard the bloody lot now,' someone at the back said.

As soon as the raffle for a packet of ciggies had been called the meeting ended, and similar to a football match when everyone anticipates the referee's full-time whistle, the room emptied dramatically. Pandemonium reigned as the stairs rattled to the clatter of footsteps, with those gasping for a pint scrambling to beat the ten 'o'clock 'last order' shout. This was always a priority for those relishing one or two for the road. Being new-comers, we stood back 'til the rush was over.

'Well Jim, that's us in. All I need now is another job before Snypy gives me the bullet like he did to poor Bonso,' Chunkie said, as the towels were carefully placed over the pumps.

I suppose some would call it fate, or plain coincidence, but a fortnight later Pitts began sacking some of the older apprentices. Arnie and Harry moved to Harding's, a reputable local firm, who guaranteed they had enough work to see them through their apprenticeship, while Chingie went down south to finish his trade with a Surrey company. Chunkie started on our job at the Cape, so joining the union had proved a fruitful move all round. Phil, Scullo, Cauly and a couple of younger lads decided to chance their luck and stay with Pitts.

Meanwhile, at Lime Street Station, Bonso was participating in a tearful farewell party with his bride of a few weeks. As expected, every member of his family had gathered to wave him off.

'You'll be all right Molly, don't start whingin' again, I'll be 'ome as soon as me square bashin' is finished,' he whispered, trying his best to lift her spirits. 'It 'ill go in no time, you'll see.'

'You're not goin' ter war lad, you're only goin' ter friggin' Aldershot,' his dad's voice roared above the loud snorts of the steam engine. 'And believe me it 'ill make a man of yer, an' put some 'airs on yer chest,' he continued. Of course his optimism wasn't shared nor was it appreciated by a senior feminine member of the family.

'Hairs on yer chest, listen to 'im. You could do with some on your bloody 'ead, never mind yer chest, short arse. An' you didn't 'ave any on your nut before you went in the army either.'

'Ar hey Ma, don't be so cruel, you know 'ow touchy he 'is about 'is 'ead,' young Rosy interrupted, as everyone laughed.

'Listen May, all I'm sayin' is that when I went in the army it was for five years solid, an' I didn't know if I was comin' back in one piece or not…. that's the difference. Not like our Berty 'ere, it will be just like goin' to a Butlins holiday camp, without the judy's that is.'

Noticing Molly's eyes filling up and sensing a sneaky leather toecap heading towards his shin, he didn't finish his intended speech.

So Bonso departed, leaving behind a young wife, a baby on the way, and with shattered dreams of becoming a tradesman; and all just three and a half years after leaving school.

Moving on

Rumours were always rife when major contracts were about to begin in the area. And with the arrival of some large companies from the big cities, the idea of a devoted loyalty became something of a lost and bygone concept. Although rates of pay were invariably the same, some of these firms paid more in travelling expenses, or would poach labour with promises of excessive overtime, thus making the final take-home pay an attractive inducement.

Tanjon's, one such company from the London area, won a local contract, and within weeks everyone from the foremen to the labourers were scurrying to leave Bailey's.

News drifting in on the bush telegraph suggested there was a contract going at Ellesmere Port, which apart from being long-term with overtime seven days a week, was also paying a lodging allowance, and this made it one of the most attractive jobs in the district.

One morning, after a fourth trip to the site telephone, Robbo bounced back into the cabin full of beans, announcing that he'd finally managed to get through to Tanjon's. Before he had chance to expand on his news or to mention the starting rates, sandwiches and cups of tea were cast aside as the shack immediately emptied. By five o'clock a substantial part of Bailey's workforce - at least two gangs of sparks and mates - had been given the green light to start for Tanjon's on the following Monday.

'What's the chances of us getting' a fix?' I enquired half-heartily the next morning, when the euphoria of the previous day's events had died down.

'If you don't try you'll get nowhere, an' after all it's only the price of a phone call,' Trunkie Davies said, generously offering 'to give 'em a ring an' see what they say.' Within the space of an hour he returned with the news that Tanjon's were prepared to consider employing four apprentices.

During the next few hours the soles and heels of our boots took a hammering as we dashed back and forth on the quarter mile stretch to the phone box. After scrounging loose change from our tradesmen and making endless calls, Chunkie, Billy Constable, Timmy McCain and myself were finally given assurances from Tanjon's site agent that he'd fulfil the agreement regarding our deferment papers and make sure that Timmy's would be honoured by the time he reached the age of eighteen.

At breaktime we could hardly contain our emotions as we discussed our good fortune at being able to jump ship. After working out the increase in benefits, we discovered that these alone would more or less equal our usual take-home pay, the kind of money that was well beyond our wildest dreams.

The contract at Bowater's Paper Mill was divided into three areas; the Old Mill isolated on the far end of the site, the Bag or Sack factory built a number of years previously, and a brand new Fibre Container building on which the groundwork had been completed recently by the travelling navvies.

There was simply no comparison between 'Bowies,' as it was commonly known, and the Cape site. As a well-established productive paper company, Bowies employed a huge workforce who enjoyed the comfort of pleasant canteens, warm and secure toilets, and individual parking spaces for the higher management. Even for the majority of the rough and ready contractors on site this was a cushy environment compared to the cold and windy sites with primitive toilets and washing facilities they'd been used to.

In the early days, just weeks before our project began, the daily routine of Bowater's staff had been severely tested by the arrival of the civil lads, the 'banjo merchants.' The trouble began when a minority of these unconventional industrial gypsies - the first contractors on site - had shown little or no respect for the feelings or privacy of the permanent staff, who soon found themselves defending basic facilities many had taken for granted.

'Bloody 'ell, a full house at this time in the mornin'. It's a bit of a bugger when you can't 'ave a decent crap when your machine breaks down,' one disgruntled worker moaned to Sam, the official lavatory attendant busily mopping the floor, seemingly oblivious to the stench drifting from the six occupied cubicles.

'Don't moan to me son, go an' complain to your manager. 'Cos it's the same every Monday mornin' since these contractors arrived. I think some of 'em must be drinkin' Epsom's Salts the state they leave the bloody pans in after they've finished.'

'We're entitled to a crap the same as you'se lot,' someone yelled from one of the cubicles, ruffling the pages of his newspaper, as a blistering blast of wind from a fellow reader in an adjacent trap muffled any likely reply.

'Listen to that lot. That's worr I've gorra put up with every day. Fartin' an' pebble dashin' the enamel at the same time,' Sam moaned.

'Oh shurrup dad, yer lucky ter be workin' at your age,' a voice piped up from one of the lock-ups.

'It's all right fer you fella's, but I've gorra clean the mess up after you'se lot 'ave finished.'

'Stop whingin' an' go an' make yerself a brew,' the original reader replied.

'Leave 'im alone,' yelled another operator, who'd just arrived clutching feverishly at the backside of his overalls. 'Come on lads, play the game,' he pleaded to the closed and locked doors of the cubicles. 'I'm dyin' for a crap, an' we've only got a few minutes before we're due on shift.'

Whether it was the urgency in his voice or a touch of conscience influencing those in the chair, the response was immediate. Without a second thought and in true militant tradition, a 'one out, all out' approach was adopted. Leaving their warm seats and swinging chains in a show of solidarity to fellow brothers of the T&G and printing unions, the banjo lads vacated the traps within seconds..

However, it came as no surprise to anyone when huge notices, 'NO CONTRACTORS ALLOWED,' appeared at the entrance to the building, thus heaping an extra responsibility on the frail shoulders of Sam the bog cleaner. Apart from keeping the toilets clean and tidy, he now had the extra and unenviable task of enforcing tough vigilante duties to deter a body of mud-covered invaders sneaking into the factory from the cold.

On my first day at Tanjon's I couldn't believe my luck when, with the other apprentices, I was placed in a gang containing a majority of the sparks and mates from the Cape; including Robbo, the Pope, Big Stan, Jimmy 'H' and Trunkie Davies. Our task, I found, was to tackle the job in the Fibre Container factory, commonly reputed to be the best of the three contracts the company had to complete.

A total of twelve sparks, eight mates and four apprentices were assigned to carry out the work, which according to the experienced tradesmen was a manageable team to tackle this size of installation. To add icing to the cake for us lads, news filtered through from the mill that Bowater's were in the process of making arrangements to recruit a number of young women to operate the machines when they were completed and ready for production.

'What more could you young rampant apprentices wish for?' Trunkie Davies commented, on hearing the news.

Our foreman, Bootsy Webster, a Lancaster lad who had five years experience with the firm was in charge of the job; and although Tanjon's wasn't as big or as well known as Bailey's, they nevertheless were reasonably organised and were more than capable of tackling a job of this size.

In the compound, the complex of temporary units rivalled any of the Capes contractor installations, and consisted of comfortable cabins, the usual cold and draughty toilets, an average size stores, a time office and workshops. Bootsy, meanwhile, had a similar but smaller arrangement for us, tucked away near the main road.

The first priority on all union jobs at that time was to organise a committee and elect a shop steward, when a show of cards would normally follow. This procedure had already been carried out at Bowies before we started, and Alf Wilson, a popular character, had been elected as shop steward to represent the workforce. Within a month of arriving on site the first meeting had taken place. To set the pattern for resolving any future conflict, Alf then explained in detail how he meant to tackle such situations. Before beginning his opening speech, however, he spent a few minutes reminding the troops just how fortunate they'd been in having landed 'a good little number' right on the doorstep. Adding a rider he then told everyone 'to keep your noses clean and look after it' - a statement which raised more than a few militant eyebrows.

'Can I 'ave your attention for a minute brothers,' he began. Just a little request from the management relatin' to complaints they've received from the maintenance section. 'Apparently, some of our lads 'ave been usin' their lavvies an' canteen facilities again. This has got ter stop. If you don't, the big cockney fella has threatened to bullet anyone caught sneaking in there. So use your loaves lads, an' for the sake of a crap park your arses in our own traps in the compound. I know it's cold an' draughty on yer ring pieces,' he continued, 'but you can't expect the management to put heaters in there can yer? 'Cos let's face it, some of you'se lot would be in there all day. So, it's a matter of grinnin' an' bearin' it for the time being. Oh, and don't give me any excuses that there's no paper in the bogs, not on this site anyway,' he re-asserted with a good-humoured chuckle.

'Who's side's 'e on? someone asked quite loudly. The militants were looking even more uncomfortable after listening to Alf's lecture.

'Through the chair,' our pal Timmy McCain's faltering voice suddenly crackled across the room, his face-changing colour to a deep scarlet from the neck upwards. 'Worra we gonna do about our toast an' bacon butties like,' he asked, 'if we can't use the cannie?' It was a brave apprentice who broached policy at such meetings.

'The lad's gorra good point there steward, an' worr about the loop-de-loop at dinner hour? ' Podgy Hogan pointed out. 'It's a long drawn-out day without somethin' warm in yer belly,' he added; sentiments shared by more than a few carrying extra weight.

After noting the complaint, Alf promised he'd do his utmost to come up with a compromise to satisfy all bodies concerned.

'Congratulations Tim, we're proud of yer, aren't we Chunkie?' I remarked as we made our way back to the Fibre factory. Timmy, a former altar boy, was a baby-faced, sensitive kind of lad. A keen train spotter, studious and forever delving into all categories of books, he was much more conscientious than the rest of us lads regarding the job or union matters, probably because his father - a well-known contracting electrician - had played a major role in influencing Timmy's principles and attitudes.

'There's nowt to it Jim, just stand up say your piece an' sit down, it's as easy as that,' he replied to my teasing remark

'I'll remember your advice when I get up to speak at the next meetin', an' try me best not to gerr a cherry on,' I answered, winking at Chunkie.

'Stop takin' the piss, it doesn't suit you Reilly,' Tim replied, uncharacteristically showing a petulant side I'd not seen before.

The work at Bowater's was significantly different to previous jobs, mainly because we were involved in the installation and wiring of machinery of all types and sizes, instead of simply doing run-of- the-mill lighting and power circuits.

Besides that, and the change in scenery, the thing that excited most of us was the way we now began taking more than a casual interest in the increasing number of young girls who were working in the Sack and the Fibre Factories. Indeed, their presence not only effected those routes that we'd normally take on missions to the stores, or when making the tea, but became the second most popular subject discussed during meal breaks in the cabins; along with football, of course.

'Did you see those two new birds workin' by the corrugater?' George Sharkey said, without addressing anyone in particular.

'The little one's smart, but I don't fancy the one you're havin'', Shifty replied, cannibalising a sausage buttie as he spoke.

'I don't see what you're all gettin' so excited about me'self,' said Billy Corker. 'They all look the same to me dressed in those green baggy ovies. An' after all, you haven't a clue what's underneath. They could 'ave legs like bamboo canes or tree trunks for that matter, an' no arses. They could even have falsies, who knows,' he observed philosophically.

'Ah! but that's all part of the pleasure, the intrigue. The element of not knowin' what you're gettin' 'til yer open the packet,' Nobby Allcock, the number one 'boss-poser' interrupted. 'It's like dippin' your fingers in a bag of liquorice all-sorts an' hopin' yer don't pick the plain black one.'

'Worra load of bloody crap,' said Frankie Turner. 'I can't believe me ears. Bloody grown men actin' like soft teenagers. No wonder the lads can't concentrate learnin' their trade properly, listenin' to tales from the likes of you'se lot.'

'I don't agree with yer there, Frank,' Trunkie Davies said, folding his paper and joining in the conversation. 'I know for a fact these lads could teach us all a trick or two. Only this mornin' Reilly had eyes on him like a bulldogs bollocks when he was watchin' the crumpet bendin' over the machine when they were lookin' round for the emergency stop button. Before you could blink he was over there,' he continued, 'pretendin' to be an expert, so he was.' 'Mind you he's not on 'is own. The other lads are just as bad as him, waitin' for an opportunity to gerr in with the judy's an' not givin' a toss about the job. So all that I'm sayin' Frank, is don't underestimate them for one minute,' he grinned, with just a hint of envy in his voice.

Temptation

Those early days when the Bowater site was being organised and we were finding our feet were truly memorable. In line with the demands of all the other contractors, the apprentices at Bowies not only learnt their trade, but ran messages and made tea for their colleagues, queued for bacon butties at the canteen, and placed their bets with the site bookie. Depending on how quickly a lad performed his official tasks or how diligently he skived, a couple of hours a day could be swallowed up in this way. .

After we'd eased into our cosy 'out-of-the-way' settlement, Bootsy, as thorough as ever, introduced a weekly rota to be carried out by the apprentices for those tasks he classed as 'mess duties.'

One particular Thursday, when Chunkie was designated 'Peggie' for the week, Bootsy added a further assignment to his list of duties, instructing him to take the time-book to the main office, hand it in to the wages clerk, wait for the hours to be recorded and then bring it back. Ambling past the toilet block, Chunkie flicked through a few pages for no other reason than a deep-seated curiosity. What he saw made him gasp. Bootsy had entered everyone's daily hours using a pencil instead of a pen.

Now, there was no denying that Chunkie was smart and streetwise, and it didn't take long for him to realise that here, staring him in the face, was an opportunity to make a few bob. Without a second thought he dashed into the bogs to borrow a pencil and a rubber from Mick, the bookies runner, who always lingered there just before the start of the first race. Then he nipped smartly into one of the empty traps and added two hours overtime for the previous Wednesday shift to his time sheet. As cool as you like, he then carried on to the office where he presented the time-book to the clerk. Minutes later, after retrieving the book, he headed to the bogs, erased the evidence, restored the earlier figure, then trotted over the hill to our compound and returned the time-book to Bootsy.

When Chunkie opened his wage packet on the following

Friday afternoon, his grin was wider than the mouth of the Mersey Tunnel.

At Tanjon's, the older apprentices had the opportunity of working two hours overtime per night and all-day Saturday at a rate of time and a half. Sunday overtime was known as 'double bubble.' However, with the majority of football fanatics opting for a twelve o'clock 'early dart,' commonly referred to as 'a half day chop,' hardly anyone worked Saturday afternoons The apprentices also had a day release and two four o'clock finishes to enable them to attend Tech College, giving them the best of both worlds. It was amongst this existing abundance of overtime galore and seemingly massive wages that Chunkie began to fiddle the books.

Never able to keep things to himself, Chunkie just couldn't keep a secret even if his life depended on it, and before the Friday shift had ended he'd spilt the beans to me, Tim, and Billy. The following Thursday, after the dinner break we waited eagerly to see if Bootsy would again ask Chunkie to take the time-book to the main office. Again the book was handed over to him, and even though we were openly sceptical that such an easy deception could work twice, the next week Chunkie again flashed an enhanced wage slip under our noses, revelling in his craftiness. From then on it was down hill all the way, with Billy the first to be convinced that the scam was foolproof. I fell by the wayside, soon after when the lure of a slice of extra cash for nothing attracted an unfortunate weakness in my character. Timmy, who was made of sterner stuff, emphatically voiced a lack enthusiasm for the scheme.

'You know it's cheatin'? don't yer lads?'

'Cheatin'...look at the basic rate we're gettin', Billy retorted. 'Without overtime we'd be on peanuts, an' I'm sure a couple of buckshee hours isn't goin' to bankrupt them.'

'Worr 'appens if Bootsy sees our wage slips then? It'll be curtains for the lorr of us if he does. Have any of you'se lot thought about that?' Timmy said, almost pleading with us.

'He doesn't open them, we do,' I replied. 'An' anyway, all we'll get is a bollickin' or suspended, that's if we're unlucky enough to be captured.'

Against his better judgement, and not wanting to be the

odd man out, Timmy finally agreed to join us; though it was obvious from his long face he felt guilty in allowing himself to be manipulated for the sake of a few dishonest hours. Three weeks later he was as corrupt as we were, his early jitters and feelings of guilt apparently forgotten, as he took the extra cash without even a blink.

.Of course success in such ventures encourages greed, and in our naivety each of us were guilty of falling into the obvious trap of adding more bogus hours than we could possibly have worked. As a result it was inevitable that our luck would eventually run out. Timmy had taken his turn in the scam in his stride, and even seemed to be revelling in the situation with a lot more confidence than the rest of us. This, I suspected, was probably because he'd not done anything dishonest in his life before, and now he'd discovered that deceit was not only profitable, but exhilarating and exciting.

I suppose it could be attributed to sods law, bad luck, or just to the run of the dice, but the next time Timmy handed over the time-book to the clerk he had no idea the bubble was about to burst, or that the next few hours would be amongst the worst he'd encountered in his short life. At that moment, though, he was on top of the world, wondering how the tradesmen would react if they found out just how devious their lads had become in such a short period of time. But his high spirits were about to be deflated, as Norman, the senior timekeeper, appeared at the doorway scratching his head as he flicked through the pages of Bootsy's records

'What day does Jimmy Reilly go to college lad?' he asked, looking bewildered. 'Only it looks as if Bootsy's booked him overtime on Tuesday by mistake,' he continued.

Tim, who flushed a deep red at the mere hint of pressure, stood transfixed as the colour drained from his face. Worse still, his usual gifted articulation failed completely and he stuttered and spluttered, unable to come up with any tangible explanation.

It's not like him,' Norman said. 'He's usually spot-on with the times. Never mind, not to worry, I'll catch up with him later an' we'll sort it out. Here, take this back with yer,' he said, handing the book to Timmy, who by now was shaking like a leaf. Norman turned to go, then glanced back peering at Tim, who seemed stuck to the spot.

'Bloody 'ell lad, what's the matter? You've gone the colour of boiled shite. Now don't be spewin' up in front of this door. Get yourself down to the bogs sharpish an' gerr a pint of cold water down yer gullet.'

Without stopping for breath Timmy fled towards the toilet block, not daring to glance over his shoulder in case he was being followed. Only when he felt safe and alone did he stop to gather his wits and compose himself.

Fortunately for Tim the navvies had dug a couple of trenches between the toilet block and the Fibre Factory to accommodate the main drainage system. These sub-service routes could not have been better positioned for an escape. After checking that the coast was clear he clambered into the sodden clay channel then slowly ducking and crawling, edged his way towards the back end of the factory to where we were working.

Billy was first to spot Timmy, as he frantically waved a crumpled white handkerchief above the trench, his ginger head bobbing up and down like a lifebuoy in a stormy sea.

'Jimmy, here a minute, I think somethin's gone wrong,' he whispered to me, pointing to the mounds of clay concealing Timmy's position.

'Bloody 'ell,' I gasped, glimpsing Timmy's mud-stained and panic-stricken face.

'Quick, go an' get Chunkie an' I'll meet yer round the other side of the building in a few minutes,' I yelled.

I ambled nonchalantly towards Robbo to make my usual excuse that I was dying to go to the lavvie and once out of view I sneaked round the corner to find the lads hiding behind a huge empty cable drum. Timmy was whinging inconsolably and utterly convinced that nothing could get us out of the dilemma we were now in.

'Me dad, 'ill murder me when 'e finds out,' he wailed. 'I don't know how many times he's drummed it in to me that honesty is the best policy. An' look worra 'ave done; lerr 'im down, 'aven't I?'

'Oh shurrup, an' gerra grip of yourself,' Billy muttered impatiently.

'Let's sort it out logically,' I said, remembering the sound advice Billy Chancer, a spark from my days at Pitts, had given me about meticulously analysing every situation before reaching a conclusion.

'Right lads, we know we're up to our eyes in it. Don't worry Tim, you're not on your own. Anyone of us could have slipped up, but the point is, how do we gerr out of it,' I said, glancing at the page in the time-book where two hours had been inserted against my name on the day I'd gone to night school.

'I'll own up that it was me, that way only one of us'll gerr in lumber,' Timmy offered.

'No way. We're all in this together, so we own up together an' take the rap,' Billy insisted, but Chunkie intervened. 'We either take a chance an' rub it out, or face the music. It's either one or the other. If we rub it out, it's only Norman's word that it was there in the first place. So then it's up to Timmy to try an' bluff it out. What d'yer reckon lads?'

'Oh I can't do that lads, me bottle 'ill go altogether, an' it's more lies on top, isn't it? No..no ..I can't do it, 'onest ter God, I can't,' Timmy wailed.

'Come on lads, we've gorra get movin' and get the book back before Bootsie smells a rat,' said Chunkie, realising that time was of the essence, no doubt helped by a glance at the newly aquired watch he'd bought from the proceeds of his dodgy overtime racket. Although Billy and I agreed with Chunkie, Timmy wouldn't budge on the proposal to remove the incriminating evidence.

I'll return it as it is, and put it on 'is desk, then I'm buggering off home, out of the way,' he muttered.

'What's up with the lads, they're quiet this avvie and not up to their usual antics,' George Sharkey observed during afternoon break. He was the youngest mate working for Tanjon's and spent most of his time mischief-making. No one felt safe when George was around. His favourite prank was hanging what we called 'tails' - made of rope, rags or trailing toilet paper - onto the behinds of the unwary visitor; or anyone else for that matter. As the victim walked through the factory, or even outside onto the open site, a fluttering tail hanging from a rear end seemed to bring endless amusement. Most of the workers would then immediately check their own backsides, just in case they in turn were parading one, for George was never one to discriminate between workers or management where the subtle art of 'tail hanging' was concerned.

Meanwhile, the time-book was now back in the foreman's office, and Timmy, pale as a lemon, had departed the site to catch the four o'clock bus. In the meantime we kept our thoughts to ourselves, observed Bootsy's every movement, and remained 'on pins,' waiting to be hauled before him and dragged over the coals.

Sharkey's right, you are bloody quiet this afternoon. That's three times you've been to the bogs. Worra you're up to?' Robbo asked, but I said it wasn't important and I'd explain later.

'Girls I suppose? When yer get to my age you'd rather 'ave a good pint of bitter, or a few bob on the gee gees. Anythin' for an easy life, that's my philosophy. Still you're only young once lad, but don't let them get yer down. Take a tip from an ould arse like me, they're not worth it in the end.'

By the time six o'clock arrived, however, and with no word from Bootsy, we accepted that our stay of execution would drift into Friday.

Even if it meant crawling in all the way or bumming a lift the twelve or thirteen miles from Woodside, no one in their right mind would miss pay day if they could help it. On that particular Friday, however, Timmy did. As the morning dragged on no one commented on his absence, and to our surprise, even when the dinner hour arrived, our leader still hadn't given the slightest hint that he was aware of our misdemeanours. In fact his attitude towards us seemed quite normal as he chatted to Chunkie about the batch of new girls due to start at the factory within days. However, lurking at the back of our minds, was the knowledge that sooner or later he'd make his way to the time office to collect the wages, and then our deception would be unmasked.

Normally, Bootsy would make the trip to the office shortly after the three o'clock break, but when Billy spotted him hurrying across just after dinner we had the feeling our number was up. Suddenly we were plunged into the dilemma of not knowing how we were going to defend ourselves against a possible sackable offence; or who might help us in our plight. With few options open, it didn't take a genius to realise our own tradesmen were the only ones we could possibly turn to.

'Robbo's all right, but there's no way I'll tell Podgy,' said Chunkie. 'You know worr 'es like. He'll clobber me for not bookin' 'im in as well.'

'You can forget about my mate,' Billy snapped quickly. 'Not only will he excommunicate me from the church, he'll 'ave me on penance 'til I finish me time.'

We all laughed, Billy was right. Confessing to the Pope was the equivalent to putting your head on a chopping block, such was his reputation for keeping a still tongue.

'What's this, a bloody Round Robin?' Robbo asked when we advanced towards him shortly after Bootsy's departure.

A Round Robin was a frequently used expression when three union members approached a shop steward to request that an unofficial meeting should be called.

After lighting a fag, Robbo listened intently as we explained the predicament we'd got ourselves into. Judging by his reactions he seemed shocked and more than a little annoyed at the mess we were in.

'You stupid little buggers. I'd 'ave credited you lads with more sense than to pull a trick like this,' he said finally. 'I just don't know how to advise you for the best, lads. But what you've gotta do is deny all knowledge of alterin' the book. 'Cos believe me, this outfit - an' any other for that matter will sack the four of yer in a jiffy. 'Then where d'yer think you'll end up? In the army, that's where. So you're goin' to 'ave to sit down and think seriously before makin' your next move.'

'An' it's no good even thinkin' of seein' the stewards,' he concluded, 'because they'll back-heel you straight away.'

In a funny sort of way we felt better after speaking with Robbo, and even though he wasn't able to give us any constructive advice there remained a glimmer of hope, when he partly blamed Bootsy for using a pencil instead of a pen.

Clinging to this tiny ray of sunshine, we construed that this could our first line of defence.

As we congregated in the compound to receive our wages,

Bootsy, showing no sign there was anything out of the ordinary, distributed the pay packets to each individual in his squad. As soon as I'd collected mine, and taking a leaf out of Chunkie and Billy's book, I was away like a flash, not even stopping to check the amount on the slip. But in my frantic attempt to put as much distance as possible between us, I failed to hear Bootsy shout, though I heard him the second time.

'REILLY! Are you going deaf or what?' he bawled. Stopping abruptly, I turned slowly, trying to conceal my nervousness as I ambled steadily back towards the compound, passing the rest of our troops as they made their way to the cabin. That is, all except Robbo, who remained standing near Bootsy, pretending to check his wages.

'What's happened to your mate, Tim, it's not like him missing out on pay day?' Bootsy said when I finally joined him in the compound.

'He's probably sick, or er.. er..maybe' he's had an accident. Or p'raps 'is granny's died or somethin', I mumbled, knowing full well I wasn't making sense. But having been caught on the hop, what else could I say in the circumstances?

Boots gave me a prolonged stare before he continued. 'Is that the best you can come up with Reilly? Tell me, out of curiosity, how many grannies do you lads have round here?'

I said nothing, I was still waiting for the real time bomb to explode. Then, to my amazement he changed the subject without mentioning the thing that was lodged like a brick at the forefront of my mind.

'Get yourself back on the job son,' he concluded. 'I'll ask Tommy Banks to drop young Timmy's wages off on his way home from work. It'll save me holdin' on to them 'til Monday.'

On the Monday morning the Crosville Bus for Bowies was about to leave Woodside at ten past seven and there was still no sign of Timmy. As he was rarely late we began thinking that he must've packed the job in. With a minute to spare, however, he came hurtling round the corner from Hamilton Square station, leaping on to the back platform, then squeezing besides us on the side-seat, looking redder than a peeled tomato. Whether this was due to his hundred yard run, or if his blood pressure was way up because of the trauma of not knowing what had happened, was debatable. There was no 'good morning lads,' or 'how are y'doin?' not that morning from Timmy. All he was interested in was Friday and what had transpired after he'd jumped ship on the Thursday.

'Worr 'appened when I didn't turn in on Friday?' he wanted to know.

'Nothin'. Boots said nothin' about the fiddle. So just act your normal self, if that's possible,' Billy replied sarcastically.

'Me dad went off his 'ead completely when I told 'im. Now he's stopped me pocket money an' he's put the block on me goin' out till me eighteenth birthday. And he's threatened to disown me if I get the bullet,' he spluttered, his bottom eyelids filling and the tears trickling down his cheeks.

'Why did yer have to tell 'im for, you soft little bugger?' Chunkie demanded.

'He knew there was somethin' up when I couldn't eat me dinner,' he moaned, searching for sympathy. And though we weren't in any mood to give him pity we couldn't help chuckling. Poor Timmy took everything so serious that anyone unaware of the situation would have thought he was about to be hung, drawn and quartered, the way he dramatised things.

'It's all right for you'se lot, your ould fella's aren't sparks,' he moaned. 'You've no idea how strict mine is, particularly with me bein' the oldest an' the only one in our family servin' their time.'

'My ould fella's just as bad,' I interrupted, 'an' he's only a docker. You can't even say 'bloody' in our 'ouse without him threatening to clip you over the ear for swearin' in front of me mam. I wouldn't mind, but me ould lady's stone deaf, but that makes no difference to him. We can't speak at the table, and we all have to go ter mass on Sunday's whether we want to or not, even though he doesn't go 'imself. Now that's worr I call strict.'

'But you're turned eighteen Jim, why don't yer kick up about it?' 'Chunkie said.

'It's a waste of time.'I replied. 'He always comes up with the same old argument: 'while you sleep under the roof of this house you obey my rules.' So rather than rock the boat, I'd sooner bite me tongue and stay put.'

Avoiding Bootsy that week was easier said than done. From the moment we arrived on site until the Thursday, whenever he appeared within walking distance the lads made themselves scarce. Then it was my turn to carry out the mess duties and my first priority - taking an early morning brew to the foreman's office - meant there was no way of missing him. As each day trickled by nothing out of the ordinary seemed to happen, until the Thursday, then, as I was carrying the time-book past the bogs, I had a funny feeling that each step was bringing me closer to the same fate as Bonso. Before reaching the end of the trail a little voice in my head urged me to stop and take stock of the situation. I knew the ball was firmly in my court and decided it was high time I put into use all the guile and the craftiness that I'd learnt since becoming an apprentice.

Oozing with an almost inexplicable new-found confidence, I swaggered into the compound, climbed the three steps to the office, rattled the door and handed the file over to a young clerk occupying a table near the entrance. Maintaining the charade, I then stepped back outside and waited for the senior timekeeper to return it to me.

Norman appeared almost immediately with the time-book held open, and a few pages fluttering as if he'd been looking for signs of any anomalies. For once, his usual barrage of jovial quips and comments seemed to have deserted him, and I was sure I caught him peering slyly over the rims of his glasses looking out for any hint of weakness in my demeanour. Of course I was ready for him, and with equal tenacity I set out to divert his attention by launching into a garbled praise about Tottenham Hotspur's recent weekend performance, a subject dear to his heart. However, my efforts seemed to fall on deaf ears and after a few uncomfortable moments of silence he closed the book, went back inside the office, only to re- appear some five minutes later with strict instructions to 'return it to my foreman intact' - strongly emphasising the word 'intact'.

I ambled back into Bootsy's cabin. He didn't even look up from studying the site drawings when I placed the book on his desk in its usual place alongside the clock cards.

A couple of days later I handed over the reigns of 'peggie' duty to Chunkie, still convinced that sooner or later the news of our indiscretions would become common knowledge on the site - and more likely sooner rather than later!

As it turned out I wasn't wrong in my prediction. On the next Thursday, as he trampled the well-worn path towards the main offices, Chunkie couldn't resist opening the book to mootch at the number of hours certain individuals had clocked up since the job began. Reaching the corner of the lavvie block he stopped dead; leaping out from the bottom of one of the pages he saw Bootsy's carefully inserted cautionary note.

> '*Anybody caught defacing this book will be fired immediately.*'

R. Webster.

Chunkie also noted that everyone's name was now entered in an indelible black ink, with the overtime hours shown in a distinctive red.

If records are meant to be broken, then Chunkie broke a few that afternoon - he was back at site almost before we'd had time to start our second shift. Gathering his wits and his composure he told us about Bootsy's warning note and of the change in recording the names and times from pencil to ink. Significantly, it seemed, Bootsy had not uttered a single word about our deceit, nor were there any immediate recriminations even when Chunkie handed the book back to him at the office.

As the weeks passed without any word or hint from Bootsy about our indiscretions, we carried on working as normal. Each of us made further trips to the time office where Norman accepted the book without so much as a second glance, and eventually we simply assumed that the silence on their part indicated an end to the matter.

Of course, Robbo, the only tradesman to be fully aware of our shaky position and the extent of our fraudulent activities, could hardly emphasise enough how fortunate we were still to be in a job; and of the huge debt we owed both to Bootsy and Norman the timekeeper for keeping the whole sorry mess under wraps.

We could only agree…wholeheartedly and contritely.

The boss poser

Norman (Nobby) Alcock was a ladies man and he knew it. And so did everyone else. His philandering was legendary, and although his exploits annoyed some of the older workers, we didn't mind joining him on his excursions through those sections of the factory where the majority of the women worked. Indeed we found that watching his technique was an interesting way for us to further our own limited education in this delicate minefield.

The huge size and expensive nature of the contract meant that all types of machinery were being bought and installed at a furious rate. As soon the machines were inspected and tested they were then handed over to the young girls who took over their operation and running. This was the phase of the work we'd looked forward to more than anything else; particularly as our voices had more or less shrugged off an adolescent squeakiness, the pimples, spots and blackheads were no longer as prominent as they'd once been, and a comb had suddenly become an essential piece of equipment.

Of course, our lack of experience had its drawbacks when it came to competing with some of the tradesmen and younger mates, all of whom played heavily on the fact that compared to them, we were mere novices; which of course we were.

Nobby was even head and shoulders above this group, and was perhaps, a perfect example of the kind of opposition we were likely to come up against should any of us even manage to try fix up a date. But of course, this did not deter us in the least from mooching through every part of the factory, even when we had no business to be there.

It was no secret that Nobby knew most of the girls in the Fibre factory by their first names, and to boost his advantage would park his brand new Ford Consul almost opposite the entrance in order to show-off as the women poured out of work.

In comparison to those like me who sported a somewhat immature and puny physique, Nobby was in a different league. He was a tall, dark-skinned type, with hazel-eyes, a fine aquiline nose and thick black hair; and as some of the older workers often said, 'thought he was God's gift to women.' So what chance did we have?

What's more, it made little difference that he was a twenty six-year old married man, with two children and one on the way, because the word, 'Fidelity' was simply not in his dictionary. One of his chat-up lines, and something we lads found amusing - but which certain tradesmen called pathetic - had to be his 'tapping up' technique, or what he effectively called 'the French connection.'

Within minutes of a new batch of girls arriving, Nobby - full of his own importance - would be hanging around waiting for an opportunity to dash across to make himself known. Usually he would approach this by going through a rigmarole of explaining certain quirks in some new machine they were about to operate, and then introduce himself as ' Norman Al-coche;' almost childishly anticipating this Gallic sounding name would be sufficient to steal a march on any competitor.

Long after the dust had settled on our time-sheet misdemeanour and news of our ill-gotten gains had made the rounds (conveniently leaked to the workforce) courtesy of the gossip centres - I resumed the roll of 'Peggie for the week.'

Taking orders first thing every morning for bacon, egg and black jock butties was something not to be treated lightly. Making a mistake and cocking an order for a workmate's greasy breakfast could make the difference between having a cushy day or experiencing a really bad one.

With the shopping list safely tucked inside my jacket pocket I set off one morning to walk the short journey to the canteen, under a dark and overcast sky. By the time I reached the open ground the heavens opened and driving rain had soaked me to the skin.

The Sack factory, running parallel to the Fibre Plant, offered some immediate protection, though few contractors ventured near there, or indeed had any reason to go there; except perhaps to sneak to the toilets if they were caught short. Compared to the new unit next door, the Sack factory was a dull and un-inviting type of building, with huge reels of paper and pallets of cardboard stacked high above the ground, littering the entrance. Of course we were hardly concerned with the layout or its appearance, our sole interest was in the younger female employees who worked there.

With a head on me like a drowned rat, I stood by the open door of the factory, feeling the warmth seeping around my body. There was no one in sight, so I crept into the building intending to take a short cut to the canteen. Out of the wind and rain, and in a comfortable environment, I ambled nonchalantly along the shadowy central passageway, gazing at women operating the various machines. Suddenly a huge figure leapt out from behind an empty stack-a-truck, gripped me by my lapels, lifted me physically off my feet and pinned me against a wall before I even had a chance to take my hands out of my Donkey coat pockets.

'Got yer, you little twerp. Can't yer friggin' well read?' a gravel voice growled from somewhere way above my head.

When I recovered my senses I found I was staring into the eyes of a six foot female goliath with short cropped hair, a chiselled chin, and a grip every bit as spectacular as that of her look-a-like, Bluto, Popeye's muscle-bound rival. Like the popular cartoon strong-man, she yanked me up without effort, my face level and within three inches of a set of gnashers that an African gorilla would have been proud of. And at that moment, if the truth were known, I felt as if I probably was three inches closer to the end of my life.

'Can't yer read?' she grimaced, twisting my neck and head so violently that I could hardly miss the NO CONTRACTORS ALLOWED notices which were prominently displayed on both walls of the passageway.

'So tell me? Where d'yer think you're goin' Short arse?'

'The cannie..I'm goin' to the cannie for the lad's butties,' I squeaked, my legs dangling in mid-air and the crutch of my ovies yanked up high as far as my belly button, sending my ollies in opposite directions.

'What's your name?' she asked, lowering her voice.

'Jimmy, er err Reilly,' I managed to splutter, as she released her grip and dropped me to the floor.

'Next time you come through 'ere, you friggin' well see me

first, 'ave yer got that?' But before I had time to assure her I had
no intention whatsoever of encroaching on this part of Bowies
Empire ever again, she poked her thick, nicotine stained finger
into my chest saying, 'an' that goes for the rest of your cronies.
So you'd better warn them that Rocky - that's me (as if I hadn't
guessed) - takes no prisoners when they enter my patch.'

'Yeah I've got yer message Rocky.' I answered, feeling for
the holes in my head where it felt the majority of the sweat
running into my eyes was leaking from.

'Come on then. Are you goin' to the cannie or what?' she
said in a softer tone. I nodded, unsure whether she intended to
punch me as a parting shot, to help me on my way. Thankfully
my physical chastisement was at an end.

'Right Shorty, for starters, you can get me twenty Woodies
while you're over there. An' don't forget me change,' she added
thrusting a ten bob note in my hand.

'Just as if,' I thought, scarpering quicker than I'd done for a
long time.

At break-time back in the sanctuary of the cabin I related my
near-death experience to Chunkie, Billy and Timmy, describing
Rocky's size and fearsome demeanour. As usual, they simply
thought I was exaggerating, but realised I was being more than
serious when I offered to bet any of them half a dollar to enter
the Sack factory on their own and come out unscathed. Needless
to say no one took me up on the wager, but in opening my big
mouth I was immediately subject to all kinds of jokes and jibes
at being terrorised by a woman, albeit a big one.

The hysterical laughter, and the mere mention of a woman
was enough to catch the attention of 'big ears' Nobby Allcock
and some of his mates, who wrongfully assumed we were
joking about yet another futile attempt on my part to break my
duck with one of the machinist. In order to capture a slice of
the action and take the Mickey at our lack of experience, they
all moved across to our part of the hut.

'It's no good you'se lads dreamin' of what you'd like to do;
gerr in there an' have a go at tryin' your hand properly. They're
just waitin' for some smart 'ansome lads like you'se lot to ask
them out,' Nobby beamed, bringing smiles of agreement from
his audience.

'What d'yer mean, dreamin' like? Jimmy's just copped off with a cracker. One that you've missed out on Nobby,' Billy said, nudging me on the quiet.

'If he's copped off, it must be one of my rejects,' Nobby sneered, glancing over his shoulder for the support of his mates.

'Anyway,' he said, as if it was of no real consequence, 'just out of curiosity, where does this bit of fluff hang out like? 'Cos there's no chance she's slipped through my net.'

We glanced at each other quickly, surprised how easily Nobby had fallen into the trap, and decided to string him along.

'What d'yer reckon Jim, d'yer want ter put Nobby onto her? After all she's a bit tall and refined for you in my opinion,' Chunkie said, with a touch of sober sincerity in his tone to help the scam along.

I didn't answer straight away, but placed my hand across my mouth to stop myself from laughing out loud, all the while contemplating the outcome and the potential mayhem if Nobby ventured into Rocky's den.

'Er.. I don't want ter let her down like,' I answered quietly, 'but I'll think about it, an' let yer know, as soon as I make me mind up.'

'What's 'er name then?' Nobby asked, at which point, the older workers sitting on the adjacent tables joined in the fun and began giving Nobby a dose of his own medicine.

'Fancy short-arse Reilly' getting fixed up,' they laughed' while you spend most of your time posing.'

'Her name's Roxanna,' I answered. 'An' I've gotta be honest with yer,' I 'lied, 'I couldn't believe me luck when she called me over an' asked me to take her out for a night.' Suddenly the more my imagination got carried away, the more I found it easier to romance. 'But, I've bin thinkin',' I said carefully, as if I had a problem. 'She might be only after me body, an' I'm not sure I'd be up to it, not with her bein' six foot tall an' all that.'

'She's six foot tall?' Trunkie Davies yelled from the bottom of the cabin. 'Christ Reilly, she'll suck yer in an' blow you out in bubbles. You'll need a friggin' scaffolding plank across yer arse if you try getting your leg over with her.'

The Pope, parked just in front of Trunkie, had his head resting on the table pretending to be asleep. But, right on cue, and as expected, his neck tilted up, as it did every time some juicy snippet was aired. Bootsy, however, appeared at this point and the conversation quickly ended as he called time on our morning break.

At half two, thirty minutes before the afternoon meal break, as I made my way to the canteen with a shopping list for ciggies, mars bars and lemonade, I deliberately headed towards the Sack factory knowing that my movements were being monitored by Nobby. Confident that I wouldn't be manhandled for the second time, I approached the area where I could see Rocky like some huge tawny owl perched way up on a cushioned seat on the stack-a-truck. Her cold, calculating eyes were not only on the girls in her charge, but were scanning the passageways for strays like me; or those who couldn't read the warning signs and fancied their chances by entering this uncompromising building.

'ROCKY,' I yelled. 'D'yer want any ciggies or anything else from the cannie?' She glared back, shaking her head without saying a word.

'Erm, d'yer wanna know somethin'?' I asked, a little more boldly.

'Worra yer talkin' about, do I wanna know something?' she replied irritably, leaving her lofty observation post.

'One of our sparks who's married and 'as bin pesterin' the girls in the Fibre to take them out, has said he'll be startin' in this buildin' next.'

'Did yer tell him about me bein' in charge in 'ere?' she roared, showing her frightening fangs for the second time that day.

'No, 'cos he wouldn't 'ave believed me anyway.'

'Well, 'es in for a friggin' big shock if 'e comes in 'ere trying ter get fresh, 'cos all those girls over there,' she said, pointing to the area where the majority worked, 'come under my thumb.' An' he'll 'ave ter fight me first to get near them. Which fella is 'e anyway? He's not that big, skinny, gormless show-off with the posh green car, is he?'

'Yeah that's 'im,' I replied delighted how quickly and easily my plan was panning out.

'Just leave 'im to me,' she said, rotating her shoulders like a boxer loosening up for a title fight.

I was still smiling when I entered the hut with the goodies, but failed to realise that Nobby was behind me, bragging to his mates that he knew the identity and the whereabouts of 'my secret bit of stuff'.

The following morning Nobby again broached the subject of my up-coming date.

'Well young fella, have yer made your mind up yet? 'Cos if you're not goin' to do the honours you can pass 'er over to me,' he smirked, displaying his usual air of confidence and macho bravado. Meanwhile, everything seemed much quieter than usual in the cabin that morning, as if everyone, except Nobby knew he was being set-up and was waiting for the crunch.

'I'm back heelin' her.' I replied. 'For a kick-off, she's far too tall for me, an' secondly, how am I goin' to gerr out 'ere without transport?'

'Yeah it's difficult without a 'danny mar' lad,' Nobby consoled me. 'But I didn't want to step on your toes an' muscle in on yer, you know that Jim, don't yer?'

'No problems. If you want ter go an' tap her up it's fine by me, I said, with a light but regretful tone to my voice. 'But don't say it was me that's put you on to her,' I added, trying to introduce a final trace of disappointment.

Walking back to the job I received a few complimentary remarks about my performance, though Robbo uttered a word of caution about the possibility of reprisals.

'You're a friggin' little liar Reilly,' he said, with a wry chuckle. 'How you kept a straight face, I don't know. 'Remember lad, and be prepared, 'Cos the fanny merchant, will get you back, one way or another. And in this life you've got to be able to take it as well as dole it out; don't forget that.'

Before reaching the entrance to the Sack factory, Nobby turned, gave the thumbs up to where we all stood, apparently enthusing over his 'boss poser' performance, and entered the building singing, 'Roxanna, I've just met a girl named Roxanna.'

Following behind, the gang dashed towards the entrance; all except me - as a precautionary measure I stayed right where I was, just out of view.

For a short while we heard nothing, then all hell broke loose. After a clattering and banging, and the initial yelps and screams had died down, all went quiet. Finally the door re-opened and Nobby crawled into view, shirt torn, blood streaming from his nose, and sporting a heavily bruised eye.

Bloody 'ell, worra monster,' he gasped.

A few of his colleagues eased him on to the dampened grass verge, while others who failed to conceal their amusement laughed openly at his misfortune and distress.

During the following weeks as Nobby's bruises disappeared, it seemed as if he'd forgotten his ordeal. And in spite of what had occurred he didn't appear to bear any malice towards me. Even more surprisingly was the way he accepted the mickey-taking of the squad with a quiet and resolute good humour.

Fortunately for our 'boss poser,' his near annihilation didn't appear to leave few physical or mental scars, nor did it deter his appetite regarding the female workforce; although, naturally, he gave the Sack factory a wide berth.

Nobby's revenge

As each section of the Fibre factory was completed, Bootsy began transferring those from his team now surplus to requirements across the site to join the majority of Tanjon's employees engaged on the installation of the main contract in the old mill. To tidy up the loose ends, and to cover any small job that needed modifying, a skeleton crew of four sparks, four apprentices and the mates, Shifty and Sharkey, remained in the Fibre.

Despite receiving two written warnings from Bootsy for spending too much time away from the job, Nobby was still chancing his luck sneaking to the 'out of bounds' areas of the factory where most of the girls worked. However, as the 'mopping up' programme accelerated, he discovered the only way he could continue his amorous activities was by forfeiting his meal break, something the rest of the tradesmen found exasperating.

After the dinner break one Wednesday afternoon, as we were busy installing a fire alarm system above the offices, Nobby arrived back on the job, late as usual. Looking mighty pleased with himself he began raving about a new girl, Maureen, a supposedly stunning brunette who he'd been pursuing all week, and who now apparently agreed to go for a drink on Friday night in Ellesmere Port town centre.

Robbo was seething. On a number of occasions he'd 'bitten the bullet' saying nothing when Nobby had sloped back late after his dinner break and left the rest of the squad a man short. Now, Robbo's patience finally snapped and he tore into the Boss Poser like a tornado, telling him in no uncertain terms to grow up and act his age for a change. Nobby, however was in such high spirits that Robbo's anger seemed to have little effect.

'You wanna see her, Robbo. Even you'd be tempted to try your hand with this piece,' he chortled. Robbo just glared before snapping back.

'Look lad, they're all the same ter me. I've gorra long haired one at home me'self, and so 'ave you. What's more, one's enough for any normal man, so don't be givin' me any more of your bullshit, an' let's 'ave you pullin' your weight for a change, like the rest of us.'

For the remainder of the afternoon we plodded on in silence, and for once Nobby didn't slope off from the job. Nor did he mention his forthcoming date. Though next morning, true to form, he slipped straight back into his normal routine, bragging loudly about previous conquests and rattling on about a couple of new girls he described as 'waiting to be interviewed.'

It was during the dinner break that same day, when he returned earlier than usual from his daily meandering, that he dropped the bombshell.

'Jimmy,' he said, 'how d'yer fancy makin' up a foursome on Friday night, with me, Mo, and her mate Maggie?'

'Why me?' I replied, completely shocked and obviously suspicious: yet, at the same time flattered in a funny sort of way that Nobby, the Boss Poser, would even contemplate allowing me - 'short arse Reilly,' to tag along with him on a date.

Of course, the rest of the lads were more wary, whispering on the quiet for me to watch my step, but I tended to ignore their concerns by searching naively for some other reason as to why he'd chosen me instead of Chunkie or any of the other lads. Eventually I came to the satisfactory conclusion that Nobby, along with everyone else, had heard of my lack of success in chatting up the factory girls, and was using his vast experience to show me the ropes. Remember this was a time when my morale had slipped to an all time low, and I was feeling more than a little sorry for myself because of my romantic failures.

The situation had come to a head one lunchtime when I was idling through the factory with Timmy and we'd come across a group of young girls having a smoke. Although we were totally out-numbered, we walked past them not expecting any comment. But when we were greeted by a fierce barrage of wolf whistles and cat calls this stopped us dead in our tracks.

'Come on Tim, our luck's changed. Let's take a shufty over and check them out,' I said, strutting and thrusting every bit of my five foot two frame as we crossed the narrow passageway that separated us, suddenly full of ideas of confronting our admirers with the latest small talk.

To my dismay I soon discovered it was the angelic choir boy

looks of the much taller Timmy - with his mop of carrot coloured hair and freckled face - that had taken their fancy; not me with my sallow complexion and sharp Roman nose. As if to rub salt into the open wound of my deflated pride, their comments on the size of my nose proved to be the straw that broke the camels back, so much so that I became paranoid about the affliction. I even adopted a bizarre measure to check on the length of my beak, by going as far as using two adjacent mirrors.

On one occasion when I was in this contortionist position in our bathroom checking my conk for the umpteenth time, Tommy popped his head round the door and asked me what I was looking for.

'Blackheads,' I said

'You must have a big nose if you can get a black head on it,' he replied, a summary which did little to improve my self-esteem.

Now, it seemed, all of this was swept aside at the prospect of being given the opportunity of a lifetime to join Nobby on one of his clandestine excursions, and without the chance of risking a 'knock-back.' Obviously I wanted to glean as much advance information as I could about my blind date; and to give Nobby his due he responded by discretely quizzing Maureen about her friend Maggie.

'Maggie's about your age,' he told me the next day. 'She's a smart piece, a blonde who likes a good laugh, can hold her ale, so with your patter and personality you'll 'ave plenty to chat about. In fact, that's why I recommended you to Maureen in the first place. What more could you ask for?' he added. 'And besides, just think of the bonus you're goin' to experience by coming along with me.' 'And don't forget, he assured me, 'you're bein' picked up and dropped at your doorstep in me new danny mar. So lad, you can't go far wrong there, can yer?'

By the time Friday arrived there wasn't a soul in the cabin who wasn't fed up with hearing Nobby's preparations and tactics being endlessly discussed

'Nobby by name and Nobby by nature,' Trunkie Davies remarked, as he listened to Nobby's last minute orders about the importance of my calling him 'Norman' on our date.

'Nob'ead more like it,' said Shifty, without raising his eyes from his newspaper.

I was home in record time that Friday night, and even before the thermostat on the immersion heater had time to regulate I'd emptied the tank, scrubbed the daily grime from my body, soaked in the warmth of a hot bath, and enjoyed the luxury of having the bathroom to myself. What a difference from the days of the tin bath in the back kitchen, boiling the water on the gas stove, and enduring the breeze blowing under the door of the outside lavvie. All of which we'd taken in our stride when we lived down town. Now I lay back, day-dreaming just what it was like to be rich, and all the while counting my blessings.

'Have you ironed me best shirt ma? I yelled, slipping into my trousers and parading in front of the mirror in the back bedroom. Our Tommy, who'd been mooching round on the landing for some mischievous reason, clattered downstairs just in time to cop mam scorching the tail end of my shirt.

'Jimmy'll go mad when he sees that,' he yelled, just loud enough for me to hear.

'What's up,' I muttered, dashing into the kitchen holding my pants up with one hand and flattening my damp hair with the other.

'It's only a little scorch mark, son, nobody will see it with your jacket on.'

'Worr 'appens if me shirt comes out of me kecks when I'm out?' I moaned.

'Don't be so damned fussy, your dad never complains about his shirts.'

'He never goes out so it doesn't matter to him, does it?' I snapped back.

'Anymore lip from you and you can iron your own shirts in future,' ma replied angrily.

In a fit of temper I grabbed hold of the shirt and bounced back up the stairs.

'Don't forget to leave your digs money before you go out our Jimmy,' ma yelled, winking at Tommy who smiled back knowing he could blackmail me for an extra shilling pocket money for keeping quiet about my latest outburst when dad came home from work.

Not all that many cars passed along our street at evening time - or during the day for that matter. So when the silence of the neighbourhood was shattered by a continuous ear-piercing blast on a horn that seemed to last for ages, we weren't the only neighbourhood family to open the front door to check the cause of the commotion. Along with a fair-sized audience I watched from our doorstep as Nobby slithered from his gleaming car, smirking from ear to ear.

Dressed to the hilt, and looking if he was going to a premiere movie he welcomed me like some long-lost friend, while our Tommy - showing off as usual - set about using the sleeve of his jersey to polish up a dull section on the bonnet which somehow had been missed.

After going overboard and discussing directions in detail, for the benefit of the audience, I slid into the passenger side while Nobby clambered into the driving seat and revved a couple of times. Glancing around the sprawl of newly-built houses, and obviously enjoying the attention that he and his jalopy had generated in this backwater council estate, Nobby then placed his foot on the accelerator and the car purred slowly away from our neck of the woods.

As we sped along the old Chester Road, relaxed and revelling in my comfortable seat, I felt a sense of exhilaration alongside Nobby. Peeping sideways I couldn't help admire my companion's choice of dress. He was decked out in a beige tweed sports jacket, grey worsted trousers and smelling as if he'd been hosed down with a gallon of cheap aftershave. He really looked the part for the occasion, and in line with its owner the walnut dashboard of the car was polished like a mirror, while the spotlessly clean upholstery presented not a stray hair or piece of fluff to mar the occasion.

If only the lads could see me now, I thought, winding the window down and scanning each passing pedestrian in the hope that at least some one I knew would pass by - even Chunkie would do.

'This is the way to travel,' I whispered to myself, heading towards the 'Port,' riding in style and feeling like a toff in this up-market jalopy.'

Half an hour later after turning into a posh tree-lined avenue,

Nobby pulled the Consul alongside a secluded detached house, stopping just past a pair of fancy cast-iron gates.

'This is it Jim,' he said, climbing out of the car. 'Phew! her ould fella must 'ave a few bob an' be on a good number to own a gaff like this,' he added, peering through the golden privet hedge surrounding a bowling green lawn, as if expecting to see a Rolls Royce or a Jaguar parked on the path;   perhaps even both.

'It's bloody good job I've gorra decent danny, or I'd 'ave no chance with Maureen,' he smiled, slipping back behind the wheel after hearing the front door slam.

'Now don't forget worra told yer this mornin' Jimmy. Remember, after we've been for a drink we'll split up an' I'll then pick you up outside the paper shop by the station, at quarter past eleven. Have you got that?'

I nodded, and for some reason that was hard to explain I began having niggling doubts as to whether I'd done the right thing in accompanying Nobby on a blind date. But when Maureen appeared looking radiant and dressed like a film star, any lingering doubts suddenly disappeared. As soon as she climbed into the seat behind me Nobby moved into gear in more ways than one, describing just what it was he had in mind for the night out. His smooth-talking line of patter was impressive, or so I thought. But then I spotted Maureen's reaction in the driving mirror, and had a feeling she'd come across his type before.

'I reckon we'd better get moving an' see if Maggie's ready,' Maureen said, cutting Nobby off in mid-sentence, just as he was about to continue with yet more exotic plans for the evening's event.

'I hope you're game for a laugh Jimmy,' she giggled, tapping me on the shoulder, 'because I've got to be honest with you, Maggie's a bit of a nut case at times. But she's got a heart of gold, so take everything in your stride and you'll have a good night out.'

Smiling nervously I glanced across at Nobby. He, as usual, seemed as if he had everything under control.

At the far side of town we drove onto a council estate containing a variety of small semi-detached houses, with the occasional grey, pebble-dashed terrace dwelling scattered here and there. Following Maureen's explicit directions we eventually stopped outside a larger town house which had a couple of boneshaker bikes propped under the lounge window and a double-decker pram parked alongside the front door.

'Right Norman, just beep once or twice and she'll be out,' Maureen said. Nobby obliged, using the side of his fist like a hammer, blasting the horn for at least thirty seconds until the front door seemed to spring open in response to the noise.

To say I was shocked when Maggie emerged would be an under statement. My ticker almost packed in as she bounced down the short path towards us wearing a set of blue short-sleeved bib and brace overalls with the distinctive Chester Zoo motif emblazoned on the breast pocket, her baggy kecks tucked into a pair of long black wellies.

My mouth fell open. I was lost for words. Her similarity in looks and physique to Rocky, the man-eater from Bowies was striking. Except that Maggie was a slightly smaller version of the Amazon who'd terrified me at work only a few weeks earlier.

'She's gorr be a relative,' I muttered eventually, glancing at Nobby, who looked to me as if he was in some sort of a coma.

'Hiya lads,' Maggie yelled, clambering into the back of the car and plonking herself next to Maureen. Snapping out of his trance-like state, Nobby suddenly turned his nose one way then the other and began sniffing loudly and exaggeratedly at the air. Then he swung round to face the girls, a look of growing alarm on his face.

'Phew! Bloody 'ell, what's the pong?' he growled, frantically winding his window down. 'It smells like bloody monkey piss to me.'

'You've got it wrong there mate,' Maggie replied in a slow and casual drawl. 'I've been workin' with the elephants this mornin' and the camels all afternoon. So now that the monkeys are out of the equation, you can take your pick from either of the other two.'

Turning back to Maureen, who had tears of laughter welling in her eyes, she then said 'give me ten minutes to get washed and changed, Mo, and I'll be with you.'

Climbing slowly from the car Maggie swaggered up the path, cockily turning back to grin at us. As I watched her disappear into the house I still harboured a strong suspicion that taking a chance on a blind date had perhaps not been a wise move on my part.

As soon as Maggie was out of view Nobby leapt into action. Hurling himself out of his drivers seat he wrenched open the rear door, crouched on all fours and began sniffing the upholstery like a dog on heat.

'Have you seen the bloody stain she's left on me seat?' he cried in anguish, using a handkerchief from his trouser pocket to try to remove what seemed to be an in-grained mark left in a valley where Maggie had been perched only a few moments earlier.

'Here, spray some of this on your precious car if it's worrying you so much,' Maureen remarked, sarcastically, retrieving a small bottle of perfume from her handbag and passing it across to him.

Realising the implications that a scented seat could inflict on his already faltering marital status Nobby refused politely, saying the smell would eventually disappear if the car windows were left open for a while after we moved off.

As we waited for Maggie to get ready Nobby asked me to swap seats with Maureen. I was only too happy to oblige, hoping that by being in the back I might come up with an opportune plan to escape the predicament I was lumbered with. But before I had chance to work out a decent excuse, Maggie re-appeared, looking smart and distinctly slimmer. The transformation certainly took me by surprise. It was such a change that I found it hard to believe this was the same 'bib and brace' clad figure who'd greeted us only some ten minutes earlier. Mind you, I still felt like a frail schoolboy in comparison.

'We'll 'ave a couple in 'The Grace' an' leave you'se two love birds to get to know each other,' Nobby said in a matter of fact way, glancing in the mirror. I couldn't help noticing an amused gleam in his eye, seeing me and my date sitting as far as possible from each other.

'Er.. any chance of droppin' us off at the Dock Hotel?' I said, the first words I'd spoken since Maggie had clambered aboard.

'Yer what! The Dock Hotel? What d'yer take me for, a bleedin' scrubber?' she hissed vehemently and I felt my face blushing as if it was on fire.

'Don't get me wrong, it's the only ale 'ouse I know round 'ere in the Port,' I stuttered, wishing I'd kept my big mouth shut and just let events take their course.

'You can get that idea right out of your head for starters,' she replied, 'cos we're stayin' all night in The Grace, whether you like it or not.'

Always the coward in any situation concerning women, I simply nodded in mute agreement. Nobby spluttered loudly, suppressing a laugh, obviously tickled at my inexperience and weakness.

After a couple of pints the tension that existed seemed to diminish, and by the time Nobby and Maureen were ready to leave, as he put it, 'to take advantage of the beauty of the prevailing countryside,' Maggie and I were chatting amiably, even if my initial intention to get as much ale down my neck as quickly as possible still hadn't changed.

As the evening progressed, with Maggie matching me pint for pint, I had visions of running out of cash. But then, as if reading my thoughts, she produced a wad of notes from her purse that could easily have choked a donkey.

'Put your dough away lad, the rest of the ale's on me,' she said.

I pretended to spurn the offer, saying I still had a few bob left. But Maggie wasn't the sort of girl you could argue with, and after a few half-hearted objections I reluctantly accepted her good natured gesture.

Shortly before the bell rang for last orders I realised I'd sunk more than I should have, when my leering eyes - no doubt playing tricks - had once again wandered in Maggie's direction. To my astonishment, I saw she was looking unbelievably attractive.

I'd also noticed my voice was slurring as we chatted on about this and that, but I still had my wits about me when she suddenly changed the subject as if intending to catch me out.

'Norman's married isn't he?' she remarked casually.

'Erm...er .. 'ow would I know if he's 'itched or not,' I replied defensively.

'You're a liar Jimmy, I can tell by your face.'

'No ..er..er ..I don't know for sure.. 'onest ter God, that's the truth,' I mumbled without conviction.

'Liar,' she repeated, only this time more aggressively.

'Let's get going,' I muttered, I'm feelin' a bit lousy.'

As I climbed from the chair I thought I felt it tilting, so I shoved it to one side. The next thing I knew my wobbly legs had buckled and I was staggering backwards, eventually landing in an old ladies lap. Before I had a chance to recover or apologise I was gripped round my waist, and then felt a wet, sloppy kiss being planted on the side of my cheek.

Give Maggie her due she was as quick as lightening. Thrusting out her huge hands, she grabbed the sliding empty pint glasses to prevent them crashing to the floor, thus saving me further embarrassment.

'Come on you, let's get yer outside,' she snarled, placing the 'empties' on the bar, all the while glaring at me as I staggered from the clutches of the sex-starved pensioner who was still chuckling loudly.

If my legs had felt wobbly inside the pub, they virtually folded when I stepped outside into the fresh air. Once again it was only the fact that Maggie kept her cool that saved me from making a holy show of myself in front of 'The Grace's' regulars. With my arm hanging limply across her shoulder she hauled me away down the street, plonking me on the floor of the first shop doorway that we came to so she could have a breather and a quick drag on a Woodbine.

As the cold from the tiles seeped through my thin gabardine pants I began taking deep and prolonged breaths. After a while I somehow found the strength to stagger to my feet, announcing to Maggie that I was fit enough now to continue the journey under my own steam.

With half an hour to spare, I realised we were only about a half-mile from the Station Hotel, which still left plenty of time for me to meet Nobby at a quarter past eleven.

'I'll walk that far with you, just to make sure you get there in one piece,' she said consolingly, slipping her heavy arm under mine to support me as I took each faltering step towards the town centre. After stopping a couple of times for a short rest, my little legs felt steadier and my speech even became a midges more coherent. This somewhat amazing transition from being bladdered one minute to becoming almost sober in less time than it takes to tell, seemed to catch Maggie by surprise. Pushing her grimacing face to within inches of mine, she now bluntly accused me of only pretending to be plastered in order to get well in with her.

'Get well in,' I thought. 'Chance would be a fine thing.'

As I rambled on making some lame excuse about being one of those fella's who recover quickly from a hangover, my reasoned argument seemed to fall on deaf ears. And that's when I decided to take the bull by the horns by suggesting we might step into an adjacent jigger to give me the chance to make amends for getting bevvied and spoiling her night out.

'Get lost,' she barked. 'You could hardly stand up five minutes ago, an' here you are tryin' ter get your leg over.'

'You've got it all wrong Maggie,' I protested. 'All I'm after is a bit of a neckin' session before I hit the road,' I lied, hoping that the one act would perhaps lead to another, just as Nobby had suggested it might.

'Alright,' she said, leading me a few yards down the jigger, stopping alongside the first backyard door. 'Stand on the step, an' listen here, Reilly, no Roman hands an' Russian fingers, and definitely no French kissin'. Have yer got that?'

'Airy muff,' I replied with a chuckle.

'Wotcha mean, airy muff?' she growled, pushing me violently against the backyard door, which fortunately withstood the velocity of my nine stone weight crashing against it.

'Fair enough...that's worra mean...fair enough. I'm only practicin' me Cockney slang, that's all, Maggie' I protested.

'Cockney slang! You want ter grow up lad. How old did yer say you are?'

'I didn't,' I replied.

At that moment my libido suddenly came to life and those salacious thoughts, almost forgotten since we'd left The Grace, now re-entered my head. From somewhere deep inside I mustered up an enormous effort, spreading my arms round her huge waist as if landing a great white whale, and managed to tug her towards me. Then, copying the style of Erol Flynn, that famous silver-screen romeo, I swung an arm round her neck, gazed into her bleary eyes, pouted my lips, and like a sacrificial lamb I put my head on the chopping block. Before I could say Jack Robinson or shout for help, Maggie gripped me like a wrestler, and then clamped her mouth over my lips so tight that for almost a minute I couldn't move or breath. To be honest, I thought I was a goner, until finally she released me.

'Right that's yer lot,' she said, straightening her coat which had risen slightly during the eternity when she'd almost smothered me.

'That's me lot?' I answered boldly. 'Why, what did I get?'

'You've had a neckin' session, haven't yer; What more do you want? Anyway, better luck next time. That's if there is a next time. And by the way lad, take a tip from me and cut down on the ale, then perhaps you'll be able to perform better.'

'Perform better! The invisible man wouldn't have a chance of performing with you,' I replied sulkily.

Without another word she turned on her heels and strode from the jigger.

When she was out of view I staggered into the main road laughing and talking to myself like a village idiot.

'Bloody 'ell, worra night. Fancy me coppin off with someone from the zoo,' I kept repeating. 'Wait till I tell the lads tomorrow, they'll never believe me.'

Outside the station there was no sign of Nobby or the magnificent Ford Consul, but I wasn't unduly alarmed, even though I was five minutes late. Nobby was never on time for work, so what chance did he have of being 'on the dot' when he had Maureen to keep him occupied.

After a quarter of an hour I'd sobered up considerably. Pacing up and down counting each pavement slab, I saw the street revellers, who I'd been watching nattering in noisy groups, gradually disappear. Then, somewhere in the town a clock tolled half eleven, and that's when I began to panic.

I knew Nobby was cutting it fine. He had only half an hour to pick me up, take me to the Woodchurch, then race to the north-end of the town before midnight, otherwise he himself would be locked out. By a quarter to twelve, and without having anywhere near enough cash for a taxi, I was resigned to the fact that if I couldn't thumb a lift, then a long, long, journey lay ahead of me.

Staggering slightly from one side of the pavement to the other, and still talking to myself, I headed north. As the town centre fell away behind me, the street lamps became fewer, the roads became darker, I realised that most of the traffic out here - which was quite sparse now - seemed to be coming at me from the direction in which I was heading.

Finally, I reached the bus stop at the corner of Rossmore Road and stopped for a breather. This was the place where the Crosville bus pulled up each morning to drop us off, and where we caught it back at night. Glancing across the road, my eyes drifted along the contour of the perimeter fence surrounding the site, and upwards to the beams from the floodlights shining down on a massive pile of logs stacked opposite the gatehouse; the dark imposing silhouette of the old Mill casting its shadow across the modern office block situated at the front.

Along with many who worked at Bowies, I knew that at sometime in the past, one of the workers had sliced an opening in a wire mesh section to provide a five-minute short-cut every morning and night-time.

Whether the remaining dregs of bitter in my system was to blame, I can't be sure, but within seconds I'd crossed the road, crawled through the gap under the fence and then lurched towards our mess hut, staggering like a drunken sailor returning to his ship after a first night on the ale following six months at sea.

Gaining an entry presented no problem, I knew the key to the cabin was always placed under a large length of angle iron. Of course I was on my guard even in my drunken state, and well aware of the large rats we often heard scurrying beneath the cabin floor, so before bending down to retrieve the key I stuffed the bottoms of my kecks into my socks; 'cos we all knew that a cornered rat would shoot up your leg and snaffle your balls.'

Once inside the cabin I crept stealthily in the darkness, gathering together as many pairs of overalls I could lay my hands on. When I had enough to serve my purpose, I plonked them on the table furthest from the door, slipped off my shoes and within seconds had fallen into a drunken stupor.

When Shifty, the first of the gang to arrive noticed the lock was off the door but the place was still in complete darkness, he peered carefully into the cabin. Catching sight of a huddled figure curled up on Robbo's table he backed out again sharply.

'There's a bloody 'paraffin lamp' kippin' on the end table,' he bawled to Sharkey, the nearest of a body of men trooping across the uneven ground towards the shacks.

'So what! Bloody shift 'im, unless you wanna wake 'im up with a cup of tea an' a round of holy ghost,' Sharkey growled irritably.

'He might be violent.' Shifty replied cautiously. 'You know what some of these fella's who sleep rough are like,'

Before Sharkey had time to react, the rest of the gang, led by Podgy Hogan reached the cabin.

Podgy glanced at his watch. Knowing for a fact that the hot water boiler hadn't been switched on for the early morning brew, he was all for getting matters resolved with the 'paraffin lamp.'

'Here, pass me that length of conduit, lad, I'll shift 'im.'

Confused by the voices and with the smell of the damp and oily overalls covering my head wafting into my nostrils, I opened my sleepy eyes as the fluorescent lights flickered on. 'Rats' was my first and frightening thought. Yelling at the top of my voice I lashed out at the phantom rodents surrounding me and then fell awkwardly from the table to the bench, before rolling onto the floor.

'Friggin' 'ell Reilly, what the friggin 'ell are you doin' 'ere?' Podgy roared, holding the conduit as if he was about to throw a javelin.

When everyone settled down to their early morning cuppa, except, of course, for the bold Nobby and a couple of stragglers - I set out describing my eventful night, and the reason I'd ended up sleeping in the cabin.

'So Nobby left yer stuck out 'ere in the Port without the price of a taxi fare, the bleedin' mingebag,' Trunkie Davies remarked.

But somehow, despite his concern, I had a feeling he was more interested in the details of my attempted conquest than of my being stranded in the wilds.

Chunkie and Billy thought the whole thing was hilarious, and when Timmy - ambling in as usual with his haversack on his shoulders - clocked me dressed in my best suit with an un-washed face, he stopped dead in his tracks.

After repeating the story, he, unlike the other apprentices, seemed more in sympathy with my predicament.

'Jimmy your ould fella will kill yer when you get 'ome. I know mine would,' he said looking even more afraid than I was.

'He's on nights,' I replied, 'and with a bit of luck he won't rumble I've been out on the tiles, that's if I can manage to sneak in when he's in bed.'

'You've gorra nerve Jim,' he said, with what I thought was a slight hint of admiration in his voice, while Chunkie and Billy carried on ribbing me. Just then Robbo intervened with some sound advice. 'Look lad, it'll perhaps be in your best interest to scoot off home before Bootsy and the rest of the gaffers arrive; the least they know about this little escapade the better. But before you leave Jim, remember me warnin' you that Nobby would be gettin' his own back after you'd set him up with Rocky in the sack factory?

'Yeah I remember,' I said, the light beginning to dawn in my still fuddled brain.

Well son, I'd call it quits if I were you, 'cos that's what he's just done, set you up.'

Before the management arrived on site I managed to board the eight-thirty to Woodside without being seen by anyone of importance. As the bus trundled along the New Chester Road, I had time to reflect on the financial losses I'd clocked up in my experience of a first blind date.

'Saturday mornin' and all day Sunday at double-time, phew! Half a chunk of next week's wage gone already,' I muttered under my breath.

Passing through Bromborough, as more passengers clambered aboard the bus and settled in their seats, I had a feeling I was being scrutinised when I caught a few of them, peering slyly over their newspapers, looking towards me with a curiosity I could only attribute to the brightness of my midnight-blue suit. When it came to my turn to leave, I saw two pretty young girls sitting on the side seat nudge one another, then place their hands across their mouths and begin tittering.

Once my feet were firmly on the pavement the bus began to move off, so I turned, smiled, and retaliated in the only way I could - by tapping the side of my temple with two fingers. As I made my way towards the Woodside ferry terminal to catch the blue 'Corpy' bus out to the Woody, I wondered when they had last been on a blind date.

Sitting alone on the top deck heading home early on that Saturday morning dressed like a crumpled nine bob note my thoughts were not on my disastrous night out, but consumed with the possible consequences, if, for some reason, dad suddenly changed his customary routine of not going straight to bed after his breakfast; as he always did when working nightshift. Before I had time to come up with a contingency plan however, the bus approached my destination and I found myself standing on the platform alongside the clippie. Some of the older travellers waiting to alight were smiling, and so I smiled back - politeness to old folk was par for the course in our family. But then, for one reason or another dad's phrase - 'here's another dirty stop-out coming home'- something he'd quote if he spotted a bedraggled drunk heading back in the early morning - came bounding into my head.

'No wonder they're smiling,' I thought, as I leapt off the crawling bus before it turned the corner into Ackers Road. With head down, shoulders bent, and the warm breeze raising my thin, straggly hair from my forehead I ambled up the hill towards our road. Suddenly, from out of a jigger or some other hiding place our Tommy appeared in front of me.

'You've gorra a big bright red ring under your nose and around yer mouth Jim?' he chuckled, pointing a grubby finger into my face.

Spitting into my palm then using it like a sponge I swiftly removed the last incriminating traces of Maggie's cheap lipstick with my cuff, and under my breath, cursed my work-mates for not telling me about my blind-date's parting shot.

'An' your shirt's hangin' out as well, showin' the scorch mark,' Tommy added.

'Have you any good news to tell me?' I replied, shoving my shirt back in my trousers.

'Yeah, me dad's in bed, me mam's down at the shops and the girls are playing in the park.'

'Did me dad miss me?' I asked urgently.

'No, but mam did. That's why she asked me to keep my eyes open for you, after I'd dossed your workin' clobber in the shed.'

'Good lad,' I replied, ruffling Tommy's head. 'I suppose that's goin' to cost me a few bob?'

'Half a dollar will do; that's if you've gorr anything left after your big night out.'

'Tommy, I replied sarcastically, 'don't bother looking around for a job when you leave school lad. The Mafia's always on the lookout for new recruits.'

The Mill and a new set of characters

The Fibre contract had been stretched to last as long as possible and now we were all set to join the rest of our colleagues at the Mill, the prominent main artery of Bowater's local empire. It was on a small jetty at the bottom of the site that huge shipments of logs, having crossed the sea from Scandinavia and Canada and transferred onto smaller vessels for the short journey along the Manchester Ship Canal, were then diligently unloaded by hand and crane.

At dinner time, during the warm weather we'd often amble down to the canal to lark about, throw stones or sometimes bathe in the highly polluted waters containing all sorts of industrial waste pumped from the oil refineries up-stream. Sometimes we'd perch on the edge of the quay, watching the huge logs travelling up the open conveyers, ready to be stripped of their bark then sawn into standard lengths, all set to begin the process of converting wood into paper.

Tanjon's, with their vast experience in the printing and paper industry were always favourites to win this huge contract from out of the clutches of their competitors. The job, according to the more experienced tradesmen was going to be quite a challenge, for not only did it involve removing and replacing old fashioned machines, but also required the stripping out of miles of defunct vulcanised rubber insulated cables, and replacing them with a modern P.V.C type.

If there was ever a contrast between two jobs on the same site, then the Mill and the Fibre were prime examples. Even before we set foot in the massive cabin that housed the majority of Tanjon's workforce, it was obvious from the dusty appearance of our colleagues that the working conditions in certain parts of the Mill were more in keeping with life in a coal mine than to the clean and cushy environment we'd just left.

As expected, shouts of 'here come the blue-eyed boys' echoed round the cabin, from those who knew us, while a large number of strange faces who were sprawled around the place viewed us with some sort of mild curiosity. But, of course, there were a few we recognised from the monthly union meetings, though we didn't know them personally.

The cabin was chock-a block, so we shuffled our way to the rear of the shack searching for an empty table. The place was heaving, with clouds of steam hissing from tea urns, mingled with stale, dense tobacco smoke as bodies scrambled for seats, or stood between benches struggling to change into overalls. Billy cans with swirling tea swishing round like miniature whirlpools passed from hand to hand, as empty cups clattered on the wooden tables, while the noise of a thousand voices vying to get their two 'a'penny opinions heard first, roared above the din.

Half way down the cabin, a familiar face leapt out at me from the past.

'Billy... Billy Chancer,' I gasped. Chunkie, who was leading the way, stopped and turned immediately.

'My word you'se lads 'ave shot up since I last seen yer,' Billy replied. 'You mightn't believe it, but it's made my day seein' two of me lads makin' the grade.' By this time he was shaking our hands vigorously and looking pleased to find someone he recognised, because like us he was new to the Mill.

'Worr 'appened to the rest of the lads?' he asked.

'Phil and Scullo stayed on at Pitts. Arnie an' Harry went off to work for..erm..er... who was it Chunks?'

'Hardtasks from Islington. D'yer know 'em?'

'Know 'em? course I do, house bashers aren't they? Another crap outfit.'

'Chingie went down 'the smoke' to work in one of 'is uncle's restaurants. An' you know worr 'appened to Bonso, don't yer?'

'No, worr happened to him?'
'Snypy finished him up. Then he had ter get married, an' he's ended up in the army,' said Chunkie.

'And his judy's in the puddin' club again,' I interrupted.

'Bloody hells bells. Two little bread snappers an' not twenty-one yet. You'd 'ave thought he'd 'ave had the brains to know when to get off at Edge Hill, wouldn't yer? Worra bloody waste. Mind you, I'm not surprised. Remember when he was messin' round with those tarts next door to Pitts, Jimmy? In an' out like a fiddlers elbow, so he was. Anyway, what mob did he end up in?'

'The Lancashire Fusiliers.'

'The Lancashire Fusiliers! Billy gasped in astonishment. 'The skin back fusiliers would 'ave been more appropriate for him, if you ask me.'

It didn't take long for us to settle into our new surroundings and before the week was out we'd fallen into a routine similar to The Cape, except that by the end of each shift we were usually covered in thick paper dust and an oily grime from the redundant machines.

In parts of the old mill, scaffolding platforms had been erected which blocked the high-bay lights, making the section dark and bleak, an ideal place for a prankster such as Sharkey to hide. Within a matter of days he'd set up shop and had become an expert with a blow-pipe, made from a thin piece of conduit. As a result, whenever Sharkey was working nearby, those with any reason to walk through that area of the mill kept their heads down. With an endless supply of putty for ammunition, he just couldn't resist potting un-wary souls.

Meanwhile, Bootsy had been commandeered by higher management to assist the office wallah's to tidy up the loose ends from the Fibre contract. And so our little squad was split up and drafted to work under the capable hands of the mill chargehands, all characters in their own right.

Despite the shortage of room in the main shack, one elderly sparks mate had a table all to himself. Referred either as P.O.W or P&W, or just plain P.W the Pole, dressed in an old army trench coat, khaki shirt and navy blue beret, he always painted a somewhat forlorn figure, with his sad eyes, sunken cheeks and mirthless, toothless grin. For some reason, he made it his business to shout derisory remarks at the chargehands whenever they set foot in the cabin to call 'time-up,' though no one seemed to take much notice.

'I wonder why no one sits next to him,' I asked, during the second week after our move from the Fibre factory.

'You'll see for yourself when you've been here a bit longer,'a spark known as Jimmy 'H' replied. Jimmy 'H', a quick-witted and gifted narrator was one of the funniest characters on site. A dab hand at winding up gullible individuals - especially the apprentices – he'd tell endless jokes, many of them howlers, and deflect the groans of the audience with his parting shot and final cry of 'am I hurting yer.'

Just as those characters such as Eggo, Rock Ferry Frank and Flatfoot Sam had lifted the gloom of the monotonous working conditions at Bailey's with their sharp retorts and sense of humour, we had similar individuals here within the workforce.

Willie the Spook for one, was a practicing spiritualist; a daunting figure who took great   delight in enthralling the apprentices with tales of headless ghosts and inexplicably spooky happenings. This was all well and good during daylight hours, but could play havoc with the imagination in the deep silence of the night.

Timmy, who assisted Willie the Spook after we first moved across to the mill, often arrived for work looking worn out. Lack of sleep turned out to be the culprit, for as he put it 'Willie is so convincing I can't help believing everything he says.'

Eventually, because of the nightmares he was experiencing, he was more than relieved when his chargehand, 'Whistling Bob,' transferred him to another gang, and well away from Willie's malignant influence.

Sid Shortwick, ex Mariner and master storyteller

Sidney Shortwick, a shrewd operator in his mid-forties didn't read newspapers. Or to be more precise, he didn't buy one. Often he'd preach a philosophy that they were anti-social objects which stifled the art of conversation and denied mans natural progress. Such pronouncements were par for the course, because Sid liked to be referred, to as a working man's intellectual. Having gained a wide experience of life as a naval engineer who'd circumnavigated the world on numerous occasions, he prided himself that he'd gleaned sufficient knowledge during his travels to be considered an authority on a host of subjects, that ranged from Greek mythology to geography and to poetry. More often though, he would be reduced to considering everyday trivia, which, he agreed, was the general conversational limit of his current companions.

'Where do nicknames originate from Sid?' Crusthead McGinty, asked one day. McGinty, not a bright spark according to a majority of the tradesmen, seemed to be trying to generate a subject worthy of discussion, though many thought his interest stemmed from a need to discover how he'd come to inherit his own particular moniker.

'The docks,' Sid replied, without raising his chin from the palms of his hands.

'How d'yer know that, like?'

'Cos I worked down there, that's why.'

'So you're a docker, not a spark,' Shifty butted in jubilantly.

'Bugger off lad, I'm time served and I've gorr all me papers to prove it. Anyway getting' back to the question. It's an accepted fact that dockers are renowned world wide for givin' one another nicknames, an' for takin' the mickey; it's a tradition that goes back donkeys years. That's how most of these names survive. They're passed from one generation to the next, then to the kids in school and finally finish up in the likes of these places, the sites. You've only gorra look round this cabin to see the effects for yourselves. Take Crust'ead fer starters. His nut reminds you of an 'ovis loaf, doesn't it? Then there's Shifty over there, which needs no explanation.'

'What d'yer mean like? Shifty retorted.

'Think about it' Sid replied, and moved on with the discussion without waiting for Shifty's next jibe. 'Or take for example young Chunkie, down the end table. He was probably a little chubby bugger at school, so the nearest description would be Chunkie.

'Maybe he was addicted to eatin' loads of pineapple chunks when he was a kid,' said Podgy Hogan, who joined the debate for the first time.

'Well I 'aven't got square balls if that's what you're hintin' at,' Chunkie yelled from the back.

'You said it lad, not me,' Sid replied, and then like a viper, he turned to me.

'I don't know what you're lookin' so smug about Reilly, 'cos you've gorra a 'ead on yer like a Killarney cabbage.

'Have I now? It's better than havin' a nose like a docker's hook,' I responded, taking a leaf out of Shifty and Chunkie's book.

'Well you're right there lad, I've got to hand it to yer,' said Sid, running his fingers down his parrot-shaped conk. 'You see how spontaneous his reaction was lads? That's the way we are round here, take the piss outa one another, retaliate, and no offence taken. Reciprocal is the correct terminology for those of you'se lads not too well read or a little backwards with your words.'

Then, after first checking over his shoulder, Sid lowered his voice to a whisper. 'Now see Chinless Brady across there lads?'

We all turned to observe Chinless, a heavy built character sprawled across a bench, enjoying a thirty minute snooze, his broad back propped against the cabin wall. From forehead to chest Brady's side-on profile was straight, almost vertical, apart from a small and insignificant nasal bump.

'I've known Chinless since we were young lads,' he continued. 'Now lookin' at 'im here today' you wouldn't believe worra great amateur boxer he was, would yer? He fought for St Teresa's you know, and as far as I can remember was never knocked down once. Mind you, it's hard to put someone on the deck if you can't find 'is chin, isn't it?' A few stifled sniggers rippled around the cabin at Sid's assessment.

'You 'avent 'eard the best yet,' said Sid, now chuckling expansively and playing to the audience, but only after checking that Chinless was still slumbering.

'Did you know when Chinless Brady was in the army during the war, he was right there, on the beaches at the invasion of Normandy? Us older fella's know there was a lorra casualties when our troops jumped off the boats into the water. You see, Jerry was no pushover. Some of them fought to the bitter end, and even though they'd thought we were coming in from Calais there was still a rough reception waitin' for us. Brady was with the second batch who were being briefed about wearin' full combat gear - includin' helmets. Now Tich Fenlon, a mate of mine, was in the same mob and he told me that when it was time to put their helmets on, Brady had nowhere to put his chin strap, except under his nose. But as yer can see for yourselves you couldn't get a bootlace under there without it slipping off.'

Sid's audience of young apprentices, once again turned around to observe Brady's tiny nose, as he continued the story.

'As you can imagine, the sergeant in charge of the troops became agitated at the sight of Brady fumblin' with his chin strap. 'Christ soldier,' he bellowed at Brady, 'if you can't get it under your chin or under your conk, stick it in your trap. It'll be safe in there.'

Obeying orders, Chinless stuck the strap into his mouth just as the Commanding Officer arrived to give his troops the once over. Stopping in front of Brady he roared, 'why has this soldier got his strap in his mouth, sergeant?'

'No chin, Sir.'

'No chin! What do you mean sergeant, no chin?'

'Take a look Sir.'

'My word you're right sergeant,' he acknowledged, scrutinising Brady from both sides and from below. Turning away from Brady, he shook his head in amazement. 'I've had fearless soldiers, brainless soldiers and spineless soldiers in my troop Sergeant, but this is the first time I've come across a chinless one.'

'Tich said he almost peed himself laughing' Sid added.

By this time most of us were almost peeing ourselves with laugher, and even those who'd been reading their newspapers had put them to one side, captivated now by Sid's story.

Sid paused, scanning the audience, aware that he'd got everyone's attention.

After completing his inspection, the C.O. returned along the line of men standing to attention. Coming to a halt in front of Brady he fixed him with a keen look. 'Don't worry soldier,' he said, 'as long as you've got a good pair of balls not having a chin doesn't really matter.'

Eventually they'd boarded the landing craft, and as it neared the Normandy beach the sergeant yelled, 'come on lads let's show these Krauts what we're made of,' and everyone leapt over the side into the swirling water.

'You've got to give credit when there's no money,' Sid continued, giving us one of his favourite clichés, 'but Chinless was first to reach the beach, way ahead of anyone else. But of course his trouble was that he couldn't warn the rest of the troop about the enemy positions because of his handicap.'

Pausing for a moment, Sid gulped a mouthful of cold tea, then carried on with tale.

'Whether it was an act of faith or whatever you want to call it, or maybe it was just plain madness - well I'll leave it to each of you to use your own judgement. But imagine the scene; bombs blowing up and shrapnel flying, the rat - tat – tat of machine guns, tracer flashes lighting up the sky, bullets whizzin' about here there and everywhere, an' Brady havin' to put up with a chin strap stuck in his gob. That's what he had to contend with, until he decided to take the weight off his head to give his mouth a rest. But then, just as he took off his tin hat and lowered it in front of his weddin' tackle, there was an almighty bang, and a bullet ricocheted off his helmet, missing his fingers by a fraction. A second earlier and he'd 'ave been mourning the loss of his D.S.O, that's for sure.

'The, D.S.O? A gallantry medal! When did he get that?' Crusthead gasped open-mouthed,now totally absorbed in the ongoing action story.

'Not a gallantry medal, you dope. D.S.O, Dick Shot Off.

Think about it.' Sid glanced round to see if anyone else besides us apprentices was laughing at his crude sense of humour.

'Are you at it again, Shortwick? Takin' the piss,' Brady's feet clattered to the floor, his gruff voice bellowing across the cabin. 'At least I fought for me King and country. Not like you, a bloody shirker. Fancy joining the Dockboard to get out of it, you yeller bellied coward.'

There were sniggers all round at Brady's revelation. But those of us anticipating that Sid might even show some mild sign of embarrassment were to be sadly mistaken.

'Yeah, you've got me there lad. I've got ter hold me hands up an' agree with yer,' he acknowledged. 'Still that's another story for another day.'

Just then, Plonker Parson arrived to call us out for the afternoon shift and yelled 'last orders lads.' Plonker, the tallest chargehand had the grotesque habit of leaving his right hand permanently in his trouser pocket, and every now and then - when he thought no one was looking - let his fingers work overtime scratching feverishly at whatever he had down there. From the moment Plonker had been promoted to chargehand, the sharp-eyed Sid had clocked this personal and secretive practice, so even before Plonker had chance to open the door, Sid shouted 'get ready lads, here comes old Scratch Me Knackers.'

Those in proximity to the doorway immediately eyed-up Plonker's posture, trying not to be seen to be looking at him, but waiting for the slightest movement from his un-seen fingers, at which point a spontaneous round of applause broke out.

'What's the score Plonker?', Sid asked. Depending on his mood, Plonker often seemed only too willing to respond and join in the game, and this was such an occasion.

'Three each, or it could possibly be four three,' he answered in his slow drolling South Cheshire accent. 'Cos I think the referee may have fallen asleep.'

Whether out of devilment or because he genuinely had a problem, Plonker would continue scratching furiously, unconcerned that everyone's eyes were pointed in his direction.

'What's the marra with him? Has he got a touch of the old Sandy McNabs?' Robbo wondered, when clocking Plonker's activities for the first time since we moved across from the Fibre.

'No, it's just 'is hobby,' Jimmy 'H' told him. 'You're only practicin', aren't yer big fella?'

'Course I am,' Plonker replied, before herding us out of the cabin with his usual plea of,

'come on now, the party's over, let's have you lads out on the road.'

'By the way' he said to Jimmy 'H,' as we made our exit, 'you get nowhere in this life unless you practice. I'm a great believer in that theory,' he added, his fingers in his trouser pocket doing a flurried dance. 'Oh, and before I forget,' he added, 'that's what you'll have to do when you come to install the heavy power trunkin' over the shredder machine.'

'What! scratch me knackers?' Jimmy 'H' replied, with a twinkle in his eye.

'No son, practice. But talkin' about knackers, I hope yours are in good nick. 'Cos the weight of that trunkin' will detect any sign of weakness you've got in that region.'

'Oooh, nice one Plonker, one nil to you,' Sid snivelled. 'Serves you right,' he chided Jimmy 'H,' 'for bein' a smart arse.'

'I wasn't bein' smart, Sid, I was just statin' a fact that if you're Puddington Village pocket billiard champion, then your fans and supporters expect you to practice. That's all I was sayin'. Am I hurtin' yer.'

'You sure are Jimmy,' said Sid, as we trooped from the cabin.

As we neared the entrance to the mill it was hard not to avoid the base of an extremely long ladder which disappeared above the lights into the roof space. From the ground, we could see that two 'youngerman boards' had been lashed together, spanning the roof trusses to form a small working platform.

'Who's that up there?' Sharkey asked, pointing up towards the platform were we could just make out a huddled figure dressed in brown overalls and wearing huge, thick-lensed glasses, which seemed to cover half his face.

'Oh him! That's the conscientious owl,' Sid replied. 'He

goes up there at eight in the mornin', takes his grub with him, an' doesn't come down 'til six at night.'

'Bloody 'ell. Worr 'appens when he wants a crap?' Robbo asked. 'Just take a decko at which way the lads are headin',' Sid answered. 'It's the wide berth tactic, cos' no one in their right mind would take a chance walkin' under that platform, just in case the Owl 'asn't gorr 'is bike clips on.'

Extra hands

Half way through the contract we were surprised to learn that Tanjon's had adopted a policy of employing additional apprentices. This was later attributed to the efforts of the shop stewards in convincing the management it would be to their advantage to change direction and go along with this line of action. Taking on lads was not only a cheap alternative to the more expensive method of employing fully qualified mates, but as the shop stewards had insisted, would benefit the rapidly expanding company in the long term.

As result of negotiations a total of five apprentices were recruited, two eighteen year olds and three aged fifteen. The older apprentices were Don Richards, a tall lean, rugged lad, keen on boxing, and the smartly dressed Louie Perrin, a good ballroom dancer with aspirations to becoming a professional. Both lads had been recently sacked by a cowboy outfit, and as the stewards acknowledged, they were extremely lucky to be given a second bite at the cherry; especially as the threat of conscription to the armed forces lurked ominously as each day passed. The other three - Nipper Hollerhead, Colin Whittaker and Peter 'Tweety' Bird - fresh youths straight out of school, were now plunged into the chaos of a huge building site, a complete contrast to the relative calm tranquillity of the school playground.

As for Billy, Chunkie and myself, we had reached the age of nineteen, which heralded a major turning point in our career. Apart from receiving a substantial wage rise, we were now expected to gain full 'hands on' experience by being allowed to use the tools and also to share duties with our respective tradesmen. To add icing to the cake, our little squad was given a cushy number working in the warmth of the plant room under the watchful eye of Plonker Parsons.

One morning, as we grafted in the narrow and airless space situated just above the large and clattering boilers, the sweat dripping from us, we stopped work for a moment when we heard something clanging noisily in the outside passageway. Sharkey, who was nearest to the door, nipped out to investigate and almost collided with young Nipper Hollerhead aimlessly kicking a tin can, using the side wall as an imaginary goal post.

Nipper then nonchalantly ambled into the boiler area to inform Robbo that Plonker had sent him across to work with us for the rest of the week.

Robbo was quiet for moment, as if pondering as to what use he could make of the lad.

'Right son, I want you to work alongside Jimmy here and help him with the trunking,' he announced.

Climbing down from the scaffold he quietly informed me that he'd be taking a back seat to give me the chance to demonstrate my skills, but at the same time would be observing my progress to see whether the knowledge he'd passed onto me had been absorbed or not. What impression I created, and whether or not my skills were worth a carrot, from that moment on Nipper followed me like a shadow.

By far the smallest of the apprentices employed at Tanjon's, Nipper certainly didn't lack confidence; nor was he slow with his backchat. Even standing on tip-toes he was probably not more than four foot ten, and a good eight inches smaller than his gangling mates - Colin and Tweety. They, unlike Nipper were as shy and awkward as most fifteen year olds were inclined to be at that particular time, but he was a rebel, and often without a cause. In many ways he reminded me of myself in my own early, faltering days and I suppose this was the reason I decided to try to help him avoid some of the many pit-falls I'd plunged into.

One morning, just days after he'd been directed to help me install the heavy duty trunking runs, Nipper turned up with a boiler suit clasped tightly under his arm. Standing away from him in the background I chuckled to myself, watching him unfold the overalls then roll them out like a carpet on one of the empty work benches, just as I'd done only a few years earlier.

Glancing at the big clock on the wall, I realised it was only a few minutes before the main body of workers would begin streaming into the cabin, so I asked tentatively 'What size are your ovies Nipper?'

'I'm not sure, but they're the smallest pair in the Army & Navy,' he said, holding them up by the shoulders with the legs trailed out across the floor. 'Why, what's the marra with 'em?'

'Nowt…They just look a bit big, that's all. And to be 'onest I wouldn't like to see the lads takin' the piss out of you like they did with me when I was your age,' I added quickly, before realising I was sounding like Billy Chancer or one of the ould-arse sparks who were forever preaching their sanctimonious 'do's and don'ts' to the likes of me and the other lads.

'Bollocks to them, they can say an' do what they like,' Nipper retorted, full of his own self-importance. 'As long as me clobber stays clean, that's all that matters to me,' he said threading one leg then the other into the bottom of the ovies, before somehow ferreting his arms down the long sleeves and hauling the top half across his frail shoulders in one swift movement. With the overalls now almost smothering him, he completed the task by rolling up the excess length on both his arms and legs. Brimming with confidence he swaggered towards the hot water urn carrying his empty cup.

Although Nipper's gear was not as large or as bulky as the pair that I'd swanned round in at the Cape, I nevertheless could see that the crotch was just inches away from dragging on the floor. I had to laugh though, here was Nipper just five minutes out of school and not giving a toss about anyone.

'It won't be long before he'll upset some of the old fella's in this game,' I thought to myself, as he set up his brew with hands that were only just peeking out from his sleeves. I was right, it was sooner than later

As the job progressed and the workforce increased, the conditions in the main cabin became even more cramped. To ease the situation a smaller shack was erected alongside. In line with the likes of Bailey's and other major contractors at that time, Tanjon's now employed a number of elderly labourers to act as Peggie's. The main task of these older men was to see that the accommodation remained 'ship-shape' and was brushed regularly. They also had to ensure the cups and plates were spotless, and that the billy-cans and tea-pots were placed at the end of each table, ready for when the men spilled into the shack from the site.

To ease the Peggies workload, the three young lads would take it in turns to run messages to the canteen mainly in the mornings when bacon butties were in great demand. Unlike us, when we'd played a similar role at the Fibre, this lot were always back before the men had filtered into the cabin. However, there was still plenty of time for these fifteen year olds to catch the 'ogling bug' - something we'd become experts at.

Even though a huge squad was now working in the Mill, the firm did everything in their power to avoid any confrontation with the stewards or the men, and to keep everyone happy.

As the ten o'clock break had always been recognised as the one the majority of workers seemed to enjoy and looked forward to, a simple system for ordering butties had been devised. Every morning before leaving the cabin to go on site, everyone would jot their names down on the sandwich list, tick their breakfast preference and their table number, and pay the Peggie accordingly. When the totals were finalised, the lad would dash across to the canteen at half eight, place the order with the girl on the till, then return at a quarter to ten to collect the steaming toasted sandwiches.

But, of course, like all well made plans someone was always likely to throw the proverbial spanner in the works, which happened one particular morning when an ordered and paid for butty was delivered and then did a vanishing trick from the end of a table. Sandy McDowell, a giant of a man was the unfortunate loser in this particular case, and found himself in a situation similar to that of Old Mother Hubbard's starving dog. Within seconds an argument had developed between big Sandy and the Peggies, who remained adamant they'd placed the correct number of sandwiches on each table. At this point someone whispered, in an off-hand way, that the aptly named Ronnie Fox had been seen munging into a sausage toastie as if his life depended on it, just minutes before the cabin began filling up.

Ronnie was not a popular character at the best of times, and those who'd been acquainted with him on previous jobs, voiced the suspicion that he wasn't the type to pay for a sausage sandwich. Naturally, as soon as Big Sandy heard these whispers his reaction was predictable.

'Hey Guzzlin' Gob,' he demanded angrily, 'did you order that sausage sarnie, or 'ave you ate mine?'

As the babble of conversation in the cabin gradually faded away, the eerie silence that followed was broken only by the sound of the water urns bubbling and spluttering in the background. It was also noticeable that those who'd been sitting near to where the quarrelsome pair stood facing each other, had now shuffled quickly out of the way of the looming confrontation.

'Are you talkin' ter me or chewin' a brick?' Foxy replied aggressively, brown sauce dribbling from the corner of his mouth, threading a path into the stubble of his shadowed chin and making him appear more ferocious than he really was.

Tommy Joyce, the deputy shop steward, leapt from his speck near the front end of the cabin and ploughed through seated bodies to reach the feuding pair.

'Steady on lads, steady on. There'll be no fisticuffs or barnies in this hut, not while I'm here.'

But the two antagonists ignored him as he continued his entreaties in the hope that words of wisdom might take the sting out of the situation. 'I'm not takin' sides lad's, but ask yourselves a simple question. Is it worth losin' your jobs for the sake of a couple of pork growlers, and burnt ones at that?'

The enraged duo again failed to respond to his placid attempts, and carried on glaring at one another, each waiting for the other to throw the first punch. However, quick as a flash, Tommy moved between the two protagonists, using his muscular arms to keep the angry pair apart. And as he did so, he yelled out to Nipper to pop over to the canteen pronto and tell the girl you're a sausage butty short.

'But I wasn't one short. I gave in the list with the right money, and the woman servin' me didn't make a mistake,' Nipper retorted.

Nipper was less than sharp when it came to spotting a bit of conciliatory subterfuge and he'd not clocked what Tommy was up to.

'Get movin' an' do as your told,'Tommy growled, and Nipper, now sensing the menace in the stewards voice took off like a rocket and was back within less than five minutes carrying a steaming hot sausage butty.

Gradually as the noise in the cabin returned to normal, a number of workers who'd known Foxy from other jobs mumbled to one another that he was at it again; and that this time he should have been sacked for his deceit.

Nipper appeared to learn from the incident and to give him his due, seemed to take the banter about his acquired overalls in his stride. Occasionally, though, he would retaliate and was duly reprimanded for being a cheeky little get, and threatened with a clip across his ear, particularly by the more impatient older workers, who didn't have the same tolerance for the apprentices as their younger counterparts.

As the weeks of the early part of 1957 rolled into months, Colin, Tweety and Nipper moved out of the adjacent cabin to squeeze into ours. Unfortunately the only space still available for them was on the table occupied by the loner P.W... PoW... or P&W - or whatever he was called.

Despite the whisperings of a few older hands, and in particular, the prediction of Jimmy 'H' that the three newcomers would be lucky to last a couple of days, the lads didn't seem all that bothered about sharing the table with the old guy. To them, he seemed to pose no problems.

What's more, P&W didn't appear to mind their intrusion; in fact he looked quite pleased that Nipper was sitting opposite him, probably because the lad was now within striking distance of a back-hander. It just so happened that P&W was one of those who resented Nipper's cheeky outbursts and was always among the first to chastise him.

Breaktimes would not have been the same without the noise and banter from the different individuals spread round the cabin. Some were louder and more vocal than others, and, of course, it was no different at our table.

'Come on then, who's gorr egg on their butties?' Podgy Hogan roared one dinner hour after everyone squelched into the cabin, drenched from the sudden cloudburst which always seemed to be waiting for us as we emerged from the Mill. With our wet donkey jackets discarded and the flat caps of the older fella's now hanging on the numerous hooks and nails scattered round the walls of the cabin, we'd all just settled at the various tables having delved into our square tin lunch boxes, or searched deep into old army haversacks for our grub.

'I aint. Mine's spam,' Chunkie said.

'I've got mouse,' I added.

'Corn jock; prem; fishpaste; beef, jam.' Each of us on our

table responded as we opened the paper wrappings to inspect our sarnies.

'So, have any of you'se lads got egg on yer butties, then?' Podgy repeated to those sitting at the adjacent tables, but they shook their heads and carried on eating.

'Well something round 'ere bloody stinks to high 'eaven,' he muttered, pinching his enormous nostrils with an index finger and thumb and exhaling through his gaping mouth like a steam train.

'It's probably him,' Nipper interrupted, pointing at P&W who was leaning the back of his head against the side of the cabin, gazing at the ceiling and chuckling at something or other that appeared to have amused him.

'Yer what! D'yer mean to tell me he's apple tarted when we're eatin' our grub,' Podgy exploded.

Everyone on our table immediately stopped eating. Robbo, tutting angrily, cocked his leg from under the table, lifted it awkwardly over the bench and then leaned across the small passageway to yank the side window open.

'Have yer got no manners, you dirty old get?' he scowled, glaring at P&W. But he simply closed his eyes, folded his arms and rested his forehead on the table.

'There's a time and place for everything,' Podgy said in a voice designed to be heard by everyone. 'And manners maketh man, that's what I was taught when I was a youngster. P&W, said nothing and pretended not to have noticed. Podgy wasn't about to let matters drop though.

Fancy breakin' wind when people are 'avin' their grub,' he growled. 'It's disgustin', bloody disgustin'or pig ignorant, one of the two,' he added, poking his bald head through the open window to fill his lungs with a mixture of the damp but fresh air blowing onto the site from the Manchester Ship Canal.

After a couple of deep breaths he returned to his seat and began tucking into his food. Meanwhile, me and Chunkie began grinning like a pair of Cheshire cats.

'What's tickled your fancies?' he muttered, peppering us with a buttered cracker spray as he spoke.

'Tell 'im Chunks, about double standards.'

'Remember last week, when we were footin' the ladder' Chunkie said, 'when you were workin' on top of the bleacher?'

'Yeah, worrabout it?' Podgy looked suspiciously down his nose at us.

'You let rip on every step, just like kick-starting a spluttering moped. Didn't he Jim?'

'Aye an' it didn't smell like me dad's roses either,' I replied.

Podgy remained silent for a moment, as if searching for the right words to counteract the accusation. But then we saw him peep slyly in P&W's direction before replying in a somewhat sheepish manner.

'Okay lads, for once I'll admit it. You're absolutely right. But bear with me for a minute 'til I finish me grub an' I'll explain it.'

He popped at least four more crackers into his mouth while we waited, then, after swilling the crumbs down with a mouthful of tea, he smacked his lips and addressed us.

'It's like this lads. You know after a plane takes off an' enters the clouds, sometimes it can encounter lots of turbulence. Well, that's what it's like with me. I've always been nervous of heights. I get light headed, you see. And as soon as me feet leave the ground, bingo...turbulence develops. Anyway, he demanded, recovering some of his lost bravado. 'What's all the fuss about. You'se weren't eatin' your grub, where yer? So it didn't effect you?'

'Yes it did,' Chunkie replied fervently. 'I was chewin' me bubbly gum, so you're just as bad as 'im over there in the corner'

'What a bloody subject to 'ave when we're eatin', said Robbo. ' Can't yer think of something better to discuss?'

Just then Jimmy 'H' ambled towards our table from the middle of the cabin, a broad smile spanning his face from ear to ear.

'Don't say you weren't warned about old custard crutch in the corner there. If you'd listened to me in the first place you wouldn't 'ave been so keen to plant yourselves down this end of the hut.

Resting a his foot on the bench between Timmy and Chunkie, he leaned over, spread his long arms across their huddled shoulders and began whispering about P&W, who he'd christened 'old dirty arse.' Before he had time to get down to the nitty gritty or reveal some salacious gossip though, 'Whistling Bob,' a pot-bellied and jovial chargehand arrived to call time. As usual, when 'Whistling Bob' entered the cabin he was serenading us all with his tune of the week, which this time was 'It's a long way to Tipperary'.

As we began filing from the hut someone mentioned this was the first time, as far as he could remember, that P&W hadn't warned us the chargehand was on his way into the cabin. We all glanced simultaneously back to the table, and were surprised to see P&W was still lying in the same position, his head resting on his arms; a posture he'd adopted when the rumpus about the smell in the cabin began.

'Give 'im a shake lad, just in case he's snuffed it,' Podgy Hogan said to Nipper.

To gain attention and showing off as usual, Nipper went back to P&W and bawled, 'WAKE UP CUSTARD CRUTCH.'

The old man's response was immediate, as he came to life. 'You've got too much of what the cat licks its arse with,' he snarled.

As quick as a flash and still playing to the audience, Nipper said, 'there's no chance of a cat goin' anywhere near yours, custard.'

No one had ever seen P&W move as quickly as he did, certainly not on this job. Now, with a rare show of agility and defying his advancing years, he leapt from his seat, grabbed hold of a billy-can and hurled what was left of the contents at his tormentor. Nipper was too sharp though, and out the door and away, even before the wet tea leaves splattered across Timmy McCain's back.

'Cheeky young bugger's got no respect whatsoever for 'is elders,' P&W hollered, without a word of apology or a second glance at Timmy, who was now protesting indignantly about the state of his tea drenched clothes.

Compared to the older workers who inevitably had a negative perception of Nipper's over - the - top actions, the younger men and the apprentices found the whole thing highly amusing. Robbo, Podgy and a couple of other tradesmen in our gang agreed with P&W that Nipper had too much lip for a young lad, and were visibly concerned at the road he seemed to be taking. They felt that if he was to upset the wrong person, there was every chance that he could very easily lose his apprenticeship.

As we trooped back towards the Mill, Robbo and his colleagues called to me to join them.

'Listen Jim, we've been chattin' amongst ourselves about Nipper, an' we think you ought to 'ave a word in his ear about the way he's behavin'. He'll probably take more notice of you than any of us, so gerra grip of him an' tell him to button up, otherwise we can see him getting' the push. And none of us would like to see that 'appen, would we?'

Feeling flushed and honoured to be trusted with this responsive role, I set about the task, determined to put my limited experience to use and direct Nipper back to the straight and narrow.

'NIPPER,' I bawled. 'Come over 'ere a minute, I wanna a word with yer.'

'What's up? 'he replied, as I beckoned him towards me like a lorry driver being guided into a tight parking spot. Somewhat sheepishly he ambled across to where I was standing alongside the stragglers, many having a last drag on a ciggie before entering the Mill.

'Go on, 'ave a word with 'im now,' Podgy urged, as Nipper came within earshot. But I didn't have the heart to belittle him in front of the lads still lingering around so I tactfully moved away.

'Look Nipper,' I began, when I thought we were away from prying ears, 'I've been asked to give you a word of advice. Y'see some of the sparks are livid at the way you've been treating some of the older fella's. I know you don't mean any harm and you probably think it's smart, but 'aving a go at old P&W that way - well you were right out of order there lad. I tried to introduce a touch of anger to my voice to show him what he'd done was unacceptable and perhaps make him realise what was expected.

'I didn't mean nowt, Jim, it was just for a laugh,' he

responded. From out of the corner of my eye I caught sight of the lads edging closer, trying to hear what was going on.

Laying on the pressure, especially as I was possibly under scrutiny myself now, I turned the screw trying to appear mature and be officious

'Look,' I told him, 'there's no need to hurt the old fella's feelin's, Nipper. We all know he stinks, an' all that, but you've still got ter learn to show some respect to your elders. Have yer got that?'

'Yeah, fair enough.'

'By the way,' I added, showing off a bit, and playing up to the audience who'd moved closer, 'did you know P&W was in the army, an' was a prisoner of war?'

'No..no, I didn't,' he answered, dropping his head as if embarrassed by the disclosure.

'Well, he was,' I said loudly and firmly. I could hear Chunkie and Timmy tittering in the background, but by now I was beginning to enjoy my position of authority even more than I could have imagined.

'Who was it told yer he was in the army, Reilly?' Jimmy 'H,' asked from the front of the group, which was now only yards away.

'Just 'cos we're apprentices we're not thick y'know Jimmy,' I replied cockily. 'We all know that P.o.W stands for prisoners of war.'

'Did yer 'ear that?' Jimmy laughed, turning to Sid Shortwick alongside him. 'Are you goin' ter tell 'im or shall I?'

Sid stepped forward, coughed and cleared his throat. Then he placed his hand on my shoulder and began enlightening me about the old fella's pedigree.

'Listen lad. First of all it's Petrioskis Androvitch Oscar Windurineski - sometimes referred to as P.W., P.o.W, or, as most of us call 'im, P&W. That's 'is real name, and he's a jam roll, okay? And to the best of my knowledge he wasn't in the army, unless he was in the Polish mob. Secondly, for pronunciation purposes it makes good sense to abbreviate that sort of appellation, d'yer get me?'

'Apple what? Never 'eard of it. What d'yer mean like?' I replied.

Jimmy 'H' chuckled loudly.

'Never mind Reilly', Sid continued, 'when your brain develops a bit I'll educate yer. Anyway, about shortening his name. On every job I've worked with him, he's always been known as Piss and Wind. So without insulting your intelligence even further lad, there's a distinct difference between being a P.o.W and blowin' off some P.a.W.

'I'll tell yer what Jim,' he said turning to Jimmy 'H,' 'when you weigh it up, 'is initials couldn't be more appropriate. They certainly fit the bill, what do you reckon?'

'I fully agree with yer Sid. I couldn't 'ave put it any better me'self,' Jimmy 'H' replied, nodding in agreement.

'So there you are lads, that's another piece of worthless information for yer,' Sid said.

Nipper sloped off with his hands thrust deep in his pockets, his head bowed low. Meanwhile, feeling quite chuffed with my own performance and not even minding my lesson in apple - something or other - or whatever they were called, I wandered across to join the lads, unaware I was about to come under quite a fair amount of flak.

'You lousy bugger Reilly. Fancy givin' young Nipper a bollickin', Timmy grumbled.

'Particularly from you, of all people,' Chunkie interjected.

'Okay, I didn't want to do it,' I explained, 'but Robbo thought he'd listen to me rather than anyone else.'

'What! After all the bollickin's you've 'ad over the years - none of which seem to have done you much good,' Billy Constable retorted vehemently.

Feeling rattled by the criticisms being hurled at me, I felt the anger rise in my body and eventually retaliated, determined to clear the air.

'Listen lads,' I blurted out. 'In another sixteen months most of us will be out of our time, and then - whether we like it or not - we'll have to be responsible, so we may as well start now.'

They all looked at me in disbelief, then began laughing uncontrollably.

Don, a quiet and athletic lad who usually said little or nothing, but was generally acknowledged as being the brightest and brainiest of the older apprentices, spoke up suddenly.

'In all sincerity Jimmy, all I can say is God 'elp these young lads if they follow your example over the next sixteen months.'

This final testament, pulled the rug from under me, so I shrugged and sulkily made my way back to the job, their unwelcome laughter still ringing in my ears.

During the early part of the afternoon when things were quiet I managed to find a speck away from Robbo's gaze to mull over the day's events. Still reeling from what I considered to be unfair criticism from my mates, I began to reflect on the number of times I'd been reprimanded by some of the more serious minded tradesmen about acting the goat, or getting involved in horseplay instead of concentrating on learning my trade. They were right, of course. The trouble with me was that I'd always been attracted, to the pranksters and jokers like a huge magnet. Take Sharkey for instance, whenever he 'hung a tail' on someone passing by, I couldn't resist the temptation to follow suit. Then there were the many site comedians rattling off a never-ending stream of 'off the cuff' jokes. I would soak them up, rehearse the punch lines, then wander the site repeating them, spending far more time away from the job than I should have done, trying to become a smart Aleck.

Attending night school - or rather not attending night school - was another of my downfalls. Sometimes I thought nothing of giving the college a wide berth when an important football match was taking place on that particular evening.

'Reilly' I eventually said to myself out loud, 'you're goin' to have to change your ways over the next year and a bit if want to be taken seriously by your mates.'

'But can a leopard change its spots,' I re-assured myself as I climbed into the light from a hidden speck above the traywork section where Sharkey often dossed down as he waited for some unwary victim to walk past.

Nipper and his final plunge

Local football results, future team fixtures, and the possibility of winning a fortune on the treble chance coupons, were among the most popular topics discussed during meal breaks; although horse racing and the glories of the card school were not that far behind in the pecking order. And usually, as soon as the food and drink had been demolished and the tables cleared of newspapers, the card schools got under way. Not a lot of money would change hands in the early part of the week, though judging by the intense concentration and fervour shown by some of the participants, a casual observer wandering into the cabin for the first time could be forgiven for assuming the combatants were playing for the town hall clock, rather than a pile of pennies.

There were exceptions of course; especially those who played a deeply serious game of poker. One such school, with Shifty Jones, Bluffer Murphy, Terry Mac and Smiler Evans making up the foursome, known as the Merseysippi gamblers played for high stakes every day.

Most of the older apprentices were wise enough to keep well away from their sacred table when a session was in progress; but not Nipper. Despite having been warned a number of times about mooching behind those players trying desperately to conceal their cards by holding them close to their chests, he just wouldn't take no for an answer.

The straw that broke the camels back came one Friday afternoon when the kitty reached a massive four pounds eight shillings. This was a record amount even for these ardent gamblers, and the kind of cash that would certainly have bought me a new set of clobber - perhaps even stretching to a pair of thick - soled brothel creepers and a night out on the ale.

The sight of ten bob notes floating on top of half crown pieces, with two bob bits mingling amongst the shillings, tanners and copper coins stacked in a heap in the centre of the table, was enough to attract the attention of even those totally uninterested in gambling, such as Billy the Minge, who'd recently arrived on site after being made redundant at the Cape.

With bated breath and straining necks the spectators followed every hesitant move, scanning the unsmiling and the conceding - nothing - at all faces, looking for the tell-tale twitch, the nervous quirk, or for some other unfamiliar oddity emanating from the quartet engaged in the quest for this veritable golden pot.

Nipper, who had been conspicuous by his absence from the intense atmosphere, suddenly re-appeared in the cabin. And like a magnet was immediately attracted by the excessive quietness seeping from those sitting around the area where the gamblers were playing. Dropping onto his thin bony knees, he slithered like a rattlesnake through the narrow gap between the crowded benches, until, eventually, he stopped directly behind Shifty.

With everyone focussing on the drama of the card school, Nipper rose to his feet without attracting too much attention. As expected, the players were watching each other for any sign of weakness, and the crowd was watching the players for any sign at all. Everyone held their collective breath as each individual made their next bid and raised the stakes even higher. Nipper, as quiet as a church mouse, eased his mop of curly hair over Shift's shoulder just as Shifty took another quick squint at his cards. Coughing lightly, Nipper suddenly muttered, almost to himself - but loud enough to be heard by everyone - 'phew, that's some hand you've got there Shifty.'

Because he was lost in concentration, focussing on the stonewall features of the other players, it seemed to take Shifty a good second or two to realise that someone was up close, standing right behind his back; and what's more, had not only seen his cards but had commented on them.

Finally the penny seemed to drop, and he spun round. With a sudden burst of seething anger, his face the colour of chalk, he made a grab for the outrageous interloper.

At times like this Nipper's survival instincts usually held him in good stead, and as Shifty flew at him he somehow managed to scramble under the tables; pushing his way through the legs of the slumberers who'd been dosing through out the dinner hour break. In the confusion and the sudden upheaval in the snoozing contingent, Nipper was able to escape Shifty's murderous clutches and flee from the shack. But later, when the commotion had died down, he was hauled back into the cabin, and before the assembled company was given a good bollicking by a couple of elderly committee members whose own gentlemanly game of rummy had been completely disrupted by the fracas and the following chaos.

As for the game, well, the hand was eventually declared null and void because of Nipper's interruption, and the cards were re-shuffled and dealt again. Needless to say, Shifty drew a load of rubbish, much to his disgust. But from this point on he displayed an open and smouldering distaste for the outlawed Nipper.

As we kind of expected, Nipper bounced back; he wasn't the type to be down in the dumps for long. A couple of days later he turned his attention to the task of keeping on the right side of the gambling fraternity by volunteering to run messages for those with a keen interest in speculating on chancy events. Often referred to by the likes of Sid Shortwick and the newly arrived Billy the Minge, as being a crowd of 'bookmaker's benefactors,' these optimists gambled on the nags, spending most of the dinner hour studying the ways and means of bankrupting the local bookie, Tom Lawson; solely relying on a combination of doubles, trebles and Yankee's to achieve their goal.

Being as fly as a cart load of monkeys, Nipper had already sniffed out the possibility of a few coppers to be earned taking and collecting the bets, which were usually written on bits of scrap paper, or more often than not, on ciggie packets. After making sure the gamblers had remembered to write their nom-de-plumes on the betting slips he would then deliver them to Pat, the bookies runner. Nipper had already sussed out that should Lady Luck happen to answer a punters prayers - then the boy delivering the bet would more than likely be rewarded with an extra tanner as a kind of good luck bonus. This entrepreneurial instinct did not go un-noticed by the other apprentices, who soon realised that, despite his age, he was well ahead of the field as far as money was concerned. Meanwhile, I tended to ignore his antics, even though he still clung to me like a shadow, and this prompted Chunkie, Don and Timmy McCain to emphasise that as Nipper was my lad, I should be held responsible for his actions and misdemeanours. I was therefore cast as Nipper's mentor or role model, but I didn't kick up too much of a fuss, because this had its advantages in more ways than one. Apart from running messages to the canteen in the afternoons for sweets and pop, Nipper, somehow or other usually managed to snaffle a couple of free bacon butties when it was his turn for breakfast duties, which he'd naturally share with me.

Although the majority of workers arrived on site between seven forty five and eight o'clock, a number of the older ones landed at half seven. This enabled them to ease slowly into the daily routine, enjoy a quiet smoke, sup a cup of tea in peace, and to read the newspapers before the main body of men converged prior to the start of the shift.

Living locally, Nipper rode the short distance to work on a bike, and was always first of the apprentices to make an appearance. So by the time we'd legged it in from the bus, he'd have the tea brewed and poured. As a result, his general usefulness first thing in the morning, was always appreciated, not only by us, but also by our respective tradesmen.

One dark morning in March, not long before the confusing hour was once again put forward on the clock, Nipper called me to one side to confront me with a dilemma that seemed to be worrying him.

'There's something strange goin' on in the next cabin,' he whispered, when we were finally alone.

'What d'yer mean like, something strange?' I replied, wondering what unknown secret had fired his imagination at this hour of the morning.

'All this week,' he told me, 'a mob have been sneakin' out of the other cabin at twenty to eight, an' comin' back at five past, laughin' an' jokin' an' not even botherin' to have a cup of tea.'

'That's odd,' I said. 'Which way do they go?'

'Across there,' he replied, pointing in the direction of the cardboard factory.

'Is Nobby Alcock one of them?'

'Yeah.'

'Ah! That explains it then. You can bet your bottom dollar there's women involved,' I said, wondering what they're were up to and as curious as Nipper to know what was going on.

'I'll tell you what I'll do Nipper,' I said, after pondering for a moment, 'I'll come to work early an' follow them.'

'Can I come with yer? 'he asked.

'As long as you make everyone's tea beforehand, an' you don't tell anyone else.'

Next morning I caught the ten to seven bus, entered the site around half past, and without anyone seeing me, hid behind the toilet block. Around twenty to eight, the door in the adjacent cabin to ours opened, and seven shadowy figures emerged.

From where I was concealed, I watched them dart across the rail track, then head off in the direction of the two factories situated on the other side of the site.

Just as I was about to set out on their trail, Nipper appeared wearing his over-sized overalls. Placing a forefinger across my lips, and pointing my other hand towards the bleak and gloomy railway lines, I beckoned him to follow.

As we skipped effortlessly across the oily wooden, tracks, we could hear from somewhere up ahead the sounds of an excited chattering and hysterical laughter drifting through the early morning murk. Within minutes the orange lights towering above us at hundred yard intervals alongside the Fibre factory perimeter had flickered through the rising mist to expose the pitched roof of the newly erected building. However, by the time we stumbled through the boggy marsh and reached the road, our workmates were nowhere to be seen.

Slinking along in the shadow of the factory wall, like fugitives on the run, we wormed our way towards the end section nearest to the canal, all the while searching for some visible sign as to where our colleagues had disappeared to. Approaching the boiler house we stopped dead in our tracks; someone had left the huge doors wide open, and these were now swinging and creaking noisily as the wind whistled between the two buildings.

Brimming with excitement, Nipper quickly overtook me and entered the building. Glancing round as if he owned the place he pointed towards tell-tale sets of muddy footprints trailing across the dusty floor then disappearing behind the massive boilers. Playing the big shot, like a scout in a cowboy film, Nipper knelt down, dipped his finger into a mud-caked foot print and held it up for me to inspect. Then, grinning like a Cheshire cat, he whispered, 'I think they're in 'ere Jim.'

'Good lad,' I whispered, moving sharply in front before he could jump in with both feet as he normally would. I then clambered over a couple of warm, un-cladded pipes and found, hidden in the shadows, a huge wooden ladder protruding into the roof space. Gripping the bottom of the ladder, I paused listening for any unusual sound coming from above. But only the buzz from the heat of the boilers disturbed the atmosphere. Then, my attention was drawn to a faded chalk message on the back wall which read: '*Chunkie Rules Ok,*'.

Suddenly, I recalled the time I'd worked here and realised that the girls changing rooms were situated somewhere around. The mystery of Nobby and his collaborators disappearing act was becoming much clearer.

Without mentioning a word of my suspicions to Nipper, I stepped onto the ladder and climbed slowly towards the darkened ceiling void, all the while conscious of his face touching the back of my calf muscles as I dallied on each rung. Reaching the top and poking my head into the darkened roof space, I was dismayed to find a configuration of enormous, square shaped ventilation ducts blocking our entry to the next section of the building.

'Follow me Nipper,' I whispered, easing my way slowly along the main duct, tentatively feeling each set of rounded rivets, until I came across the long protruding bolts inserted through the coupling plates to join the sections together. Using these as foot grips, I stretched every inch of my five foot four frame clawing my way up the top of the vent without making too much of a racket After lying prone for a few moments waiting for my eyes to adjust to the dark, I focussed in on a number of figures, some six or seven feet below, each stretched out on planks of wood that had been carefully positioned across the tops of the aluminium angle supports holding the ceiling tiles in place.

By now, eager to get a glimpse of the action, Nipper was struggling to join me, so I knelt to give him a helping hand. Unfortunately, as I leaned over to grip him by his boiler suit, my knees sank into the thinly manufactured tin duct, which buckled and twanged loudly, the noise clearly startling the voyeurs. One of them whispered frantically across, who's that? Who's over there?'

'Shurrup, before the girls hear us,' I heard Nobby hiss.

After waiting for our frayed nerves to calm, I resumed my efforts to drag Nipper onto the duct. Gripping him with both hands I gave one mighty heave and finally managed to yank him up, but disaster was only seconds away. Instead of landing next to me the momentum seemed to carry him right past where I squatted, and before I could grab him for a second time he'd slid across to the far corner and toppled over the edge.

Like the England goalie of the day, Big Frank Swift, I dived across the vent just in time to see him lashing out with his arms and out-stretched fingers as he tried frantically to prevent himself from plunging through the gaping hole made by his feet. Horrified, I watched him disappear through the ceiling, grasping in slow motion at broken tiles, jagged pieces of aluminium, ragged strands of fibreglass, and yelling as if he was about to meet his doom. To add to the fiasco, a small scaffolding plank, which had been balancing precariously on the edge of the opening, slowly slid through the gap and crashed down below.

An eerie silence prevailed as a dusty mist began to rise from the mound of debris splattered across the changing room floor. Then, all hell broke loose, as girls, in various stages of undress began to scream and wail, as if the building was on fire or the end of the world was in progress. The noise swiftly brought me back to my senses, and as I scrambled to my feet, I took a last look at the hole - now the size of a massive crater. Before legging it, I glanced across at the distraught faces of the 'blimp squad', frozen to the spot, all looking mesmerised by the pandemonium raging below.

Without a second's thought I leapt from the vent, slid down the ladder, hurdled the huge pipes spanning the boiler house, and like a bullet, I shot down the track without thinking what I was doing. In record time I'd reached the sanctuary of the main toilet block, confident that not many of our squad would be using the lavvies before the working day began. After sitting for some time in a locked cubicle gathering my composure, and carefully removing the white dust from my navy blue jacket, I cautiously let myself out and slid past the empty traps. Turning the corner by the wash basins and urinal troughs, I heard someone whistling and immediately stopped in my tracks.

Silently, I tiptoed forward and came across Nipper standing there as bold as brass, calmly combing his hair as if he didn't have a care in the world. I couldn't believe my eyes.

'Obviously you escaped in one piece,' I said, watching him slapping the back of his overalls which were covered in the bits of fibre glass and dusty grey powder he'd gathered during his un-orthodox flight from the roof space to the changing room floor.

'Yeah, except I've ripped me kecks on one of those ceilin' brackets,' he answered, probing the damage under the crutch of his overalls with his right hand.

'You wouldn't be standing looking so bloody smug if you'd landed on one of those girls,' I replied sarcastically. There was a long silence as he contemplated the possibility.

'What'll 'appen now? Will they sack us?' he blurted, finally showing his concern and fear for the predicament we were both in.

Before I could answer I heard one of the doors to the traps closing, and beckoned him to keep quiet.

'Get cleaned up, then go into the cabin and act normal,' I whispered.

'Worrabout the others, they're bound to blow us in, aren't they?' he agonised.

'Shush! Forget them, and get movin' before the chargehands arrive.'

Everything seemed to be in place when I followed Nipper into the hut. Crucial footy results on the back pages of the daily newspapers were being discussed, mugs were clattering, thick blue cigarette smoke hung in the corners above the doorways, and no one took much notice of us. Though I thought I detected a few glares from the older apprentices, particularly Chunkie, who sneaked a peep at his watch as we sat down to drain our mugs of cold tea.

Chunkie, who was closer than any of the other lads, knew I wouldn't venture near the job, or even use the bogs before eight o'clock, unless I was involved in some sort of racket or other so I wasn't surprised when he slid across to ask what I'd been up to.

'I'll tell you later, when we're on our own,' I replied.

A few minutes before the main body got themselves moving, I slipped from the cabin and moseyed next door, just as Bootsy was checking out his newly formed squad.

'What's happened to my lads this morning?' he asked, addressing no one in particular. 'Has anyone seen them?'

'They must have gone straight onto the job, 'cos they were here early on,' Trunkie Davies said, leaning back, sucking his empty pipe. 'I saw them walking from the bus stop, but not afterwards,' he whispered under his breath. Not knowing their whereabouts or what they were up to worried him, because if Trunkie didn't know what was happening on the job, it was unlikely anyone else would.

'They've got to be up to something,' Bootsy said, looking more concerned than usual. 'I hope they're not into my slummy pile.'

'Slummy,' was the local name for the scrap cable ends, strips of lead, brass bars, or any other bits of non-ferrous metals which were collected at the end of each shift, then stacked in a secure compound. When the price was right - usually before a holiday period - the slummy was then sold on in bulk to the 'scrappie,' and the proceeds shared out amongst the 'gaffers' as a kind of perk.

As the cabins emptied, the workers would usually troop the three hundred yards to the job, then stop for a few minutes outside the Mill entrance. Some would enjoy a last drag on a ciggie while the rest would hang round, waiting for the chargehands to ferry them to their various work places. Normally the apprentices would arrive first, but on this particular morning I deliberately stayed well back from the other lads, the bold Nipper trailing a few yards behind me. From a safe distance we scoured the groups of workers, searching for Nobby and his fellow blimpers. Eventually, the sharp-eyed Nipper spotted them huddled together in one of the unused mill doorways. For some reason, however, his bottle seemed to go at this point. Before I could open my mouth to offer a calming word he was off like a greyhound and across the tarmac road. Within seconds he'd caught up with the rest of the lads and dodged out of sight in the crowd.

Turning away I decided to take the bull by the horns and ambled towards the conspirators. Surprisingly, my presence had little or no effect; they simply stood there whispering to each another; so I turned away and headed to the job. As soon as I set foot in the Mill, Chunkie was across to quiz me about my odd behaviour. So, I rattled off the details of our great escape, and the drama that Nipper and I had just undergone.

By the time the ten o'clock break arrived the news had spread like wildfire. There were rumours that the security men knew the names of the 'Blimp squad,' and it was only a matter of time before they'd be named and shamed, then hauled before the management to be dealt with. Others spoke about the cost and the amount of damage to the ceiling; while the Pope, from his pulpit, lectured everyone on the low moral character of the deviants involved, and of the embarrassment endured by the girls who'd been spied on as they changed into their working clothes.

Of course, even though our mates were faithful and kept the secret of our involvement, Nipper and I nevertheless came in for a fair share of the ribbing. Especially me. As Chunkie was quick to point out, I was supposed to be the one keeping Nipper on the straight and narrow.

Although Nobby and his 'Blimp Squad' knew it was Nipper who'd fallen through the ceiling, they still seemed uncertain that I was his accomplice. To his credit, Nipper stood his ground, refusing point blank to reveal my involvement, and by late afternoon the incident had been exaggerated so much I began to wonder if the Fibre Factory had any ceiling left at all, or if anyone was still working in there.

As five o'clock approached the rumours had become rife, with the painters and the laggers - the only trades - to have outstanding work to complete in the boiler house becoming the prime 'Peeping Tom'suspects. Nobby's mob welcomed the news gleefully. Of course they were careful not to show their jubilation or to celebrate too openly in front of big Jock Burns. According to Trunkie Davies, Jock's only sister had been in the changing room at the time of Nipper's plunge, and Jock had threatened to skin alive every single one of the culprits involved; that's if he could get definite proof of their identity.

No one on the site disputed Trunkie's assessment that there

were few capable of outdoing the big Caledonian when it came to imposing the laws of the jungle on those who'd offended him.

Meanwhile, the laggers and the painters management were angry as well as adamant that their employees were innocent of the Fibre factory fiasco. They then took the unprecedented step of allowing their workers to hold an unofficial union meeting, knowing that this would eventually involve the rest of the site in their grievance.

As a result, a mass meeting was later convened outside the main gate with the case against the two trades being outlined by a well-spoken orator. After discussions for and against the accusations, a vote was taken to support their cause, with an overwhelming response in their favour.

Standing alongside Nobby and his blimping mob as each hand was raised, I was relieved in a way that he did indeed seem to have some sort of principle when he urged each of his devious squad to vote in favour of strike action to support the innocence of the laggers and painters.

Needless to say, with the contract at a crucial stage of completion, the threat of a 'walk out,' was sufficient to resolve the problem, and the good name of the laggers and painters was restored when they were exonerated from the blame for the whole sorry mess.

Like all things that happened at Tanjon's, most incidents, savoury - or un-savoury - were forgotten within weeks as some other incident occurred to take their place. Meanwhile, after his infamous plunge, Nipper appeared to have turned over a new leaf, and it was noticeable that he seemed to have changed for the better. He'd not upset anyone on site or in the cabin, and his willingness to run additional errands, made him popular with the whole squad, including the younger apprentices. Naturally, I made sure I was credited with most of the praise for this improvement.

A week or two later, after the dinner break, Jimmy 'H' arrived like a mini tornado as the squad congregated outside the mill gates waiting to be hustled into the Mill. Mildly curious, we watched him dash from group to group spreading some sort of news to the assembled smokers and gossips. Seeing the effect his disclosure had on those he'd spoken to, our little band became more than inquisitive.

'What's 'appened?' Chunkie yelled at Jimmy 'H', as we slouched across to join the main body of workers.

'Some dirty bastard's nicked young Nipper's wallet,' Podgy Hogan blurted out.

'You've gorra be kiddin'. I've only just left 'im a few minutes ago,' I gasped.

'JIMMY' 'Come over 'ere an' tell the lads what you've just told us, 'Podgy bawled.

Someone's pinched Nipper's wallet out of his arse pocket,' Jimmy 'H' yelled across as he passed the news to yet another group.

'Christ! Don't say we've gorra bloody tea leaf in the camp,' Robbo growled. 'Has anyone informed the stewards?'

'Let's not get them involved,' said Billy the Minge. 'It'll mean a bloody collection, an' I've only gorra short week to pick up this Friday.'

'What's goin' on here?' Plonker Parson roared, striding ahead of the other chargehands straggling a few yards behind. He listened to the explanation as to why the men seemed to be reluctant to enter the Mill, then muttered with just a hint of sarcasm,'how do you know the lad hasn't dropped it somewhere on site, or left it in one of the traps where he spends most of his time.'

Podgy, who wasn't impressed by Plonker's flippancy or his tone of voice, yelled as loud as he could muster, ' HEY JIMMY COME OVER 'ERE AN' TELL THE BIG FELLA ABOUT THE ROBBERY.'

Jimmy 'H' ambled across at his usual steady pace. Everyone gathered to hear the details straight from the horse's mouth, to see what light he could shed on the missing article.

'Right lads,' Jimmy 'H' began. He was frowning for a change and looking serious. 'From what I've been told,' he continued, 'someone's pinched Nippers wallet from his arse pocket.'

'His arse pocket?' Plonker replied, repeating Jimmy's words parrot fashion.

'Yeah, 'is arse pocket' Jimmy said, with a solemn emphasis. There was a stunned silence for a moment. Then, before anyone had chance to ask any further questions about this serious allegation, Jimmy 'H' added, 'I didn't really think anyone could stoop so low.' Turning briskly he walked away, his usual straight face displayed for his gullible audience.

As we trundled on the job even the chargehands were chuckling at Jimmy 'H' latest wise- crack which had fooled everyone, including themselves. Robbo, turning to us as we opened his toolbox, casually remarked that the job wouldn't be worth a carrot if we didn't have the likes of Jimmy 'H' to liven the place up. Everyone agreed, as Nipper shrugged and grinned at the way his small frame had been used to produce such fun and laughter.

'Here he is,' Chunkie said, as Nipper went past him, 'not yet sixteen and already he's become a legend - and there's five more years to go before he finishes his time.'

Summer holidays and the noble art of self defence

It was only those poor unfortunates whose finances were stretched to the limit and couldn't afford the time-off who didn't look forward to the summer holidays. For the rest of us - and the majority of contractors who were closing down for a fortnight - the last week in July and the first week in August was a time for jubilation. Regardless of the loss of pay and the chance of overtime, well, this was simply 'The Best Time of the Year'!

At last those carefully made plans were to be put to the test. By the time we broke up on the final Friday night we were determined to spread our wings, throw caution to the wind, and cast away the pressures of work and months of studying at night school and particularly, the following exams. With the results of our efforts now safely in the lap of the Gods, and the indifferent marks thrust to the back of our minds until next term, we left the site like a bunch of released convicts suddenly tasting freedom for the first time in years.

Big Don, now senior apprentice, was among the first half dozen who fled through the gates that night. A few months earlier he and five of his mates had booked a week at Butlins Pwllheli Camp in North Wales. They were amateur boxers belonging to The Star club in Ellesmere Port, all with a passionate ambition to win glory for themselves and for their club in the main boxing competition at the holiday camp.

For some reason, when Don invited the older apprentices at Tanjon's to join his troop, I was the only one to accept his invitation, though the chance to compete in such a sport was not one I particularly relished. Light as a feather and blessed with a puny five foot four and a bit frame, there seemed little chance for me to make a dignified exit from the ring other than in a horizontal fashion. Yet, despite being surrounded by the group and their dangerous practice of trading blows for sport, in a perverse kind of way, I was ready, willing and more than able to rise to any challenge that lay ahead. Even if it turned out to be less than perfect, I still had the second week of my holiday to look forward to. This was to be spent touring the sights of Dublin, soaking up the culture, and improving my drinking prowess by exploring the many bars to be found in that city. To keep his eye on me and act as a calming influence, my companion for the week was the studious Timmy McCain, whose role was not only to be my boozing pal, but to hold me in check and keep my feet firmly on the ground

During the two-hour road journey to Wales everyone was in high spirits, with Don and his mates in top form. We kept ourselves amused by playing cards, singing the pop songs of the day as loud as we could, and generally fooling and messing around. Eventually, after crawling through the picturesque valleys and mountain passes of North Wales and then skirting round Porthmadog Bay, our Harding's Holiday coach pulled into the car park outside the main entrance to Butlin's resort in Pwllheli, the holiday Mecca of North Wales.

Before the driver had time to switch off the engine, we were on our feet and off the coach, hauling our battered army haversacks and imitation leather pre-war suitcases towards a party of female redcoats, who, after welcoming us, then guided us towards a reception located just inside the ornate main gates.

With an exaggerated sway of confidence that was as much to do with our fevered imaginations than with any actual reality, we swaggered forward, dressed in the latest summer gear and more than ready to take the place by storm. After signing our monikers on a bundle of sheets pinned to a clip-board to claim our right of entry, and a cursory glance at the camp rules on the notice board, we traipsed behind our first female redcoat, ogling her rear end as she led us towards a row of smart looking chalets in the 'singles section' of the camp. With families making up the majority of holiday makers frequenting the Billy Butlin leisure-time revolution, the need to segregate and dampen down the noisy behaviour of the younger single parties and groups was only to be expected. And this young raven-haired beauty had her work cut out with our group. Despite entertaining her with a running banter of the latest gags, the giggling redcoat declined our invitation to stay for a bevvy, and turned away. Watching her short, white pleated skirt, swinging back and forwards in unison with her long, provocative Hollywood-style legs, taking her back to reception, we decided this was definitely the place to be.

Half an hour later with our travelling gear tucked away, and now changed into baggy blue shorts, we paraded outside the chalet, mainly to take in the sunshine and also to weigh up the opposition - male and female. But there was no sign of any other group to challenge us to a game of footy, so in order to make our presence known, we galloped off across the grass to invade the areas where the happy campers would be likely to congregate and plunged into the nearest swimming pool.

'Fools rush in,' as the old saying goes, and it was fortunate that we had leapt into the three-foot end of the kid's pool, and not the six-inch deep paddling end. Luckily there was no one around and our dignity was still intact as we crawled out, with only the odd scraped knee to show for our rash and foolish plunge.

That first night in the huge dining room we joined hundreds of others ready to demolish every morsel the catering staff could place before us. We then jokingly begged for seconds from the most attractive of the waitresses, all the while hoping that whatever was about to develop might produce more than an extra bowl of spuds

As soon as the food was cleared we steam-rolled into the Calypso bar and nabbed a set of tables nearest to the dance floor, intending to claim them for the rest of the week.

Keen to get the show on the road, but more importantly to impress the vast array of talent beginning to fill the place, we ordered double rounds, and within no time our tables were flowing with booze. Then it was down to the serious business of swallowing the golden liquid in case it suddenly evaporated or went out of fashion. And in between gulps, we ogled the girls strutting around the bar or out on the dance floor, openly promenading their wares waiting for the first of our team to chance his luck.

Eager to show my new-found friends the proper way to perform, I eventually staggered from the table and headed towards the dance floor, determined to put into practice all of Bonso's teachings and experience in the art of bopping and jiving; just as we'd done on our Saturday night's out in the 'Pool'.

After a couple of knock-backs, which I attributed to the natives being unable to understand my guttural accent - rather than any slight on my looks or personality - I managed to save my reputation by creeping up behind a suave looking Teddy boy, as he was about to 'cut in' on a pair of blonde dolly birds. Without saying a word, I stepped in and held out my hand in order to save the girl from becoming a wallflower, and, of course, from losing face. From that moment to the end of the dance, my little feet rattled the boards as if they were on fire, because I was Gene Kelly, Fred Astaire and perhaps a bit of Mickey Rooney all rolled into one.

'See yer later, lad, for another twirl,' my blonde partner said, as we finished our session with a flourish, smiling at me across her shoulder as she made her way off the floor with her mate.

Playing the cool dude, just as I'd done many times before in the Grafton, I gave her the thumbs up, then shuffled back to the tables, where I found the lads arguing the toss as to whose turn it was to get the next round in. I then realised no one had noticed or for that matter shown the least interest in my performance.

'GOOD MORNING CAMPERS.WAKEY..WAKEY.' The voice over the loud speakers blasted a hearty and penetrating reveille. I struggled to open my eyes. 'What time is it?' I muttered, 'Surely it's not that long since we crashed into bed.' But no, it seemed that several hours had passed, and even though my brain told me it was still time to sleep, my watch said it was breakfast time; and as usual, I was hungry.

After stuffing ourselves with enough groceries to last a week, the team got down to the serious business of checking out the sporting calendar, and enrolling in what, for Don and his mates, was the main event of the week - the boxing championship - a competition they were more than confident of winning.

As for me, well, I reckoned a couple of games of football and the odd game of cricket - without having to demonstrate my inability with the bat - would be sufficient exercise to keep me going.

On the Monday morning, with my first game of football scheduled for that afternoon, I slipped into the gym to watch the rest of the lads begin a savage and physical routine of belting punch bags, shadow boxing, skipping over flailing ropes, and sparring with each other; a punishing schedule designed for the sole purpose of getting into shape for the up-coming competition. They all looked extremely impressive, so in order to show an interest and at the same time release a little of my own hidden bravado, I staked my somewhat dubious pugilistic reputation by ambling across the gym to join in the training schedule; confident I'd never be a likely participant in any contest

Unfortunately, as Robbie Burns reminds us,' *the best laid plans of mice and men aft gang astray.* ' For as soon as the trainers began to pair off the contestants it became obvious there was an extra man - a spare fighter without an opponent. To save face, and to keep up the vague pretence of being handy with the gloves, I had no option but to reluctantly allow myself to be cajoled into volunteering to make up the numbers for the squad.

If energetic coaching and loud verbal encouragement won fights, there's little doubt I would have become the world lightweight champion as I soaked up my team mates and trainers advice like a sponge, drinking their words of guidance and comfort as if they were mother's milk. But then I discovered that once you climb through the ropes and enter the ring there's no lonelier place in the world - except perhaps the solitary confinement wing in Alcatraz.

My first contest, on the Wednesday afternoon, was against a freckle-faced lad from Birmingham, who, like me, was a novice. The opening round was spent keeping our distance by at least six foot - I think it's called weighing up each others weaknesses - I'd hardly dare call them strengths. As soon as I returned to my corner, my ringside seconds reminded me that although avoiding a clout on the chin was a laudable move, my tactic of keeping out of my rival's shadow had little to do with the rudiments of boxing, which was to attempt to knock big lumps off the other fella. As they pointed out, the fight would end in a draw if neither of us threw a punch. And this, as I was well aware, could hardly enhance my boastful claim 'to be handy with the gloves'.

Responding to this sound advice and urged on by screams of derision from my mates - as well as some of the audience - the moment the bell rang for the second round I shot out from my corner determined to make an impact. Catching my fellow dancer on the hop with my instant response, I slipped my right arm round his neck, gripped the top rope to prevent him getting away, then pummelled him with my left fist; an act of aggression which caught him (and even me) by surprise. As he quickly dropped to his knees, blood gushing from his nose, I watched him stare up at me. Suddenly I realised he had tears in his eyes, and for a moment I felt a twinge of sympathy for the brutality I'd inflicted on him. That is, until to my amazement, the referee shoved me back then raised my hand as the winner. At this point any sentiment I had for him disappeared like a puff of smoke as the joy of success overwhelmed me.

There was no holding me back now, and on the Thursday as I warmed up for my next bout, I was more than ready to take on another contestant, this time a Yorkshire lad from Barnsley. Whether or not I'd have beaten him is something I'll never know, but Lady Luck was definitely on my side that day. As he made his way from the back of the hall, he somehow or other tripped on the steps leading up to the ring, fell awkwardly, and because of the encumbering boxing gloves was unable to save himself with his hands. With his gloves bent beneath his falling body, he lay in a heap nursing a badly sprained a wrist, an accident which gained me an instant bye into the next round of the competition on the Friday.

Of a possible eight entries in the Friday finals, the 'Star' boxing club had a total of five lads representing them. To add spice to the occasion - or in my case, a drop of custard, the organisers decided to include a novice event. And so Deadwood Jimmy Reilly, with one fight and one bye under his belt, was nominated to box against another so-called 'no hoper' from Cardiff.

For the big finale, the banked hall was full of screaming holidaymakers, each supporting their own favourites. And as Don, the captain of our team, climbed into the ring ready to take on the first of the challengers, I can only describe the atmosphere as being electric.

From our perch, way up at the back of the hall we had a birds-eye view as Don put on a brilliant show, stopping his opponent in the second round. Further successes followed quickly, as our lads won the next two fights. However, the fourth and fifth were much more heavily contested encounters, with equally matched opponents, and resulted in us losing one and drawing the other.

Finally, as the tension grew and the noise in the hall reached a deafening pitch, it was my turn to perform. I was escorted to the ring with one of the team on either side to act as seconds and to prevent my waning self esteem from slipping away. They also had to help me stop the shakes - which I felt certain were unlikely to be caused by the previous evening's morale boosting drinking session. With a show of confidence I was not sure that I truly felt, I climbed up, ducked between the ropes, and danced round on my toes, just as I'd seen Joe Louis do on the Pathe newsreel. I then threw a flurry of imaginary punches and grunted a few times, as the lads in the previous fights had done. The crowd went mad and the noise grew even louder.

As I leaned on the corner of the ropes to receive a last minute instruction from my tutor, 'the expert'- a former professional British light weight contender - my eyes wandered off into the crowd. Across the heads of the spectators I could see a row of seats in the banked auditorium where the girls we'd teamed up with during the week were gathered. At this point I felt like a gladiator about to do battle in the famous Colosseum in Rome.

Suddenly everything went quiet and there was a pregnant pause before a ripple of applause spread round the hall. I turned away from the crowds and the girls I'd been grinning up at in the fifth row as my curiosity got the better of me. To say I almost dropped with fright would be an understatement. There, standing before me, on the opposite side of the ring and waiting to do battle, was the meanest, toughest, muscle-bound character that I'd ever seen in my life. 'Surely that's not a lightweight,' I told myself. 'He's got to be a super heavyweight' was the thought that skittered across my shocked and dumbstruck mind.

During that first round, if there'd been an Olympic medal for back peddling I'd have been a serious contender for gold that night. In a frantic attempt to put as much distance between me and my opponent, my little legs rotated like set of over-worked pistons. Meanwhile, in order to stop my adversary penetrating a remarkable defensive posture that I'd just invented to protect my body and face, I began flaying my arms in windmill fashion; a strategy I reckoned might just enable me to leave the ring in one piece.

One whole minute may not seem too long when you're

messing about doing nothing in particular, but when you're in the ring being pursued by someone who's clearly intent on removing your head from your shoulders, then those sixty seconds can seem like a lifetime - or even longer! How I managed to escape the clutches of my Tiger Bay opponent is a mystery to this day, and at the bell, when I plonked myself down on the stool in the corner I could hardly believe my luck - that I was still alive.

Wearing a groove in the canvas deck during those harrowing few minutes had taken its toll, however, for instead of following instructions to swill my mouth out with a small swig of water to combat the threat of dehydration, I snatched the bottle from my trainer and gulped the lot down.

What's more, it seemed the crowd had sensed blood, hearing them baying and screaming; and I was sure it was my blood they were after, not Tiger Bay's. At the same time the advice from my 'expert' was coming at me, blunt and straight to the point, giving no indication of recognising my precarious position.

'Stop back peddlin' and stand your ground, lad,' he growled at me, 'then let him feel the full weight of your left hook.'

'What left hook?' I asked myself incredulously, but said nothing as he urged me to 'think of your reputation while your at it,' glancing over his shoulder at the rest of the lads who by now were parked in the ringside seats.

'Reputation, for what? Cowardice' I whispered to myself.

Fortunately the 'expert' missed my defeatist parley, and continued his careful pep talk.

'And if he does catch you properly, son, don't forget to take a mandatory count of eight, just for a breather,' he added as a final nugget of fighting wisdom, all the while wafting an old white towel in my face. This, I fully expected to see come flying into the ring sometime during the bout.

As the bell sounded for round two I stood up and rolled my shoulders a couple of times and glared across at the corner where my opponent was just rising. Suddenly, propelled by a less than gentle push in the back from the 'expert', I shot across the ring, determined to catch the Tiger by surprise and land the punch of a lifetime - just as I had done in my first bout when I'd caught the 'dancer' on the hop. The surprise was as much mine as it was his, however, for the punch I delivered did indeed smack him on the chin; and what's more it was as sweet as a nut. I stood back a pace feeling mighty pleased with myself and glanced back to my corner to see what they thought, waiting for the so-called Cardiff assassin to slump to the floor, ready to be counted out.

Keeping up my guard as advised by the 'expert', I then blimped across the top of the sixteen-ounce gloves to see what was going on, just as a searing thud tore through my guard landing in the region of my solar plexus. Immediately heeding the advice to take a count of eight if I was hurt in any way, I was about to begin the short journey to the deck when another savage clout was delivered to the side of my head. The power of this sledgehammer blow was such that it left me in little doubt that the assassin now intended to finish me off in double-quick time, and this was enough to hasten my trip to the canvas.

Crouching on all fours, I tried to improve my lowly position further by simultaneously letting my arms and my legs slip away from my body, to allow my chest and belly to reach the comfort and safety of the floor; a state I reckoned would look more authentic when I was stretchered from the ring.

'One...Two..Three..' the ref counted out, firmly and slowly. For some reason, at that moment I remembered my trainer's last minute consoling instruction that if I was really hurt he would toss in the towel to stop the fight. To remind him of this tactical move, or in case it had slipped his memory, I opened my left eye to glance towards my corner, and was horrified to hear him urging me to get up. I could hardly believe my ears.

'Gerrup, come one gerrup! You've won this Jimmy. Gerrup, come on gerrup. He's finished,' he bawled, waving his arms in an upward gesture.

More from shock than anything else I opened my other eye and looked towards my opponent - big Tiger, or whatever he was really called. I could see he was in obvious pain, because he was dancing up and down, gingerly holding his right hand with his left, as it hung limply and uselessly down by his thigh. It seemed that like me, he was in no hurry to continue to fight.

'Seven... Eight... Nine...' the ref counted on.

How I managed to beat the count as I staggered to my feet

just before he got to ten, is not something you'll find in the boxing annals. But having gained the vertical once again, I sloped across to Tiger, all the while trying to look like a winner. The ref looked hard into my eyes when I reached the opposition, then ushered me back to my corner just as a greyish white towel bearing an image of the red Welsh Dragon came floating in the ring from Tiger's corner.

'Sit down son. Sit down for a second' the 'expert' said, as he half drowned me by pouring a bucket full of cold water over my head. This swiftly brought me to my senses and stopped my incoherent ramblings.

The ref was now standing in the centre of the ring with Tiger. Looking forlorn and slightly dejected the Cardiff mauler still managed a menacing glare in my direction. Then, beckoning me with his finger to join them in the centre, the official announced to the audience that Tiger had sustained a broken thumb - which was no surprise to me, considering that searing thud to my solar plexus - and proclaimed me to be the winner. He then grabbed my wrist and raised my hand, much to my delight.

With my both hands held high I gave a little jig as I danced back to my corner, keen to impress the girls in the fifth row; who, I couldn't help noticing, were still yelling their support for me.

Standing proudly with the lads from the Star boxing team that night, as the awards were being dished out, I wondered if, perhaps, it would worth my while joining the club. But when I mentioned the possibility to them, Don did the honourable and logical thing and shot my self-inflated dreams to pieces, saying that in his opinion and that of the 'expert,' I'd be much better taking up field events – perhaps running, or maybe even backwards running.

I got the message. And for this memorable and pugilistic experience - which, if I was honest, could well have resulted in a fatality - I earned myself a silver plated cup which I received from the reigning Miss Butlin.

Mind you, this was not the outstanding award it might seem; the cup could hardly be compared to the Lonsdale belt, and would have struggled to hold an averaged sized hen's egg. On the other hand, after mulling over Don's words of wisdom,

I was in no doubt that my trophy was considerably larger than the remnants of my previously over inflated ego.

The second week of my holidays could, I suppose, be compared to a retreat in a monastery after the hectic time I'd crammed in at Butlin's.

Timmy had arranged to meet me in Holyhead, and though I slept during the journey by coach, when I eventually woke I felt is if I'd had enough ale and late nights to last a lifetime. Despite my dishevelled appearance, he was pleased to see me arrive in one piece, and as I kind of expected, took the responsibility for treating my obvious hang-over by dosing me with a couple of cups of strong black coffee, before escorting me towards a tap and a freezing cold water wash in the toilet area.

The ferry left the harbour on time and as it ploughed through the choppy Irish sea on the three hour journey to Dun Laoghaire, Timmy pranced round the deck eager to let everyone know it was his first journey overseas. Meanwhile, like a bloated dog with eyes too big for its belly, I sprawled alongside the bogs on one of the slatted benches, tucked out of the wind between the Port and Starboard side of the vessel.

To afford this holiday on his lowly apprentice wage, Timmy had arranged for us to stay in a Youth hostel right in the heart of Dublin, and it was from this spartan base that he plotted an itinerary that emphasised all the historical sights the great city had to offer. Of course, having unwillingly traipsed around most of places of note with dad on a previous visit to Dublin, I didn't share Tim's enthusiasm. However, in my present state, and determined not to rock the boat, I gave him the reins and fell in line with his plans.

Next morning and every morning after that, Timmy was up like a lark, often scoffing his breakfast long before I had a chance to clear my head, or to dig the sleep from my eyes or to swill my face. And so around nine o'clock we'd hit the road, ready to begin our incursions into Dublin city.

Although there were times that I moaned about Tim's relentless attempts to learn all he could about past events, I began to understand his fervour when he told me his relatives hailed from County Wicklow, and how a distant uncle, sometime during the last century, had been executed for being a member of the Republican Army. But what he kept to himself until the end of a drinking session in Mooney's bar on our last night in Dublin had me choking on my Guinness.

With a face the colour of a red balloon, he began reminiscing about the time he'd worked with 'Willie the Spook;' and how the Spook had explained in detail, the subject of reincarnation. He also reckoned that in a previous life, Timmy had been involved in a Fenian uprising and had come to a sticky end. No wonder I almost ruined my best shirt spluttering with laughter as the Porta dribbled from my mouth like treacle. It was later that night I remembered the time Tim worked with Willie and how it had affected his nerves, so that ultimately he'd been moved to another gang.

I must confess that even though I was fifteen months older I learnt a lot from Tim that week. He was a lad of principles and without his strong leadership I'd have probably spent most of my time aggravating the stools in the O'Connell Street bars instead of ambling along the banks of the River Liffey, breathing in Dublin's illustrious past and visiting the likes of the Phoenix Park, Croke Park, and even hob-nobbing with the 'in crowd' at the famous Abbey Theatre.

As our holiday came to a close I came to the conclusion that maybe Timmy might now swap his childhood passion of train spotting for priest spotting. From day one, the sight of relentless armies of priests steering their 'sit up and beg' bikes through the narrow gaps in Dublin's busy roads always stopped him in his tracks. He would stand around St Stephens Green area for ages marvelling at this spectacle, while I, having seen it all before, relished the chance to rest my aching feet

.After a fairly smooth crossing, we arrived back in Holyhead in the early hours of Saturday morning, refreshed and ready for the three hour train journey home. Compared to Butlin's, it had been a leisurely week, although we still managed to sup more than our fair share of Guinness during those long drawn out evenings spent savouring the balmy atmosphere of the Dublin city night life.

More gaffers, more changes

Perhaps for the first time since I'd left school I had no need for dad's thunderous roar to stir me from the land of nod. I was up, bright as a lark, my enthusiasm even taking him by surprise, and with a bounce in my step I reached Woodside in record time. As I boarded the bus to take me to the Port, a buzz of light hearted banter erupted from the passengers, who were mainly contractors, their patter in direct contrast to the grumpy Monday blues that would normally herald the beginning of a new week.

There was a similar atmosphere in the cabins, with the excited chatter of those who'd been on holiday drowning the extraneous outside noises, as highlights of the past two weeks experiences were exchanged.

'Bloody 'ell Reilly, you've got eyes like piss 'oles in the snow,' Trunkie Davies yelled, as I was about to settle in my usual speck beside the main window, next to Chunkie.

Now I was that little bit older and with more experience under my belt, I didn't immediately respond. Apart from being generally nosy, I'd sussed that Trunkie - like the Pope - showed an unhealthy interest when we lads were discussing our sexual exploits.

'Did you score, or what like?' He asked, determined to glean the explicit details of any failed or successful conquest from my time at Butlin's.

'Of course I did,' I replied eventually, lingering over a mouthful of sugary tea, and playing for time to gain those few vital seconds that might induce a touch of inspiration and allow me to string him along.

'I managed to score on the first Saturday,' I said, rolling my eyes as if reliving a provocative experience.

'Good lad', he said, in an encouraging manner, resting his chin on the palms of his hands to take in the details of everything I was about to divulge.

'Mind you, I missed out on the Sunday, though I tried all the tricks in the book,' I continued. 'Monday and Tuesday, to be honest I bounced back right on form.

'Are yer listenin' lads', Trunkie blabbered, appealing to the rest of the gang as the lies slipped from my tongue as natural as the day was light.

'Wednesday and Thursday I took it nice and easy. You know worra mean, Trunk? To gather my strength for the run in.'

'Exactly, I know what yer mean lad. Go on finish your story', he added, his face glowing an unusual shade of red.

'Friday afternoon I was back to my best, I even managed a hat trick.'

'A hat trick! Well done son,' Trunkie beamed.

Did you hear that lads? he bawled, almost falling off the end of the bench in excitement. So don't be expectin' too much graft from young Reilly this week, not after all he's been up to at Butlin's', he said, turning to the adjacent tables to address those who were not reading their newspapers.

'Just out of interest Jimmy', he continued in a much quieter voice, 'tell us which of 'em performed best? An' what did they look like? Come on give us a bit of detail? Were they fat, thin, tall, small, or what like?'

'Just average', I told him, noticing the lecherous gleam in his eyes as he waited for me to disclose further tit bits to stimulate his overworked imagination.

'And as I said, they just got better as the week wore on.'

It was at this point that I noticed the Pope moving closer, almost snuggling up into Trunkie's shoulder.

'I must say they took it well though', I mumbled on.

'Wotcha mean, took it well?' Trunkie asked, his eyes almost popping out of his head.

'Bloody good losers, that's worra mean. They were only playing with ten men, an' almost held us to a draw on the Friday, until I scored the winner, my hat trick in the dying seconds.'

I watched as Trunkie's smile turned to a scowl, while the Pope tutted for a second, straightened his glasses, then flipped open his newspaper, which was upside down.

'We're not talkin' about football you dope, Trunkie growled. We're supposed to be talkin' about bits of skirt; about birds. An' I don't mean the friggin' seagulls that bombard us when we're on our way to the Mill. I was talkin' about dolly birds, those with curvy figures. You do know what I mean, don't yer Reilly, or 'ave I got to spell it out to yer?'

'Of course I do, I'm not thick Trunkie. You seem to forget I've been coached by Nobby Alcock, the Boss Poser, one of the best gigolos on site. Anyway, what would happen if you'd keeled over when I was right in the middle of describing one of my famous Reilly clinches, eh? I don't want to be held responsible to the lads for havin'to have a collection for you. Billy the Minge would never gerr over it? He'd haunt me from his grave for the rest of my life.'

'Famous clinches my arse, you haven't gorra clue Reilly,' he spluttered, his face red with anger.

'Well done Jimmy, I'm proud of yer,' Billy Chancer interrupted, pleased to see Trunkie taken down a peg or two

Lifting his newspaper from the table Trunkie muttered sulkily, 'anyone who doesn't score at Butlin's must be canned goods.'

To gain a bit of further attention and to raise a laugh during the morning break, I casually mentioned my performance in winning a cup in the Butlin's boxing finals. Delving deep in my haversack I then pretended to struggle with an incredibly heavy object, before fishing out my tiny trophy for all to see. Holding it above my head like a world champion receiving the adulation of his fans I waved it back and forwards. But then, as I sat down, I listened as my credibility was torn to pieces, as big Don described just how I'd achieved my success in the face of an almost overwhelmingly run of events.

'Christ this can't be much bigger than one of me mam's thimbles,' Billy Constable said, lifting the cup with his little finger and inspecting the inscription.

'What weight were you fightin' at Reilly, paperweight or featherweight?' Chunkie joked. 'Cos you can't be more than nine stone ringin' wet.'

'Chunks, because of all the training I did I was just under eight stone for my first fight,' I answered steadfastly - rolling up my right sleeve to show my tiny but firm bicep.

'With all that back peddlin' Don's been tellin' us about, I reckon you'd probably lost over a stone by the time of you entered the ring for your last fight,' Podgy Hogan added, joining the apprentices in the mickey taking. 'We'd better watch our steps lads, what with havin' a champion in our midst', he continued.

'Champion, worr of? The children's 'ospital,' chuckled Chinless Brady, who was an ex-North West County middleweight champion from St Teresa's, one of Liverpool's most famous boxing clubs.

Suddenly, as the Pope sitting quietly on the next table, began to rise, Chinless - already on his feet - crouched in a southpaw stance and threw a number of right hand punches that whistled just inches above the Papal father's head. As Robbo, laughingly remarked, 'for a so called man of the cloth the Pope can't half move when danger threatens.'

At this point the timely appearance of the chargehands ended the fun, and my blushes were spared, as Don had just started to describe not only my drunken performance in the dance hall; but my outrageous ambition to join the Star Boxing Club.

After a holiday period it usually took a day or two to pick up the pieces on a job, but this time it was different. A couple of weeks before the summer break, the stewards had called a meeting to outline a few important management proposals. To ensure the Mill contract would be completed on time, Tanjon's were now considering drafting in groups of men and their respective chargehands from the newly completed office job. And so Bootsy (now promoted to senior chargehand), Plonker Parson and Whistling Bob Baines, were joined by three more supervisors. First there was loud-mouthed Terry Collins, better known to everyone as Tear-Arse. Next in line was Tommy 'Dosser' Dobson, and finally, the ebullient and likeable local personality, Sailor Waverly the Third. Rob Shepherd, a Staff engineer was also appointed as senior supervisor to oversee the job. He'd arrived six months earlier from down south bringing with him a reputation for being a no-nonsense hard liner. According to the lads, though, Rob was no more than glorified chancer and never an engineer.

So, for the first time since starting at Bowaters I was transferred to another squad, away from my mentor, the wise and ever faithful Robbo. It was Robbo who'd been responsible for saving my skin on more occasions than I could care to remember, and who was always on hand to offer sound advice to me and the rest of the apprentices whenever we fell foul of authority.

To gain experience in the skills of panel wiring it had been decided that Chunkie, Timmy McCain, Big Don, George Sharkey the prankster, and I would be transferred into 'Whistling Bob's' gang. However, before we'd had chance to settle into our new surrounds and suss out the best specks in the switchroom, we were immediately paired off with Jimmy 'H', Podgy Hogan, and Billy Chancer - the self-styled philosopher from my early days at Pitts.

Everyone had a good word for 'Whistling Bob.' He was a jovial, roly-poly character, never miserable or sarcastic, and according to those with experience of working for other chargehands, was perhaps the easiest going gaffer at Tanjon's.

Bob had one less than endearing habit, however, which was an unconscious tendency to whistle the same tune over and over again, from early morning 'til five o'clock finishing time.

Of course the lads working for Bob knew his favourite melodies off by heart, and were acutely aware of his compulsion to take onboard whatever song someone else was whistling. So, for a laugh - and out of mischief - someone would strike up a tune for Bob to latch on to; then somebody else would whistle a different one, and this would be repeated again and again. The record number of these implanted whistling diversions we managed to achieve was eight in one morning, but whether Bob was aware of his manipulators ploys, we never found out. He wasn't the type to let slip that he knew anything unusual was happening. As happy as Larry, he was simply content to whistle the time away. And not surprising those of us who were feeding a stream of new tunes soon became known as the Trillo Brigade.

Unlike 'Whistling Bob,' Terry Collins was a different kettle of fish. Only those with a naive ambition for fame and grandeur, or those who were a bit soft in the head would volunteer to work for him. A stickler for getting on with the job, he'd earned his reputation and his nickname of 'Tear Arse' by not tolerating slackness and idle talk - an attitude that delighted the management.

As soon as 'Tear Arse' got wind of a rush job - which usually meant working overtime, or even through the night (commonly known as a ghoster) - he would head off to the agents cabin before any other chargehand had heard a whisper that a 'double-bubble' wage buster was on the cards.

Out of a simple curiosity, we would often blimp his squad as they huddled together before setting off to perform their duties. This assembly was like an army operation, because as soon as 'Tear Arse' fathomed out the best way to tackle a job he'd hit the button and his lads would be off like the clappers, all out to finish it as quickly as possible. The more militants maintained that 'Tear Arse's methods were detrimental to the ultimate good of those of us on the job, and complained that he was too thick to realise that the quicker the work was done, the quicker everyone would 'be up the road'. Of course, even though many resented 'Tear arse's' bullish, steam-rolling approach, no one could argue that his compulsive commitment wasn't in the best interest of the firm and its profits.

Thomas Dobson, who was appropriately nicknamed 'Dosser' or 'Tosser' by the more out-spoken of the workers was the complete opposite of his workaholic comrade 'Tear Arse.'

'Dosser' was so laid back his squad were often forced to take the bull by the horns and motivate themselves in order to show progress and to keep a grip on the work. For reasons not too difficult to fathom out, 'Dosser' had taken it upon himself to encourage the men to express their skills without the need for his prolonged appearance, or interference and presence on the job.

As it happened this job was tailor made for 'Dosser's' easy going attitude. And fortunately he'd inherited a squad of conscientious workers, which enabled him to spend most of his time scanning blueprints and fiddling with progress charts in the comparative warmth of the chargehand's cabin. It was only a matter of time though, before his unorthodox and slow moving methods began to raise a few eyebrows amongst his fellow supervisors. But when they began to question 'Dosser's' style of supervision, they found that he just happened to be married to 'Bootsy's' sister, and as such, was a protected species. This revelation forced a swift change of tune and naturally, a quick U - turn.

Of course the workforce had been well aware of the situation long before the chargehands rumbled that 'Dosser' was a relation of the more senior 'Bootsy,' or that there was another good reason he'd been recommended by his brother in law. On good authority the grapevine let it be known that 'Dosser' had mastered the complicated act of reading schematic blue prints, while 'Bootsy, it seemed had not.'

And so no one was surprised when these rumours reached the ears of the gossip merchants; there was always a suspicion of nepotism when someone with a different accent to the locals turned up on site from out of the blue, especially if they were immediately given their stripes.

'Sailor Waverley the Third,' to give him his full and commonly used title, completed the quintet. Now someone with enough cheek to live with such a Hollywood style tag - especially on a construction site - would seem to deserve the torrent of ridicule and mockery from the many wind-up merchants lined up to take a pot shot. And our site was no exception.

Sid Shortwick, the champion story teller, having worked alongside Sailor on other sites, had a tale to reveal, and he didn't waste much time before putting everyone in the picture about Sailor's origins. As expected, Sid deliberately chose a ripe moment during a mid-week dinner hour to tell all, when those not engaged in the serious pursuit of gambling were either nodding off or generally looking bored. We were all killing time, waiting for the chargehands to appear, when Sid suddenly mentioned the new chargehands and began comparing 'Tear Arse' and 'Dosser' to the likes of 'Plonker' and 'Bootsy,' before turning his attention to Sailor.

'I'll tell you something about Sailor,' he began, 'he's the real McCoy y'know, a genuine article? 'Yep' he continued, 'he's the third generation of the Waverley family bearin' the Sailor moniker? Without waiting for anyone to respond to his opening gambit he carried on.

'Right, I'll put you in the picture lads, as I always do…Step by step… so you can follow me. You know how thorough I am with my research.'

'Go on, give us a laugh an' surprise us for a change,' Podgy Hogan said, spreading his massive, fat legs on either side of the bench and comfortably resting his head on the side of the cabin wall, all set to listen to Sid's version of the Waverley family tree.

'I'll start at the beginning, way back in time, in the early days of the great sailin' ships,' Sid began. 'That's when Sailor's grandad kicked off with the sea. Fourteen years of age, that's all he was when he signed on as a deck hand. Then straight out ter sea, even before he could get used to his long trousers warmin' his legs. He began his career on sailin' ships, yer know - the ones that ploughed the Atlantic from the 'Pool to the States. Now those lads were proper sailors. Not your bronzie merchants. Not like some of today's cowboys who only go ter sea to gerr a tan an' to show off to their judy's when they get back home.

Sid was just warming up now, and turned the volume up a notch or two.

'Anyway, getting' back to Sailor's grandad. Can yer imagine haulin' in those massive sails in mountainous seas? Then relyin' on the wind ter get yer from A ter B, an' bein' tossed outa yer hammock when yer half asleep? Bloody 'ell that must have been hard goin'. And the times when some poor soul had to climb the main mast to the crows nest just to blimp if pirates or worr-ever there was ahead on the horizon. An' that was an every day fact ... worra life that must 'ave been... Christ that's what you call tough.'

'Pirates?' said Crusthead McGinty, frowning and looking a little shocked.

'Shush,' Sid replied putting his finger across his lips, 'story first, questions later.'

'Now then, from the info I have, I know this was Sailor's grandad's party piece during the whole of the time he was at sea. In fact he became known far and wide as Dickie Sam's number one look-out.' Of course, this is all second hand 'gen.' But according to a good source which I'm lucky to have access to,' Sid told his audience as he took a quick puff on a stump that was burning perilously low in his fingers - 'as the ship sailed into Liverpool Bay after Grandad's first trip, it was greeted by a load of seagulls flying in a sort of halo fashion. The sailors in them days of course, were suspicious of anything unusual, and many reckoned this was actually a sign – a phenomena or an omen of good luck to mark their arrival home - safe and sound. And all because of this phenomena – Yes, Crust'ead phenomena, Sid repeated as Crusthead was again about to open his mouth.

'Right, where was I up to? Oh yeah! So Sailor Waverley's grandad's name became part of the folklore of famous mariners who'd sailed out of the 'Pool. So now then, I reckon that's one for those of you'se lads interested in local seafaring history.'

'What was the name of the ship then Sid? It wasn't the famous old confederate ship 'The Alabama,' was it? Crustead McGinty asked, keen as ever to display his own knowledge on nautical matters.

A ripple of laughter echoed around the cabin from the older listeners, while us lads, not being conversant with naval history, just sat there with straight faces.

'Don't talk daft la, how old d'yer reckon young Sailor is?' Sid retorted.

'Any road, getting' back to what I was sayin' before bein' interrupted by soft arse over 'ere,' Sid muttered, glancing towards Crusthead, who appeared totally unaffected by Sid's derogatory response.

'Then Sailor's dad, known as Sailor junior, followed the call of the sea just like 'is ould fella before 'im. Only by now the sailing ships were being scrapped and modern steam ships were all the rage. So, after getting a bit of practice in on the ferry boats, sailing up and down the river and dockin' at the Pier 'ead, an' New Brighton, Seacombe and Woodside, he then managed to sign up on a 'skin boat' voyagin' to the Canaries and Africa. Now for you'se lads not conversant with the merch, the skin boats belonged to Elders and Fife, a subsidiary of the famous Elder Dempster Line,' Sid added, once again reminding everyone just how vast his knowledge of past and present shipping companies was.

'His maiden voyage down to the West Coast of Africa turned out to be his first and last, though,' he added with a snigger. 'But before I go any further I've got ter point out to you'se fella's that Sailor's old man was a real nark, an argumentative bugger. Not a bit like his lad, who, as we all know, is a good skin.' This carefully added rider was for the benefit of any listening stool pigeon who was likely to repeat his story to Sailor.

'Then the ship, .. er.. what was it called? Let me think now,' he said, scratching his head as if to prod his memory into action. 'Ah that's it, 'The Ivory Coaster' or something like that,' he continued, as if the name was significant; but more likely to perhaps save further interruption from Crusthead.

'Anyway, after the Ivory Coaster dropped anchor in Lagos, the locals immediately began unloading the bulk of the cargo, which was mainly farm machinery and the other domestic bits and bobs Fifes regularly shipped from the U.K. Of course, it was roastin' at the time, with the temperature touching the high nineties, and even before the ship's cargo had been properly cleared, a convoy of old fashioned bullock wagons packed to the hilt with bananas began arriving at the quay.

Now, for the rest of the crew - except Sailor, who was new to the event - the novelty of seeing bananas arrive in this manner and then be slung up and loaded onto the ship usin' a variety of bamboo canes had long worn off. So most of those off-duty had gone ashore to spend time moseying round the Lagos docks area, or to get stuck into the local rum - or anything else worth getting' stuck into, if you know what I mean.' He chuckled, winking at the gawping Pope, who hurriedly dropped his head and closed his eyes as if he hadn't been listening to the tale.

'For some reason at this point the bold Sailor took it on himself to get involved in the situation, acting as some sort of inspector and almost caused a bloody strike.'

'We're not havin' THEM,' he raved, pointing at the clumps of bananas being carried up the gangway onto the deck. 'Your not kiddin' us, we're not thick y'know, he ranted and yelled. 'We 'aven't come over on the banana boat.'

There was a chuckle from a couple of Welsh lads resting on a table behind us.

'We 'aven't come all the way from the Pool ter pick up green 'uns when we can gerr em from Paddy's market all nice an' yeller like,' he bawled, leaning across the hand rail.

'Of course, with Sailor rattlin' so fast and with him havin' a broad Scotty Road accent, well the natives couldn't make heads nor tails of what he was mumblin' about,' Sid said. 'So they ignored 'im and carried on loadin' the bananas. By this time Sailor had seen 'is arse and in a blind rage he blocked the top section of the gangway, spreadin 'is thick arms across the ropes, threatening to flatten anyone who came aboard. Naturally - an' you couldn't blame em,' Sid continued, 'the locals took one look at Sailor - who, like his son, was built like the Titanic - an' fearing for their safety they dropped the bananas, leaving them scattered all over the wharf.'

'When the skipper got wind of Sailor's uncalled for interference and heard about his aggressive attitude he summoned the bosun and a few crew members to help lock Sailor in his cabin 'til the ship was properly loaded and ready to sail.

Sid yawning noisily, closed his eyes, then stretched his hands above his head before continuing in a quieter voice

'Just over a week later, when they docked in the 'Pool,' the skipper put the boot in good style by reporting the incident to his bosses. He told them Sailor was nothing but a bully, and besides he had nowt upstairs. The gaffers had no option then, but to mark Sailor's book as 'unsuitable for deep sea journeys.' And in a way, that was the end of Sailor's long-haul seagoing career.

Before anyone had chance to question Sid's exaggerated account, he pushed on with his tale. 'Mind you lads, Sailor wasn't the kind to take no for an answer, and somehow he managed to kid his way on to the trawlers sailing out of Fleetwood. Believe it or not he lasted years before finishing right back where he started, on the ferryboats. Not bad for a chancer! Eh lads?' Sid said glancing round at his audience, some of whom were now fast asleep.

'And now,' Sid continued, 'if you'll bear with me 'til I've supped the last dregs of me rosy lea, I'll bring you up to date on the ups and downs of our very own, Sailor the Third.'

'Oh no, not more bloody drivel,' Billy the Minge complained. But with eight minutes to go to the end of dinner break, and no one else objecting, Sid simply carried on, ignoring Billy's whinging remark.

'For starters, Young Waverley was known as a 'dry land sailor,' Sid began, his voice rising considerably, bringing a few of the slumberers back to life.

'When he was only twelve years old he upset the Waverley

crowd by breaking ranks with his merchant naval blood, and joining the Royal Navy sea cadets. His first trip was on H.M.S Neverbudge, you know the one that's berthed down in the docks. Truth is, lads,' Sid whispered, to those of us still awake. The truth is - SAILOR NEVER WENT TO SEA IN HIS LIFE,' he roared vigorously.

An unusual silence lasting for a few moments followed the revelation.

'You're jokin'?' Podgy Hogan responded finally. 'Sailor's been round the world more times than we've 'ad hot dinners,' he continued. 'Any fool knows that. I mean ter say, you've only got ter listen to the way the fella speaks about the different places and the ports he's called at to realise he's a born mariner.'

Podgy was right, Sailor had a way of describing in detail those dodgy, no-go areas of the main ports in many exotic countries scattered round the world.

Whether Sailor had memorised and adopted the tales of seamen he drank with, or he'd heard them from his grandad or dad was now a matter of much debate. Yet no one could deny he constantly used nautical terms such as 'welcome aboard, keep the place ship shape, don't desert a sinking ship, or, it's a good little vessel this one' and others he had off to a fine art. This alone was sufficient to convince many that he was indeed a real salt of the sea, a true jack-tar mariner. But, unlike 'Tear arse Rawlston,' Sailor was an extremely popular chargehand with the majority of workers. Loyal and fair minded, he would never pass the buck, something which was second nature to some of the other chargehands. And if a rush job appeared to be slipping, he wouldn't panic or go running to his superiors. Instead, he would respond with a typical expression, such as 'don't worry shipmates, no one will go down with this vessel while you've got me for your skipper;' a declaration which always endeared him to his squad. What's more, in addition to his nautical lingo, like many seamen who'd been away for months and who swayed as they walked, Sailor's western roll swagger was so exaggerated, that if you happened to be walking alongside him, you had to concede at least three feet to avoid being buffeted by his broad shoulders.

Before Sid had a chance to continue and perhaps to become the judge, jury and the executor in this bizarre quest to nail

Sailor Waverley the Third, the chargehands - including the subject himself - swung open the door and yelled 'time's up lads, let's get this show on the road.'

And so we filtered out, headed towards the mill, taking with us whatever tit - bits from Sid's stories we found acceptable, and never knowing if Sailor had indeed crossed the seven seas.

Since the reshuffle of labour, the installation work appeared to be going faster than before the holidays. This unusual burst of conscientious energy was firstly attributed to some unknown devious person who'd suggested they'd heard whispers that a 'pump list' was being strung together. This rumour was quickly squashed by the stewards, who rightly condemned the foolishness of putting such an idea into circulation, which might just seep into the heads of the management.

Then the more liberal attitude shown by Bootsy and his chargehands towards the workers was suggested as the reason for this strange work phenomena. However, behind the scenes, someone else was apparently blowing his own trumpet, by claiming responsibility for the sudden spurt in production. This was Rob Shepherd, the so called engineer, on his granny's side, and who was - as I mentioned above - a grey haired, round-shouldered Essex man, who'd suddenly appeared on site at a time when the stewards were in dispute with the management regarding the contentious subject of abnormal condition moneys (A.C.Ms) - an inducement which were paid to men working in exceptionally bad conditions. It was now that someone in the office declared that Rob had originally been brought in by the firm as a trouble-shooter.

Openly boasting he was a disciple of the old school, Rob, if he could, would have demanded a full ten and a half hours work from each man, even if it meant the chargehands timing each individual and standing over them to push the job along. Naturally, such an approach was never likely to go down well with the stewards, or those on the shop floor for that matter.

Unfortunately for Rob, before he'd left the 'Smoke' no-one had mentioned that there were two 'Ellesmere's up north;' the one with the distinctive Port after its name, and the other in Shropshire with no handle attached. Consequently, he arrived, equipped with the pre-conceived idea he would be dealing with a pitch-fork wielding community of yokels, and not one from a population whose citizens were well-versed and practised in resisting the heavy handed approaches of trouble-shooters, particularly when they were 'foreigners.'

Of course, management realised it was too late in the day to consider introducing Rob's out-landish theories and practices. And so with the job reaching a critical stage, the argument then swung in favour of the men, with the A.C.M. payment somewhat grudgingly being awarded to those working long periods in dark and cramped areas in certain parts of the old mill; a clear result to the stewards.

Instead of drafting Rob back to the Smoke after the dispute had been resolved, Jack Poulson, Tanjon's jovial, cockney site engineer decided to keep him in the office to work with the planners sorting and up-dating drawings. But following another reshuffle, Rob was handed the reins and given a senior supervisor's position in charge of progress on the shop floor.

Now Jack Poulson had a habit of calling everyone - 'old Jack,' old 'Jim,'and so on. Rob was no exception, but instead of using his Christian name as he did with the other office wallahs, he always referred to him as 'old Shep.' Before long this somewhat innocent and colloquial nickname was seized on by the lads, so everytime Rob passed through the mill he was greeted with a stream of yelps and barks, ranging from poodle yaps to deep throated woofs. Inevitably, it was only a matter of time before some bright spark christened him 'the dog.'

It was about this time, that he began to realise his earlier geographical mistake in placing 'Ellesmere Port' in the rural backwaters, moaning to his fellow supervisors that ' I can't understand these 'scarser's.' Everytime I walk through the mill they all start barking.' Yet, regardless of this misunderstanding, it seemed Rob was now claiming credit for the increase in productivity and progress on the job, insisting to the management that it was all due to what he called 'good old fashioned surveillance, or 'close supervision.' Obviously, on the shop floor his claims was vehemently disputed, until, that is, the antagonism seemed simply to disappear when news leaked out that 'the dog's' fiftieth birthday was approaching. On the day of the big event Rob walked into the chargehands office with an uncharacteristic smile on his face. From behind his back he produced a huge birthday card and said, 'it's from the lads. And look what's with it, a present in a shoebox.'

'Wotcha reckon on these, me old cockers, he beamed,' placing the box and the card on the table besides his sandwiches. 'It just goes to prove my point, that the iron fist of disciplin' never fails,' he added, plonking himself on the bench between Tear Arse Rowlands and Bob Baines.

After gulping a mouthful of tea, he began carefully un-wrapping the creased, tinsel paper round the box. 'I hope they've got the right size,' he chuckled, slipping the lid away from the box.

'There was an eerie silence for a second or two, then his face erupted in fury.

'Barstid's... fackin' barstids,' he repeated, flinging the box angrily towards the waste bin. As it clattered towards the door, a huge juicy bone with scraps of meat clinging to either end rolled across the floor.

Tails and spooks

The beginning of 1958 was the start of a memorable year for me. After a Christmas merry - go - round of seemingly never-ending days and nights spent tanking up, staggering round local dance floors, and then aggravating the palliasse 'til the clock struck mid-day, the proverbial penny dropped. And as the fumes which had clouded my thick-headed performance during the holiday period suddenly drifted away, I realised, I had but twelve short months to get my act together and become a tradesman. So by the time I returned to the cold, dank atmosphere of Bowies half-completed Mill job, I'd taken stock of the situation and was more determined than ever to finish my apprenticeship with at least some degree of credibility to my name.

A couple of weeks before the holiday period, the portly, grey-haired, charismatic figure of 'Willie the Spook,' had joined our squad along with several others, drafted in to boost the numbers. The decision to about-turn on the usual policy of keeping the squads short-handed had been decided by the engineers at the top. They recognised the job was running so far behind schedule that any further delay in progress might seriously jeopardise the contract, and risk the chance that the client would impose the previously agreed penalty clauses.

Since he'd left Bootsy's job in 'the Fibre' a few months previous, Willie had been shuttled between the different squads like a well-worn ping-bong ball, and now it seemed, we were to be the next in line to benefit from his vast experiences; not just in the art of 'panel wiring' but to be educated into the shadowy and secret domain of the spirit world.

Of course everyone at Tanjon's knew that Willie, besides being a first class tradesman, was a practising medium. Possessed with an unusual and exaggeratedly dark sense of humour that came into its own whenever he embarked on a round of tales about ghosts, graveyards ghouls and mysterious emanations that seemed suddenly to appear and then disappear right before his rheumy old eyes, he would finished one of his long and rambling stories and then calmly wait for the reaction from one of the many doubters in his audience; and this was usually not long in coming. As the discussion became totally over-heated and his vision of the 'other world' intensified, he would clamber onto a metaphorical soap box to fiercely defend his belief in these somewhat controversial doctrines; though religion and associated offshoots, such as spiritualism, was reckoned to be a taboo subject for discussion - as it was with politics.

To the apprentices, Willie's line of patter and fevered arguments in support of his dogmatic beliefs were simply double dutch. We were more than happy to let his hot air float aimlessly above our heads, as we continued to brag about our never-ending, never failing conquests with the girls, or our football triumphs.

As far as we were concerned, religion with all its palaver and complications was yesterday's news. Yet even as I took a braggart's comfort in a dismissive and derisory stance, there was a small part of me that had to admit there was still that tiny chink in my armour. And so when Chunkie happened to mention Timmy McCain's nightmares during the time he'd worked with the 'ghost man' in the Fibre factory, we were once again reminded that whenever 'Willie the Spook' was around there was often an odd and very unusual atmosphere.

It therefore was no surprise when not a single hand was raised when 'Whistling Bob' asked for a volunteer to work with Willie. Indeed, there was a rare and unusual silence amongst the apprentices, while Timmy took on a pale and frightened look.

True to form, Bob did not repeat his request for a volunteer, but simply began to whistle his first tune of the day - 'There's no business like show business,' - always a favourite. Halfway through, just when everyone had relaxed and resumed their normal activities, he stopped in mid-stream, glanced across to where I was perched, winked at me then nodded his head in Willie's direction; and I knew I'd become the chosen victim.

'You've got the kiss of death 'Reilly,' Billy Constable chuckled.

'The dreaded black spot,' said another.

I shrugged my shoulders, making out it was no great deal and set off to collect Willie's toolbox from the compound. As I trudged from the cabin Timmy was unable to keep his big mouth closed for a second longer.

'Bloody 'ell. That's the best news I've 'eard for yonks. Now then smart arse, let's see how you like workin' with spooks for a change.'

Compared to the other tradesmen I'd worked with, being alongside Willie was something of an enigma, and it certainly came as a kind of culture shock. Right from the beginning of that first shift he set about improving my skills, and, after grilling me in an oblique way about my awareness of general knowledge - or my lack of awareness - he began to educate me in a range of subjects. This kind of patter would have sent me to sleep a few months earlier, yet this time it was different. From the start his commanding use of long sounding words often left me floundering, and in a moment of madness I even considered investing in a Collins dictionary - but then, as fleetingly as the thought had crossed my mind, it disappeared just as quickly. However, to my shock and surprise, after a short while, I began to take on board some of Willie's language and his long words, and even on occasions to use them correctly - much to the amusement of the sparks and apprentices alike.

As we plodded on with our work schedules I began to fall in line with Willie's easy-going approach, instead of daydreaming, as I'd tended to do in the past. And though some of his ideas were beyond my intellectual reach, he kept ploughing on with his teaching like a man possessed, patiently describing and analysing world events, outlining major historical happenings, emphasising the history and circumstance of geological and geographical features, touching on wars, on great statesmen, describing influential authors and philosophers, and outlining their philosophic ideas. I suppose it was like being taught by someone who'd just graduated from teaching college, and who was full of pent-up enthusiasm as he practised his techniques on a first year student

Within a matter of time, as my confidence soared, I found myself learning more about my trade and current events than I ever thought possible. What was strange though, was that despite Willie's attempts to cover as broad and as far reaching range of subjects possible, to everyone's surprise - and not the least my own - he hadn't mentioned one word about ghosts, or life after death, or re-incarnation, or resurrection, or ectoplasm or spiritualism, or anything about eerie spooks and phantoms that go bump in the night. Indeed, it seemed as if he'd run out of tales on his favourite subject; or perhaps was simply waiting for me to make the first move on what was almost a forbidden topic for the rest of the squad.

Of course it was only a matter of time before I fell for the proverbial three card trick, and like a fool, I broached the subject one morning when curiosity got the better of me.

'Worra about this spiritualism lark then Willie?' I asked in an offhand manner. 'And your involvement with the nether world, or worr ever it's called?'

Before I could escape to the bogs to bite off the tongue that had always been responsible for getting me into all kinds of trouble and scrapes, he was in like a flash. And without drawing breath, he launched into a long and complex history of his involvement and his close encounters with a range of psychic experiences. These took us on a journey from the time he'd wandered into a meeting at the Liverpool Truth Society by accident, right up to that very moment, when we were wiring the panel in Tanjon's.

Trapped inside the panel, with Willie blocking the only escape route, I didn't need to be a brain surgeon to realise I was well and truly snookered, and in a position which left me with little option but to listen patiently to what he described as 'the stages in his search for the ultimate truth.'

My only hope for a reprieve rested on the chance that 'Whistling Bob' would make a snap inspection, something that might just have broken Willie's non-stop ear bashing. Unfortunately for me, on this occasion Bob failed to put in an appearance.

Willie began by describing a harsh childhood, of being brought up in humble circumstances by parents absorbed in the Protestant faith, and then attending Art college as a teenager. This had drawn him into a fervent belief in a rigorous Leninist/ Marxist communism, which he'd seen then as being the social and political panacea for all ills. In turn this inevitably had led him into becoming a dyed-in-the wool atheist, until a chance meeting with a Catholic girl and the ensuing all-embracing strings of love had then tipped him across a divide, straight into the arms of the Holy Roman faith. The act of falling in love had put unseen pressure on Willie, who found himself cajoled into pursuing that most honourable of undertakings and becoming a religious convert. This complex search for the truth, which had taken him through these different journeys into the various aspects of faith and belief was delivered to me in a sort of galloping discourse, and all in less than ten minutes flat.

Pausing for breath, Willie then told me of his doubts and his eventual scepticism with the stringent moral codes of practise his newly faith demanded, and how he'd stumbled, by chance into the world of Spiritualism while making his way home from college. Passing the building where the Liverpool Truth Society was holding one of its meetings, he described to me in hushed terms how he'd suddenly felt a compelling urge to find out exactly what this spiritualism business was all about.

'More out of nosiness, than anything else,' he said, 'I climbed the steps and opened the door, then wandered inside into a fairly large hall where an elderly man was addressing a sparse audience. I stood at the back, and the preacher - or whatever he was called - because I didn't know their lingo then - suddenly stopped speaking in mid-sentence, came down off the stage and across to the entrance. Without a word from anyone else he looked me straight in the eye, then went on to describe explicit details from my childhood – telling things he couldn't possibly have had prior knowledge of.'

I sat mouth open - what could I say?

'Warra-ye think of that Jimmy?' he whispered.

'Go on,' I said, in a way of reply, because I couldn't think of anything that would make sense to a believer like Willie.

He needed no second urging and off he went again, describing how the man had then told him his path was chosen, and that from now on he had to follow and champion the Spiritualist cause.

I realised much later that Willie was one of those men who badly needed the comfort and sustenance provided by a deep and abiding faith in something or other, simply to sustain and confirm their social beliefs and actions. And of course, up to that point the conventional religions, as well as the more extreme political movements, had failed to nurture this fierce and implacable desire within him. At that time, however, I sat looking at him as if he was offering the keys to the castle. A castle, I might add, that I had no wish to enter.

'Since that moment, Jimmy,' 'Willie the Spook' continued, 'I've attended every weekly meeting; I've followed the Spiritualist teachings with sincere conviction, and I've found my true vocation in life.'

I'd have though that our vocation was to be relatively competent and successful electricians, but it seems I was wrong; well in Willie's case I was.

'I hope, young Reilly, this little chat gives you some idea of the way I think, and how I've reached my conclusions on life,' Willie said with a contented sigh. 'And what's more,' he continued - there was always more - 'to tell you the truth, with all the knowledge and progress I've made I'm more than happy with the dedicated work I've been assigned to, and which I'm responsible for carrying out.'

He lost me there. Was he talking about wiring the panel? I wasn't sure, so I played dumb.

'What work are you talkin' about Willie?' I asked, curious to learn that little bit more about the Spook's strange beliefs than my mates.

'My job, young Reilly,' he announced in an almost reverent manner, 'is rescuing lost souls; rescuing those poor beings that're stuck in limbo.'

Even for a Catholic lad like myself the idea of limbo had always been a bit vague, so I let him rattle on, encouraging him with a question.

'Stuck in limbo! Whereabouts is that Willie?'

'Ah, young man,' Willie replied gravely, and with that air of superiority that often comes from having special knowledge that others aren't privy to. 'Limbo' he intoned, 'could be anywhere.'

And with that he began to unravel a tale of ghostly figures, of weird happenings and eerie places, of the antics mischievous poltergeists got up to in empty houses, and of spirits adrift in dark untrammelled localities - all of which began to put the wind up me, trapped as I was with 'the Spook' in the narrow confines of the section of the panel we were supposed to be working on.

The tale wound on until he stopped for a moment and screwed up his eyes, concentrating on the next part of his outlandish paranormal experiences; at which point, seizing the opportunity, I squeezed behind him and nipped away from the panel. Within seconds I shot out of the control room and legged it without stopping until I reached the bogs.

From that point on my imagination ran riot. And as the days went by Willie continued to pour his spooky tales into my somewhat receptive ear, describing the torments of the crowds of phantom sticklers trapped in the wilderness of limbo, all of whom it seemed were waiting for the likes of 'Willie the Spook' - or one of his spiritualist cronies - to move in and use their special powers and talents and give them a gentle shove into what Willie pronounced was called 'the other side of the veil.'

The problem is that when you're susceptible to such stories their influence tends to spread like the ripples on a pond, and soon I found I was unable to sleep properly, as my fears of joining these nocturnal limbo-lurkers created a steady flow of wild and debilitating nightmares.

One night I was dreaming that I'd trapped my foot in what seemed to be a thin and ghostly net-like material, - in essence, caught halfway through Willie's 'veil' but still halfway on this side of reality. A wild and totally improbable idea that I might have to spend the whole of eternity and a day dangling in limbo by my trapped foot almost caused my ticker to pack in altogether, and I woke everyone in the house yelling at the top of my voice. As I came too, dripping in a cold sweat, I realised with a gasp of relief that I wasn't in the grip of some hideous poltergeist, but was simply caught up in the sheets and blankets on my bed.

Back at work, the only chance I had of escaping 'the Spooks' increasingly bizarre tales of the after life was at breaktime; as Willie was based in the other cabin. This respite, short as it was, gave me an opportunity to voice my fears and my concerns about how convincing these tales of limbo and the spirit world of Willie's really were. Of course I might have known I would get little sympathy from my fellow apprentices, and should have guessed they would respond with howls of cynical laughter at my vulnerability: and these were supposed to be my pals.

'What did I tell yer' Timmy yelled. 'Now you know how I felt when I worked with 'im.'

Robbo was more sympathetic though, and decided to air his views on events. Interrupting the humorous laughter ricocheting round the cabin, he placed his butties in the centre of a loose page of the Daily Herald, then wrapped them carefully before leaning against the cabin wall. Flicking his thumb against the flint wheel of his old pre-war, brass cigarette lighter - which eventually spluttered an intermittent flame to the tip of his Player's Weight ciggy - he inhaled a couple of long drags before giving his ten-penn'orth of ancient wisdom on the subject.

The cabin fell quiet - when Robbo wrapped his sarnies and became sombre, then you listened to what was being said.

'You probably won't remember this,' he began, 'but I worked out of town with 'Willie the Spook' many years ago. And take it from me, there's definitely something odd about the way he acts; or I should say, about what he attracts'.

By now he had the cabin's undivided attention, so we sat like church mice as he strode around working up an atmosphere for his revelations. 'While we've got a few minutes to spare,' he finally declared, 'let's make ourselves comfortable, and I'll tell you about it.' And with that he sat in an easy chair and lifted his feet up onto the end of a bench to make himself at home.

'I'd been sent to a site in Redcar,' he began, 'workin' for Smith's of Bromborough - a good outfit, by the way - and when I got there, I found myself sharing the same digs as Willie. Now then, like most lads here in this cabin, I didn't believe any of the crap doin' the rounds at the time about ghost's and the likes. As far as I was concerned it was a load of bullshit,' he added, stretching his long arm and stubbing the end of his ciggy on the floor.

'Then, after a month - it was our first weekend off, if my memory serves me right,' he pondered for a moment, looking a bit sheepish before taking up the tale. 'That's when something happened that I just can't put my finger on, and it's bothered me ever since.'

'Y'see, unknown to me, the landlady in the digs heard from some smart-arse that Willie was into the spirits and the like, and that he was a medium. So she'd kidded him into holdin' a seance in the parlour that Friday night. Of course I knew nowt about this, and didn't want to know. An' besides I was as dry as a bloody bone. After me tea, I couldn't get away from the place quick enough and off to the pub. Mind you, I'd been sweatin' me bollocks off dragging bleedin' mains cables half way across the site all day, so I was gaspin' for a pint.'

'Anyway, as soon as I was outside, I took a short cut and headed straight for the sea front, on me jaxie of course,' he added quickly, in case anyone got the impression he'd been playing away, as well as working away.

The tale was taking a hold by now, so Robbo lit up the stump of his ciggie again, sucked a long, hard drag and then blew out a cloud of smoke that almost blotted Chunkie and me from view. He knew how to hold an audience, did Robbo; closing his eyes for a second, he took another deep breath.

'Ah! Just feelin' that warm breeze and fresh air comin' in from the North Sea was something different altogether lads, he enthused, 'Aye, that's some place worth goin' to, believe me.'

I said nothing, but seemed to remember some of the lads who'd been to the north-east speaking of a wind that came straight out of Siberia then crossed over to Russia and the North Sea, before it blew up your kecks and froze your knacker's right off.

'Anyway getting' back to worr I was sayin', Robbo murmured, shaking his head as if reminding himself he wasn't on the sun drenched beaches of Redcar, but holding the fort at Bowies, in the industrial heart of Ellesmere Port. 'Now, as I made my way along the sea front, surrounded on all sides by loads of long-legged beauty queens out for a night of fun and frolic, all dressed to the hilt and ready for the taking,' he laughed at this point, knowing the mention of yards of available crumpet would keep our attention focused on his story. 'As I made my way through this bevvy of beauties,' he continued, 'I came across a nice little ale 'ouse which, accordin' to the locals, sold the best pint of bitter on the whole of the east coast, never mind Redcar. Believe me lads, they were spot-on, and boy, did I give it the bifters after all that slog. I reckon the barmaid's arm must've been achin' for a fortnight after I left,' he chuckled, smacking his lips as if still tasting the froth rising over the top of the glass.

'Anyway, by the time I found me way back to the digs, I

was in right old state. How the 'ell I managed to get there, God only knows. But it's funny how you can tell when you're well-pissed, when your legs feel like jelly and you stagger all over the place tryin' to walk in a straight line, and you're singin' an' talkin' nonsense to yourself - or to anyone else who 'appens to come across yer, for that matter.'

'I can just about remember dragging me'self up the steps into the foyer, trippin' over a thick coconut mat, then falling - arse - over tit into the lounge,' Robbo continued.

'When I looked up, I spotted big Berty Thomson. Some of you'se lads might know him - Dingle Berty, the darkie with one eye. At first he didn't notice me 'cos he was sprawled on the couch with his head restin' on his chest. I thought he was out for the count, until he jumped up suddenly and began gibberin' away about the nutters who owned the guesthouse.'

'Hey Berty, calm down lad,' I said. 'And anyway, where's everyone gone?'

His head shot up then he began fumblin'around for a few seconds prodding his dodgy eye with the tip of his finger. Clutching an empty whiskey glass he raised his hand, pointed towards the parlour and muttered words to the effect that Willie was holdin' a séance in there, for a crowd of well - dressed crackpots.

'A seance! You've got ter be jokin', I gasped. 'And before I knew what was happening I'd flung open the parlour door, ready to liven the place up with my own special version of 'Danny Boy.'

He grinned and we grinned back, because we knew how lousy Robbo's singing could be.

'Anyway,' he continued, 'that's when I got the shock of me life. Christ, even thinkin' about it all these years later still sends shivers down me spine.' He scratched nervously at the bald patch at the crown of his head, before pausing to take a swift couple of drags on what was left of his second fag.

'It's hard to explain lads, but as soon as I stepped inside that room, it felt as if I'd stumbled into a butcher's freezer. Willie was perched in some sort trance at the end of a table, but I could only see part of his face in the dark. Small flashing lights darting like meteorites were shooting all over the place and a white mist seemed to be floatin'above his head. But what happened next, I'll take to me bloody grave.' Robbo paused again, as if searching for the right words to describe his harrowing experience.

'A blast of wind, an' I mean a blast, almost lifted me off me feet and when I felt waves lappin' against me legs, well that was the last straw.'

'Jesus! talk about followin' through; I don't mind admittin' I almost touched cloth that night.'

The cabin was silent now as we all tried to imagine ourselves in Robbo's place in this nightmare situation. But there was more to come. 'With me feet rooted to the deck, the 'airs on the back of me neck risin' like bristles on a backyard sweepin' brush, and me eyes as wide open as me mouth, I was in a right old state. I'll tell you somethin' lads, if the Guinness Book of Records had a section for the fastest time for soberin' up, I'd 'ave won it hands down - by a friggin mile. In fact, had there been a category for it I could've won a gold at the Olympics, believe me.'

Never one to over exaggerate, Robbo now had everyone's close and undivided attention at our end of the cabin. Even the Pope, from his speck five tables away from ours, was straining his neck to hear the outcome of the tale.

'To this day I don't know where I got the bottle or the strength for that matter from, to slam the door shut, considerin' I was like a window cleaner's wet rag. But somehow I managed it, and when I'd stopped shakin' I glanced across at poor Dingle Berty, who was as white as a bloody sheet; or as near to white as you can get when you're his colour to start with.'

'Bloody 'ell Robbo,' Dingle spluttered, tremblin' with fright, 'I've never seen anything like it in all me bleedin' life, an' by Christ I don't want ter see it again, thank you very much.'

'Now remember lads,' Robbo cautioned us, 'it was a sweltering night, and perhaps you can understand why Berty took it so bad. Imagine bein' half-pissed when a blast of icy cold air almost lifts you off the bloody couch an' onto the deck. And then clocking me standing there, with me hair standin' on end, blockin' the parlour door, frozen to the spot like a statue. It's a wonder he didn't snuff it there and then.'

'I shouldn't laugh,' he added with a wry chuckle, 'but

I reckon it's a good job Berty hadn't opened the door before me. I mean, just imagine - his great mop of black crinkly hair standing up on end; now that would 'ave been a real sight for sore eyes. All the same though, there was no doubt in my mind he'd definitely spotted something with that good eye of his when I opened the door, and whatever it was - ectoplasm perhaps, or some spirit or other - well, it knocked him for six. 'Cos no sooner had I slammed the door shut, than he took off and flew straight up the dancers to his bedroom, hell for leather. As for me, well, despite all these so-called entities from the other side creeping into the lounge when I opened the door, at that moment the only kind of spirit I wanted was one of those distilled in Scotland. And a very large one at that - to settle me nerves.'

That was it, it seemed that Robbo was going to give no further details as he unfolded himself from his easy chair and picked up his parcel of unfinished butties. But then, just as he was about to leave, he finished off the tale.

'So lads, that's just one of the experiences I've had with Willie and his invisible friends.' And if any of you'se 'appen to come across Dingle Berty, well just ask 'im about Redcar and mention 'Willie the Spook,' then watch his face change colour.'

As we were walking back to the mill, Billy Chancer caught up with me and in his usual furtive manner offered his opinion about the rubbish 'Willie the Spook' had been dishing out earlier. What's more, he seemed to have similar opinions as to the merits of Robbo's tale of his spiritual experiences.

'Y' know my methods by now Jim,' he said, checking to make sure he wasn't being overheard. 'And I hope you always remember to put into practice all those little gems I gave during those coaching lessons when you were just fifteen and still wet behind the ears.'

'Yep, I've still got it all up here Billy,' I said, tapping the side of my temple with my forefinger.

'So think on son,' he advised, 'analyse everything - especially when it comes from someone as sharp and as devious as 'Willie the Spook.' 'Cos believe me, he's out to brainwash you and all the others about things you can't see, and which probably aren't there anyway. I mean most of it's a load of crap, take it from me.'

He paused for a moment then continued. 'Y'see, only last night I mentioned to my better half about the way Willie carries on with you'se lads - about ghosts and spirits and contacting' the dead. An' Maisie could hardly believe what I told her, an' she should know.'

'Contacting' the dead?' she said, 'why that's a subject for old widows an' crackpots, and certainly not for healthy young lads to be getting' involved in.'

'To be 'onest Jim,' Billy admitted, 'I promised her I'd 'ave a quiet word in your ear this mornin'.'

That was okay with me,'cos I was all ears anyway. I knew that Maisie, Billy Chancer's wife, was well versed in these matters, and that Billy himself was no slouch when it came to bursting someone's pompous self-importance.

'Y'see son,' he continued, 'I couldn't help listenin' to the drivel Robbo was dishin' out about Redcar. Well that's easily solved, with all the ale he guzzled that night he was probably pissed out of his mind, and more than likely hallucinatin'. I ask yer - seeing this ectoplasm stuff and spooks, instead of the pink elephants that most of us see when we've had a few too many - what next? And I'm not bein' critical of Robbo in any way Jim,' he cautioned, 'he's a good skin, and entitled ter get pissed whenever he feels like it. But when he rants on about freezin winds and water lappin' round his legs, well, anyone with a brain in their head would have to question his state of mind. Especially in those circumstances,' he added quickly: no doubt wisely covering his back because of how popular Robbo was with me and the rest of the squad.

'Anyroad, getting' back to Willie and his far-fetched beliefs,' the Chancer continued. 'take a tip from me son and don't ask questions about spooks an' the likes, 'cos it only encourages him to gerrup on his soap box an' bore the kecks off the rest of us with all the nonsense he turns out at the drop of a hat; fair enough Jim?'

'Fair enough,' I replied, and knew that for the moment the subject was closed.

As we left the daylight behind and entered the Mill, Billy

muttered that he was having a problem keeping his mate, George Sharkey, in check. This was not surprising because the Mill was a massive old building with lots of unlit areas and dark scaffolded corridors, all of which provided an ideal place for a prankster like George Sharkey to carry out a constant round of mischievous tricks on a steady stream of unsuspecting victims.

'Give me an apprentice everytime lad,' Billy sighed, 'cos when you've got a grown man helping yer, even though he acts like a soft schoolboy at times, well it's difficult to show 'im the right and proper way to do the job; or to bollock 'im like you can if he was a lad.'

We were halfway down a narrow passageway leading to the control room when we were startled by voice screaming frantically from somewhere above our heads, 'BELOW ... BELOW.. WATCH OUT...BELOW' - the usual cry when someone on a gantry or a scaffold dropped a tool or some other piece of equipment. This time a huge metal flange thwacked noisily onto the concrete floor, just a yard or two behind us. As it landed, the clattering, metallic thud caused both of us to hurl ourselves forward, our hands vainly trying to protect our heads, like some ancient warriors about to be decapitated by a samurai sword.

'WATCH WHAT YOU'RE DOIN' YOU STUPID IDIOT. YOU COULD 'AVE KILLED BOTH OF US' ' Billy yelled, glaring into the darkness above the low-level lights.

We both scrambled to our feet, but there was no response from who ever it was who'd dropped the heavy flange, just an eerie silence.

'Y'see,' the Chancer said quietly and firmly when he was back on his feet, 'Willie the Spook' would've looked for the involvement of some ghost or poltergeist if he was with us now; but incidents like this, Jimmy, mean that we all 'ave to act responsible and be careful how we handle our tools and things when we're workin' up top.'

He was back in control of his emotions now, though still visibly shaken by the crashing noise the eighteen-inch steel flange had made on its impact with the ground.

'You're right Billy,' I replied, glancing over my shoulder just in time to see Sharkey creep down a ladder from a scaffolding platform erected immediately above the passageway we'd just passed along. I wondered if Billy's advice about 'being responsible for our actions' was something I could pass on to Sharkey, but decided it would probably fall on deaf ears. George was a law unto himself, and everyone knew the Chancer had more on his plate than he could chew. Of course, the apprentices held an entirely different sense of humour than their peers and mentors, and in a way we openly encouraged the bold Sharkey by laughing at his outrageous behaviour; just as we had done on the Monday morning, only days before he'd scared the life out of me and Billy with the flange in the mill.

George, had hurtled down the hill at Woodside to catch the ten past seven bus, where four of us - Chunkie, Timmy McCain, Billy Constable and I - were already parked on the side seat, blimping the young clippie as she bent over to fix the leather strap across the doorway to prevent anyone else from boarding the bus, which was already full. Of course, even though Sharkey was late, we knew it was a brave soul who would try to prevent him from barging to the front of the waiting queue and lift the strap from its hook, then to try to sneak aboard.

'Hey! Are you blind or what? Can't you see we're full up?' the conductress yelled. 'What d'yer think you're playin' at anyway.' But George took no notice and shot up the stairs to check if there were any spare seats up top. We were laughing as he stomped back down and then checked out the lower deck.

'Are you satisfied now, smart arse?' the clippie snapped when George had finished counting the passengers downstairs and returned to where we were sitting. Ignoring her scowl and frosty comments, he began for a second time to scan the heads of passengers sitting at either side, and those standing in the middle of the aisle.

'There's a spare speck,' he said to the clippie, pointing triumphantly to a side seat opposite us, where three very large workmen had filled the four spaces with their giant bodies. She looked at the narrow space on the seat, then at the enormous size of the men now holding their newspapers high, their heads and unseen faces buried in the pages, before turning back with a look which told Sharkey, 'the best of luck if you can squeeze your arse in there mate'. But of course our team was the only one on the bus who knew what Sharkey was capable of. And so we watched with interest - he was always eager to take up a challenge. Turning his face to us he began bending over, as if intending to touch his toes. With his head now on Chunkies lap, the whole thing reminded me of Eggo's performance on the Littlewood's Pool bus all those years ago, when he'd wriggled his bum between those two old birds into a space that was no bigger than a couple of bags of sugar.

As the ongoing drama continued everyone on the bottom deck seemed to have given up hope of the clippie ringing the bell to signal the driver to start up the engine and move off; and by the sound of things, some of the passengers upstairs were losing their patience and kicking up a rumpus at the delay.

By this time we were in hysterics watching Sharkey twist one way then another without making any visible sign of progress, and could sense this wasn't looking too promising for our man, the 'champion tail hanger.' As the minutes ticked slowly by, with the three heavies showing no sign of compromise, it seemed as if Sharkey had indeed met his match.

But Sharkey was no defeatist, not by a long chalk. He looked up and smiled across at us, in the way he usually did when he had another trick up his sleeve. This time, however, it was a region further down his anatomy that held the trump card.
With his bum jammed between the outsides of his protagonist's massive thighs, he closed his eyes, grimaced, and then broke wind with such force it sounded like a tornado crashing into a mountain.

I'd never seen anything move so fast in my life, as the two heavyweight rear ends shot sideward as if they'd been stabbed by a pitchfork, their reaction relinquishing the disputed territory immediately. Needless to say, Sharkey's bum settled into the vacant space in a flash, and although the clippie blushed like a cherry, she could hardly contain a nervous giggle, while we were in stitches laughing.

As we began to regain a bit of control, a grey-haired midnight reveller, still bevied from a night on the tiles, turned round and yelled: 'I know that one. Eddie Calvert's "Oh my Papa." That's right isn't it lads?' There was no immediate verbal response to his claim, just more laughter.

When Billy Chancer heard us joking about the way George

had claimed his seat on the bus he was not amused. Somewhat uncharacteristically, he took us to one side, and gave us a severe tongue-lashing for encouraging Sharkey, who he said, had let the team down by acting like a guttersnipe on public transport, and especially in front of a woman.

Despite sitting at the back of the cabin, Sid Shortwick - who was not one to miss out on anything - heard the full tale, but then disagreed wholeheartedly with his colleague, saying 'listen Billy lad, if you were in church at a wedding and someone let a rasper off just as the vicar was about to seal the marriage vows, I reckon nine out of ten would find it difficult not to burst out laughing - and the odd one out would probably be the culprit.'

'Or the vicar,' Podgy Hogan added, ruining the Chancer's attempts to install a sense of decorum into us.

Sussed out by the Chancer

Although the work in the Main Control Room was no different than in other parts of the mill, before they began tackling the immense task of installing and terminating the various types of cables, the sparks would usually spend a fair bit of time assessing the best possible positions to carry out each task. The panels - walk in types - were fitted wall to wall and from floor to ceiling, having been manufactured in such a way as to allow them to accept the huge multi-core cables through the back sections of the units. They were not designed, however, for anyone who was grossly over weight to work inside.

The older more experienced tradesmen usually drilled rows of small holes into square pieces of thick hardboard or plywood to create a simple method of separating the individual cores of each multi-core cable. And before a single core had been terminated, these cores - sometimes as many as sixty or more - were then threaded through the small holes, before the tedious and laborious task of looming, numbering and terminating them began.

Rather than suffer the discomfort of working in a crouched position, because of the limited space behind the panels, everyone engaged in the job had their own makeshift chairs. These ranged from small oil drums with a circle of padded sponge taped round the top to act as a kind of cushion, to a variety of wooden boxes of various shapes and strengths. In some instances, where two men had to work together on a panel, a small plank would be placed across to form a sort of tiny bench.

It was in such a compact and cosy environment that I, with the other final year apprentices, had been sent to gain experience from the experts in panel wiring. In my case, of course, I was having the dubious benefit of a few extra curricular lessons from 'Willie the Spook' who was still keen to lecture me on a range of worthy and other worldly topics. This, as he always put it, was to improve my understanding of life on this planet and of life on the next.

To relieve the boredom of being crammed in one position for hours on end, the panels were awash with stories - tales of war, of fly-by-night merchants pulling stunts, yarns about mickey taking, and a non-stop round of filthy, ale-house jokes. This was the daily bread and butter for most of the fully-fledged sparks, while we would rattle on about the girls we'd met or hoped to meet, about the dances we'd been to or were going to, and the music or the latest bits of football chit-chat doing the rounds. On occasions, usually towards the end of the week when the mood took us, we'd entertain our peers with some golden oldie songs, which everyone joined in. But, if we happened to break into a modern 1950s catchy tune, we'd be told in no uncertain terms to quit making a racket and pay more attention to the important things, such as learning the job we were supposed to be doing.

A stickler for keeping his eye on the job, 'Whistling Bob' would usually pop his head into the control room a couple of times between breaks, and on those occasions when we were in full throttle and singing our heads off, he'd join in for a couple of numbers before leaving with the evergreen remark 'that a happy, contented squad was worth its weight in gold, and could be generally relied on to turn out a first-class job.'

One morning Bob wandered in just minutes after Sharkey had been hanging carefully manufactured tails on everyone's rear end as they laboured away with their heads buried deep in the panel, leaving their back sides sticking prominently in the air.

'Bob chuckled when he saw the result. 'It's just like a bloody circus in here,' he said before bawling at the stooping workers, 'what's happened lads, have you all be readin' Teddy Tail in the Daily Mail this mornin an' copying him?'

But at that moment we were giving it our- all with a rendition of Little Richard's latest hit - 'be-bop-a-lula,' and the din was so loud that there was no response to his crack about the favourite newspaper cartoon character of the moment. What's more, as we were all working conscientiously, the shattering noise of our vocals had not only masked Sharkey's tail fastening antics, but also masked Bob's entry.

During his visits Bob would diligently check the work we'd done, mark up the drawings, then set off for a morning progress meeting with his own immediate boss - 'The Dog.' Satisfied on this morning of the 'hanging tails' that all was proceeding nicely, he left, still chuckling at what he'd seen, and whistling a tune which he'd unconsciously picked up from the songsters he'd just left. As he trundled off along the corridor Bob bumped into Plonker Parson who stepped out of a passageway in front of him.

'If you want a good laugh, Plonker,' he said, 'pop your head in there an' have a decko at my squad with their arses stuck out of the panel. And while you're there, why don't you shout in 'worra you'se lot tryin'' to be - mice or men? Then watch their faces an' let me know what went on.' And he giggled, waddling off towards the entrance with his own tail - a straggly thick piece of twine - trailing along the floor behind him.

Throughout all of this, Willie was as determined as ever to continue his mission of indoctrinating and trying to convert me by recalling a string of spiritual adventures. But Billy Chancer, despite his quiet and timid disposition, had decided it was high time for him to intervene and to act on my behalf. One day, soon after he'd concluded Robbo's encounter with the spirits of Redcar had been helped by too much contact with the bottom of an empty ale glass, he cornered the 'Spook.'

'Y'know, Willie, with all due respects to you, I reckon all this mumbo - jumbo, talking to the dead malarkey, is goin' too far. And, I think I'm correct in sayin' that we're all fed up to the back teeth with the same old subject being trotted out all the time. And don't forget mate, these lads are still servin' their time, so we should be makin' sure they've learnt their trade properly, not fillin' 'em up with tales of ghosts, phantoms and visitations from the other side, and the likes.'

This was quite a speech from the Chancer, and it spluttered to a halt as though he suddenly wondered if he had perhaps over stepped his mark.

'You're not offended are you Willie?' he asked, almost as an after thought, and as if to make sure 'the Spook's feelings weren't too badly bruised.

'Course not, Billy,' the 'Spook' replied, 'everyone's entitled to their point of view. But before we put my experiences to bed for the time being, I'd like to hear your opinion on some short stories in The Psychic News - my favourite journal.' Chuckling loudly, he then stuffed a few copies of the controversial publication into Billy's panel.

Everyone was laughing as Billy snatched the copies of the magazine and hurled them back, shaking his hands as if they were contaminated by some kind of radioactive material.

When things had settled down and the squad were busy working, George Sharkey ambled quietly across the switchroom, picked up one of the discarded journals and slipped it inside his overalls. Later, as we hurried from the cabin after finishing our afternoon shift, I doubt if anyone suspected that a copy of The Psychic News now rested beneath an empty sandwich box at the bottom of Billy Chancer's haversack, or realised that it had begun its journey to its new home at the Chancer abode in Bootle.

The following morning when George asked if my mate Billy had mentioned anything about the Psychic News, I was able to say 'no' in all innocence. That is until he revealed he'd slipped a copy of Willies spooky newspaper into Billy's haversack on the previous evening.

Later in the day Billy collared me as we were walking back from the dinner break, and once we were out of ear-shot of the rest of the squad, the worried spark told me that Maisie had been shocked to find a copy of Willie's paper stuffed inside his haversack when she'd come to empty it. Although Billy had his suspicions as to how the magazine had got from the control room into the haversack, he couldn't fairly and squarely pin the blame on Sharkey without having some kind of proof to back his claim.

To add fuel to the fire, and to his consternation, it seemed Maisie had skipped through the journal, more out of curiosity than anything else, and was immediately convinced there might be something in Willies claims after all; and wondered if the paper had found its way into his bag as some kind of divine message.

'I find it hard to believe,' Billy moaned, but she's seriously talkin' about visiting a spiritualist church, or one of those other daft meetin' places where those sort of people hang out. To make matters worse, she thinks there's half a chance of contactin' her old lady... her BLOODY OLD LADY,' he repeated with a groan.

I made a few conciliatory grunts, but Billy ignored them as he continued his tale of woe.

'Y'know I'm not one for swearin' lad, but I tell you, if my mother- in - law hadn't popped 'er cloggs when she did, I'd be more than likely in a friggin' nut 'ouse by now. To say she ruled the roost, would be the understatement of the year. And as for me, well no matter what I did or how hard I tried, I could do nothin' right in 'er eyes. Bloody 'ell! She was a tough old bird, believe me. And now Maisie want's to try an' get in touch again. I ask yer lad, worr 'ave I done to deserve this?'

Before I could think of any suitably consoling words, Billy screwed up his face and let fly at the one he blamed for all this

It's that bloody 'Willie the Spook's' fault. I wish ter God I'd never set eyes on 'im or even heard of 'im. And I'm not one for puttin' anyone down so readily, as you know Jim.'

Even though Sharkey continued to pester me whether Billy had mentioned the Psychic News being planted in his haversack, of course I said nothing, because Billy had told me in confidence about his tribulations. What's more I couldn't for the life of me feed him any further ammunition to use against my mild-mannered mate.

As the days wore on, however, Billy seemed to be getting more and more depressed, so when he called me to one side to tell me he hadn't slept properly for night's on end, I really began to wonder if he wasn't taking things a bit too seriously; or worse still, was on the verge of a nervous breakdown.

'I know it's crazy Jim,' he said, 'but when I'm in bed an' half asleep I keep hearin' footsteps on the landing. Then, last night, I swear the bathroom light flicked on and then off again. I tell you I was so scared I stuck me 'ead under the blankets and held me breath for ages. I reckon if a burglar had broken in to screw the place he'd 'ave had a field day, 'cos I wouldn't 'ave been able to move a single muscle to stop him or defend me'self.'

'Are you sure no one else was there?' I gasped.

'Honest ter God, I'd swear on my Maisie's life, there wasn't a bleedin' soul.'

'Phew! I tell yer...' he choked, as if glad to have got the whole thing out in the open, 'fancy a grown man being terrified over such a stupid thing; and in his own 'ouse. I don't know if it's just my imagination Jimmy, or if it has anything to do with

Willie, but I ask you what's the point in tryin' to contact the dead? I mean ter say, we've got more than enough problems on our plate havin' to talk to some of the livin' zombies that work here without getting' involved in all that spooky stuff Willie preaches.'

As we reached the panel he slowed to a stop, then pleaded with me in a low whisper. 'Look, don't tell the lads what we've been discussin' Jim. They'll think I'm goin' doo lally, an' who could 'onestly blame them.'

Sharkey, of course, did nothing to help ease the Chancer's miserable situation. Besides continuing to hang tails on whoever happened to visit the control room, or splash water from the fire buckets on anyone walking nearby, he also began secretly mooching into Billy's pride and joy - his lunchbox. As soon as he saw Billy head off in the direction of the bogs and the coast was clear, Sharkey would then nip into the cabin and delve into Billy's lunchbox, swapping Maisie's delicate roast beef sandwiches for an equivalent number of own home-made mousetrap butties, each heavily plastered in brown sauce. Then, when it came to the lunchbreak, he'd calmly plonk himself down to read his paper, acting as if nothing out of the ordinary had taken place.

Because of his temperament, Billy was not the type to say anything, or to kick up a fuss about the decline in his lunchtime grub. Indeed, he seemed to accept the reason for the drop in the decidedly sub-standard sarnies was probably due to Maisie's new distraction with the spirit world.

'She's probably got in touch with her old lady, and she'll be knifin' me in the back for celebratin' her passing, and gettin' pissed on the day she was buried,' he muttered as he surveyed the latest set of cheese doorsteps smothered in H.P. sauce

On Friday morning, after four consecutive days of 'making do' with stodgy bread and cheese butties, Billy lifted his carrying-out box from the end of the table where it was sat on his copy of the 'Daily Express. As he flipped open the lid, he spotted a very large, dark thumb print planted prominently on the top of the first sandwich. His jowl fell and he slowly stood up, and then let rip with a volley of vehement obscenities.

Swinging round, shaking and burning with anger, he was just

in time to spot the bold Sharkey smacking his lips as he hungrily polished off a slither of lean beef that hung from what, to Billy, looked very much like one of Maisie's specialities. In a fit of blind rage he hurled his brown tin box at Sharkey, splattering him with a mixture of thick lumps of rough bread, hard yellow cheese, brown sauce and piccalilli. To everyone's surprise, the previously mild and equable Chancer then threatened to take on his much taller and younger colleague, and to sort him out with a proverbial bunch of fives.

By the time the break was over Billy had somehow or other calmed down and regained his composure and we ambled back to the job. Halfway through the shift, 'Whistling Bob' put in one of regular appearances. Addressing the Spook, he chuckled. 'Hey Willie, seen any dead bodies lately?'

'Indeed I 'ave,' Willie responded, sharp as a knife, 'if you act quickly and pop your head round the back here you'll find a couple of the brain-dead who certainly need stoking up.'

'How's things with you Billy,' 'Whistling Bob' asked, turning his attention to the Chancer, 'and more to the point, are you keepin' a watchful eye on that mate of yours?'

Before Billy had chance to tell him what he thought of Sharkey, Podgy Hogan jumped in.

'Bob,' he roared, 'what with Billy havin' a permanent tail hangin' from 'is kecks every day, and the amount of rat-bag cheese he's had to eat this week, well, you almost had a Mickey Mouse look-alike in your gang.'

Everyone, even including Billy, had a good laugh, though Sharkey failed to add to the hilarity; unusually, he was nowhere to be seen.

'Right lads,' Bob said, addressing the squad when everyone had quietened down, 'I've got a little problem on me hands. I've been in touch with the lads in production and they tell me there's no way I can have a shutdown 'til the weekend. Now I don't want to rock the boat by goin' above their heads, but in order to stay ahead of schedule, and more to the point, to keep 'The Dog' off me back, I need someone to work on the live side of the panel.'

'I will Bob,' Podgy yelled, 'I will,' before anyone had time to think what this implied, or had given a thought to the safety factor.

'Suck 'ole' a familiar voice muttered from somewhere behind the panel, and Sharkey crept into view. If looks could kill and had he not moved like a rocket, I reckon he would have be in line for a measurement for a coffin. Then again 'Suck 'ole' was probably what most of us were thinking, because I'm certain the majority of the sparks were struck dumb by Podgy's enthusiastic offer to carry out the task. But it wasn't just a case of the panel being powered up that took the sparks by surprise - working on live equipment was an everyday hazard for a qualified electrician. It was more to do with Podgy's vast size - he'd not been given his nickname for nothing. The awkward position of the terminal rail meant he'd have to lie flat out, at full stretch, between two sections of the panel, and in a space which only the likes of Billy Chancer or Jimmy 'H' could squeeze into with any degree of ease.

Undeterred by the well-meaning concern of his colleagues, Podgy set about preparing for the job, huffing and puffing as he struggled to discard his massive boiler suit, and then removing a heavy woollen jumper and a thick plaid-check working shirt. This left him standing in a white vest and dark brown corduroy pants, his huge pot-belly, hanging slumped like a roll of lino over a leather belt that was stretched to its ultimate limits.

His next move was to ensure the temporary lights were plugged in properly, and that the working area was sufficiently illuminated, before he trundled across the room to collect a large sheet of corrugated cardboard, spreading it like a carpet across the base of the panel. Although he'd not yet laid a finger on the job, a few of us couldn't help noticing that Podgy was already sweating profusely. Nevertheless, oozing a heart warming confidence - along with a gallon or two of sweat - the big man seemed satisfied he'd covered all the eventualities necessary to terminate the cables in the most comfortable of positions. After stretching on his toes and taking a couple of deep breaths, like a heavy weight boxer preparing to enter the ring, he then dropped slowly onto his knees, rolled onto his belly, and began easing himself head-first into the panel.

By this time the rest of the workers were pushing on with their own jobs, at which point the bold Sharkey returned unseen to the control room, carrying a sack full of materials from the stores. Since his escape some fifteen minutes earlier, an unusually quiet atmosphere had settled on the place, so out of curiosity he popped his head round the back of the panels to see what was happening, and of course discovered Podgy down there, flat out on his belly, already in position, and all set to begin the task.

Widely acknowledged to be an expert in the art of being neither seen nor heard, Sharkey watched silently as Podgy, now soaked from forehead to chest in a lather of sweat, nervously and carefully ease his insulated screwdriver towards the live connection. At the vital moment, Sharkey knelt quickly, produced a two pound hammer from behind his back, and in one swift movement he belted the plated metal floor with such a force that the temporary lights went out.

For a few frantic seconds the place was in a state of complete pandemonium, with Podgy screaming like one of Willie's wounded banshee's, and everyone else scrambling panic stricken from behind their respective panels. When the lights were eventually switched back on, Podgy was found lying in a crumpled heap, slobbering like a baby, his wet face as white as his vest. Meanwhile, as stealthily as he'd entered, will of the wisp, Sharkey had once again vanished from the scene.

Ultimately a concerted effort by four of Tanjon's stockiest mates - who were fortunately pulling cables outside the control room - managed to tug Podgy away from the panel. When the big man had sufficiently recovered from his trauma and was back on his feet, he made no bones about his intention of murdering Sharkey at the first opportunity.

Bob then appeared for a second time that morning, with Sharkey by his side. Showing little or no sign of regret nor concern for the chaos he'd caused, the bold Sharkey was whistling in tune, along with Bob, and was carrying a bundle of angle-iron brackets in one hand with the offending hammer clearly visible in the other.

Usually he was way ahead of the game, but on this occasion George could only offer what seemed to be a very lame excuse that he'd been testing the hammer-head before using it on the brackets, just to make sure it wasn't loose. This raised chuckles all round from the sparks and the lads alike. We were all acutely aware that such a feeble explanation would not be enough to save him from a severe dressing down.

When Podgy saw Sharkey's smirking face, it took the strength of the same four workers who'd freed him from the panel to restrain him from carrying out his threat to annihilate the culprit. Bob, however, came to the rescue, remarking - with tongue firmly in cheek - that it was a good job Podgy hadn't frizzled inside the panel - because of the mess he'd have made. He then asserted his authority and called Sharkey to one side, announcing he was transferring him to the cable gang. As he quietly explained, Sharkey was 'likely to do less harm in that squad.'

Once George departed it was much quieter in the control room, and in a perverse kind of way he was sorely missed by us apprentices - and by a fair number of the squad if the truth were known. There's no doubt we all enjoyed his pranks and mischief - making, though Billy Chancer and Podgy Hogan were the exceptions, of course. Billy had more than enough of having George as a mate, and Podgy was still smarting at the way his high-pitched squeals of terror and uncontrollable sobs had then been exaggerated by the mickey-takers in the squad. What's more, he was still certain that only by the Grace of God and the skin of his teeth, he'd avoided having a fatal heart attack

As the days passed, the job eventually returned to normal. Bob whistled from morning 'til knocking off time. Billy Chancer moaned continually about Maisie's obsession with spiritualism and how his life had changed since she'd got involved. Podgy ceased mentioning Sharkey's nerve- shattering prank and was back to breaking wind behind the panels, then laughing hysterically as everyone scrambled from their cramped quarters to escape the resulting stench in which he would happily wallow. And, Jimmy 'H,' as sharp as ever, kept the troops happy and amused with a stream of quips, ale house jokes and salacious innuendo's.

'Willie the Spook,' who'd not said a thing about ghosts, phantoms, or anything to do with the supernatural world since Sharkey's enforced exit from the squad, suddenly broached the subject once again, when, in a round about way, he mentioned 'a doddle of a job' he'd worked on in Lancaster.

Unfortunately, we'd been lulled into a sense of false security, and with our guards well and truly down, we walked straight into 'the Spooks' well-set trap.

'Have you heard this one,' he began - the usual opening gambit for a joke or a tale.

'I was on a 'job and knock' five weeks before Christmas, three or four years ago. A small factory unit where you had to gerr in, an' gerr out with just three of us to strip it completely, then re-wire and test the lot. By the way, as anyone of you'se lads come across Rashly Phipps, a Manchester outfit, or worked for them?' he asked, searching everyone's faces.

'No?' he said, after a momentary silence greeted his question. Then, you won't know Frankie Clarke and Tommy Patterson?' To be honest, I'd be more than surprised if any of you had come across them ' he added, a wisp of a smile on his face.

'Why? What's so special about two 'airy arse Mancunian sparks?' Jimmy 'H' demanded.

'Well, if you want to hear this yarn, give me a few minutes of your time, Willie replied firmly, 'and then you'll find out.' So we all settled down to listen to the tale as we worked on the panels.

'After we'd got into the nitty-gritty, arse-end of the job,' he began, 'my first impression was that whatever outfit these lads had served their time with had done a fine job. But once I got to know them properly I discovered they were as different as chalk and cheese. Take Tommy, for instance; a studious kid, skinny as a rake, well over six-foot tall, an' easy to get on with.'

'The other fella, though - Frankie - now just you lot sit back for a moment while I tell yer about him.' Willie's emphasis left us in no doubt that Frankie was about to become the butt of the tale.

'Unlike his mate,' Willie explained, 'Frankie was self-centred and a right cocky bugger. What's more, if you believed everything he said and took him at his word, then he was one of the hardest hitters the city of Manchester had ever produced. He was tall, dark skinned and well built. A good-lookin' lad, and boy did he know it. Football daft! Man U fan, of course, but with nothing up top worth talkin' about. Typical of that old proverb 'empty barrels make the most noise.'

'Without braggin' about my abilities,' the Spook continued, now well into his stride, 'it didn't take me long to suss out that Frankie had a serious drink problem. Half the time he was in

- 259 -

cloud cuckoo land and just didn't seem to know when enough was enough, or when to call it a day. Most mornin's he was still half- pissed at ten o'clock. To be honest somedays you'd get more sense talkin' to the concrete wall. And, of course, it goes without sayin', Willie continued, 'apart from a love of the ale, he was also a bit of a 'jack the lad' when it came to the girls, if you get me drift,'

He turned towards me as he said this, which, I assumed, was because I happened to be nearest to him. 'It's funny, young Reilly,' he said half jokingly, but he reminds me of you in a way.'

'Come off it Willie,' I protested sharply. 'The only experience I've 'ad so far was that cock-up of a night with the boss Poser in the Port, and a week at Butlin's.'

Suddenly I saw Billy Chancer poke his face out from behind the panel where he was dossing. He glanced across to me, shook his head a couple of time, then stared long and hard at Willie, before placing the palms of his hands over his ears as if to warn me that yet another ghost story was on the cards.

'Well,' said Willie, warming to his tale, 'as I was about to say, everyone here knows of my interest in the human species and about my understanding of world events and the likes - and if I may be so bold as to risk a torrent of abuse from all you doubters - about the secrets of the paranormal.'

'Oh no! Norra another ghost story,' moaned Podgy Hogan.

'Bear with me and hear me out,' Willie cried.

'Now gettin' back to Frankie. Apart from havin' a massive chip on his shoulder, the lad had a personality problem that sat on his head like an oversized trilby. 'Cos no matter which way I approached him, or whatever piece of advice I gave - always offered with the best intention in mind - he had this infuriatin' habit of contradicting everything I said. But you'se lads - well, you know my style,' he purred smoothly, hurrying on before we could tell him just what we thought of his style. 'An as y'know lads I've never been one for throwin' in the towel.'

'Reilly knows all about throwin' in the towel,' Big Don yelled, again interrupting the flow. 'Ask 'im about the boxin' at Butlin's.'

But Willie was not to be deflected, and surged on.

'Y'see, unlike some of the old timer's who would 'ave given the young upstart a swift back-hander an' thought nothing of it, I don't believe in violence under any circumstances. So I held my hand, and had good reason to thank the good Lord for havin' blessed me with the patience of a saint. Because that's when I took it upon myself to try an' broaden Frankie's education and outlook in the more important things in life, besides boozing an' fightin' an' football, an' stoppin' out all night with bits of stuff. Just as I've tried to do with you young fella's here,' he added, a look of self-satisfaction crinkling his smug face as he nodded in the direction of me, Chunky, Big Don and Louie.

Of course trying to tell Willie that his vision of the important things in life had gone straight down the plug-hole was not something he'd want to hear, so me and Chunkie, Big Don and Louie just said nothing.

'Now, with this bein' 'a job and knock', Willie rambled on, 'and with us being on the go from mornin' 'til night, well, the only time I really had a chance to get to grips with Frankie's education was in 'the Angel' bar next to our digs, on our way home from work.

'Good God! How long is this yarn goin' to last,' Podgy yawned, stretching his legs then belching loudly - a gastric reminder from somewhere deep inside that told him brew-time was fast approaching.

'Plenty of time yet, Podgy, plenty of time, so stop panicking,' Willie replied, before launching again on his tale.

'Now, slowly but surely, and by weighing up the titbits and topics that the lads discussed during the day, I was able to worm my way into their conversations and draw them into talking about a wider range of subjects - about their ambitions, about the purpose of life, and about their fears and beliefs. Before finally,' he bragged, 'I played my trump card, telling them I was a practising spiritualist'

'Oh, you bloody would,' Jimmy 'H' groaned.

'You finally told them! What took you so long Willie? You'd only been in our squad five minutes and everyone knew about your dammed spirits,' Billy Chancer ranted from behind the panel, an admission that even he was following the story.

Despite these interruptions and frosty comments, Willie was not to be swayed, and he simply carried on with the tale.

'It seemed as if I'd touched a raw nerve when I told him this, 'cos straight away gobby Frankie, went for the jugular - even before I'd had a chance to explain the ins and outs of my beliefs.' Willie's voice was raised high now, in a decidedly uncharacteristic manner.

'To tell yer the truth when the lad stared at me like a madman, for a brief moment it crossed my mind that maybe he was possessed with some kind of evil spirit or demon - now that would have been an interesting challenge and right up my street for psychic investigating.'

Billy Chancer tutted loudly and disdainfully from behind the panel, but Willie again ignored him, for the narrative was hotting up.

'I knew when we first met, there was somethin' odd about you,' Frankie snarled at me. 'Ghosts,' he shouted, 'what do you know about ghosts, Willie? Anyone who believes in that load of crap must 'ave somethin' missin' up here,' and he pointed to the large scar spanning his shaven head from one side to the other.

Despite our reservations Willie had us hooked now. Even the Chancer was sneaking a look round the panel again.

'D'yer know lads,' Willie's voice subsided again, 'he gave me no peace afterwards. At me throat day and night, tryin' his best to goad me or trick me into revealing all the astral experiences I'd gathered on my long and arduous spiritual journey. In the end I was so fed up with his piss-taking that I made my mind up to put the fear of God up him, and to get him off me back once and for all. So a few days I allowed things to rest, just talkin' about everyday trivia. Then I deliberately let slip about hearin' strange voices and clanging chains as I was dozin' off in the digs on the first night we'd landed. And I told them that a voice had cried out that the pub next door and the block of houses we were lodged in were built on sacred ground.

'And of course he bit, didn't he? Jumped right in with both feet, with a silly grin spread across his arrogant face.

'Sacred ground? Worra yer talkin' about now soft arse?' he growled.

'Now listen here,' I said, addressing the bully boy as if he was a spoilt and naughty child, 'I've not mentioned this before,' but if you cast your mind back to the night I had business to attend to and couldn't join you lads in the Angel for a pint? Well then, I think it's time I told you where I went and what I was up to.'

'That got 'im! Drew him further into my trap; so now I moved in to lay the bait for the first part of my plan.'

'Y'see, Frankie,' I reasoned with him calmly, ' being a believer in the spirits, I made it my business to make an appointment with the local vicar and librarian, and after checking some sixteenth century records in the old archives, they confirmed that there had indeed been a Benedictine Priory, right where our digs and the pub are.'

'He wasn't convinced.' 'That's shite,'he snarled at me. 'Pure un-adulterated shite.'

'Right then- know all,' I said, calling his bluff. 'Come with me an' have a chat with the vicar or the librarian fella yourself, an' hear what they have to say on the matter.'

'But Frankie was up against a brick wall. He just stared, lost for words and snarled, then shrugged and walked away.

'Now, a couple of night's later I put the next part of me plan into action. Frankie had left the pub a bit earlier than usual, to claim the bathroom before anyone else could get the chance; so I grabbed young Tommy Patterson, hoping he'd help me to put Frank firmly in his place. And what a success story that turned out to be!'

'Y'see,' Willie continued, 'Friday night was his big night out.'

By now we were all listening carefully as we plodded along, looming masses of cables, keen to hear how Willie had managed to get one over on this mouthy Mancunian from the other end of the East Lancs Road.

'First let me tell you what I had in mind,' Willie explained. 'With the cold weather settling in, me missus - always one for a bargain - had bought me an arctic white duffel coat from the Army & Navy stores in Byron Street. As it turned out, it wasn't too cold so I left it in me room, out of sight and out of mind.'

Once again he stopped to take stock, then continued in a nonchalant, matter of fact way.

'Now then, lads, without wanting to bore you to tears, I'd better give you the run down on our digs, for it's essential to the tale.'

'Bore us to tears? for Christ's sake, ' Jimmy'H' growled impatiently, 'how many parts as this story got?'

'Not long now, Jimmy, not long now,' Willie replied soothingly.

'Y'see, the house was just a run-of-the- mill, three story mid-terrace,' he explained. ' Front lounge, rear kitchen, straight stairway to the first floor; with two bedrooms and a bathroom, then another set of stairs to a boxroom on the top landing, with a tank and linen cupboard outside the door. I must mention that as soon as we set foot in the place those two buggers were up the dancers like greyhounds, snaffling the largest bedroom opposite the bathroom, while Joe Soap here had to make do with the tiny box-room. But this, as it turned out, couldn't have been better placed for what I had planned.'

'Our routine rarely varied,' Willie said. 'Each night we'd settle into our usual spot at the end of the bar in the Angel, and the first couple of pints would never even touch the sides,' he reflected nostalgically.

'Gerron with it you old misery,' Billy Chancer growled from behind the panel.

'Okay, okay, as I was sayin', Willie moved back into gear. 'After suppin' our quota - usually three pints apiece - we'd amble back to the digs, get washed and changed, then pop down stairs for our dinner. More often than not we'd hit the sack, even before the ten o'clock news. Of course, Frankie was the exception to the rule, especially at the weekends when he was out playing the field. And then young Tommy could never be certain of getting' a decent night's kip, 'cos it all depended on whether the bold Frankie had scored or not.

'Now if you were to ask me my opinion,' Willie began again.

'We'd gerrit whether we want it or not,' Podgy Hogan muttered, as the saga ran on.

'For what it's worth, I reckon it was this total disregard for Tommy's feelings that eventually gave the lad the impetus to throw caution to the wind, and to help me set Frankie up.

'Bloody 'ell Willie, we know your workin' as fast as you're gabbin', but how much longer do we 'ave to suffer, waitin' for the punch line to this story?' Jimmy 'H' asked for a second time.

'We're nearly there now Jimmy, just give me a few more minutes lad,' Willie replied, before plunging on.

'Now from the very first week we'd set foot on the site, Frankie made it abundantly clear he preferred going dancing on his own. So, every Friday, as Tommy and I downed our regular three pints before dinner, Frankie would limit himself to a half of bitter before dashing off to have his customary shower and shave. This particular Friday night, though, 'Frank the lad' was in for a bit of a shock.' Willie was smiling at the recollection.

'As he flew up the stairs, we were already hard on his heels, hiding in the shadows in the hall which was only lit by a miserable forty watt bulb. After a minute or so we clocked him skippin' across the landing heading for the bathroom, crooning like Bing Crosby, with only a towel covering his bits and bobs.'

'Wait a mo lads, hang on I'm nearly finished,' Willie pleaded, as we began congregating near the control room door ready for the inevitable dash when the hooter sounded. But it seemed we'd timed it wrongly, or Willie's tale had driven us out early, because we had a few minutes to kill and this gave him the chance to continue - but now with a distinct note of urgency in his voice.

'As soon as we heard the shower flowing and Frankie 'Singin' in the Rain,' the two of us sneaked upstairs, stopping outside the bathroom long enough to allow young Tommy to remove the light bulb on the landing. Then, as quiet as mice, we climbed the stairs up to the top landing where the lad stretched his long arm and took that bulb out as well.'

By now the place was in complete darkness so we tiptoed into my attic room. Quick as a wink I dragged a black pullover over me head and face, and slipped the white duffel coat on. With the hood pulled up I then stepped onto the landing, just as Frankie emerged from the bathroom. Through the gap in the immersion cupboard door I watched him fiddle and fart about with the light switch, flicking it up and down a couple of times, then scratching his head as if he'd run out of ideas as to how a bloody switch worked. At this point I stepped out onto the landing and wailed like a banshee.

'Terror…Bloody 'ell, I've never seen such terror in anyone's face,' Willie giggled at the memory of his moment of triumph. 'In fact I thought he was about to keel over on the spot. He looked up to where I was standing, dropped his towel and screamed at the top of his voice. I'm sure those drinking in the bar next door must 'ave thought a murder was being committed.' Laughing as he spoke, Willie described how Frankie had shot bare-bollocked across the landing into his bedroom, slamming the door with great force, before sliding home the heavy bolts at top and bottom.

'This gave us enough time to put the bulbs back in their holders, slip downstairs and nip next door to resume our positions at the bar, waiting for the return of our mate Frankie.'

Just then, the hooter sounded, blasting three monotonous drones across site to remind everyone it was break time.

'Come on,' Chunkie murmured, as we moved towards the control room door, 'worr 'appened next Willie?'

'Well, I've never seen such a change in a fella in all me life,' Willie said. 'He came hurtlin' into the bar, a hundred miles an hour, shirt hangin' out, grippin' his kecks at the waist. His hair was ringin' wet, his laces were un-done, and his face was the colour of boiled shite.'

'Willie, Willie, he spluttered, grabbin' hold of me in a right old panic, 'you'll never believe it, but I've just seen a friggin' monk appear from behind that water cylinder outside your bedroom door.'

'A monk! Don't talk daft lad.' I told him, 'you're lettin' your imagination run away with yer. There are no monks up there. The only place you're likely to see a monk is in the pantry, on the Birds Eye Custard powder label.'

'On me mother's life, Willie,' I know what I saw,' he gibbered, shaking visibly, 'I know what I saw.' Then he turned to Tommy. 'Do me a favour mate,' he pleaded, grabbing Tommy's pint and lifting it to his lips as the ale lapped from one edge to the other, 'will yer go an' check it out, 'cos there's no way I'm goin' back in there an sleepin' in a house that's haunted.'

By this time we were halfway to the cabins, but still listening to Willie's tale.

'Right Tommy,' I said to the lad, 'let's go an' see what all the fuss is about, while we leave Frank here to gather his wits and composure.' As soon as we were out of earshot and safely next door in the digs, well, you can imagine the state we were in tryin' to keep a straight face an' control the tears. Tommy, who'd been nervous and fidgety from the time Frankie staggered into the pub, plonked himself on the bottom of the stairs an' couldn't move for laughing. When he eventually calmed down he begged me not to tell anyone about being his involved in the set-up, 'cos Frankie was related to a notorious Moss Side family, a clan never known to take prisoners, nor leave any stone un-turned when it came to gaining revenge on anyone who'd put one over on them.'

As we lined up outside our cabin, Willie shouted the last bits of the story across from his place in the queue outside the other cabin.

'Talk about a reformed character,' he chuckled, pleased as punch at the way the story was still panning out.

'I've never seen anyone change so much in such a short time. Far from being his usual aggressive self Frankie became as mild as a day old lamb. And when he began pesterin' the life out of me about my spiritual beliefs - well - I did all I could to put him on the right road - like I've tried doin' with you'se lads.'

'An' guess what?' he concluded triumphantly,' 'before the job wrapped up, he only wanted to make arrangements to jump a train from Piccadilly to Lime Street to meet me and pay a visit to The Liverpool Truth Society.'

'It'a lorra shite,' Podgy bawled over his shoulder as we moved into the cabin; but then for some reason or other he changed his tune.

'What did you say his name was Willie? He asked, 'y'know just in case he lands 'imself on one of our jobs in this area.

'Don't worry yourself Podgy, there's no chance of that happening. You see, I deliberately changed the names of the characters in the tale in order to protect the innocent,' Willie chuckled, before disappearing with his mob into the smaller of the two mess cabins that housed the Tanjon's full labour force.

After a week-end spent drifting round town, sampling ale from any of the pumps that caught my eye, and drinking far too much for my own good, the last person I wanted to meet on my way to the mill on the following Monday morning was Billy Chancer. But when I spotted him I had to look twice to make sure my eyes weren't deceiving me. Here he was for the first time in months looking as pleased as punch, smiling away like a big Cheshire cat, his mouthful of stained yellow teeth exposed like a row of well-worn ivories, adorning an ancient bar-room piano.

Curious to know the reason for this sudden change in mood or good fortune, I headed directly towards him, instead of taking my usual Monday morning evasive manoeuvre of sliding off to hide in the bogs 'til he was out of sight.

'I'm glad I've managed to catch you on yer own Jimmy,' he said, placing an affectionate arm across my shoulders.

'Why, what's happened,' I replied pleasantly, 'you haven't won the treble chance have yer?

'As good as lad, as good as, believe me,' he grinned.

'Okay, tell me about it Billy, you can trust me to keep a secret, so fire away,' I said, all the time wondering just what sort of good news could be responsible for lifting Bill out of the doldrums and into a state of almost child-like euphoria.

'Well son, you know how I've always preached about analysing things properly before making a decisions, haven't I?'

'You can say that again Billy,' I agreed.

'You're a bright lad Jim, so you must've spotted that for the past six weeks I just haven't been me'self. No matter how hard I tried, son, I just couldn't seem to put things together in their right order. Then bang - out of the blue - everything came together. When I think on, it was so simple. I don't know how the hell it took me so long to suss things out.'

'You see, Maisie's been all wrapped in this crap about

spirits, ghosts and mediums and the like. Well, last night she came home from a meetin' in a right sweat, and d'yer know what lad, in all me married life I've never seen her as wild and in such a mood. My initial thought was that she'd gone off her rocker. But then, for the first time in ages she sat down to tell me all her troubles. Just like she would in the old days, before she got herself involved with that crowd of manipulators down the road at the spiritualist church. And when she told me she'd forked out seven bob for a private hearin' with one of the charlatans, well, I nearly had a dicky fit. I ask yer! 'Bloody seven bob, lad? If that's not daylight robbery, nothin' is.' he cried.

I listened intently, 'cos this was getting interesting; I knew for a fact that seven bob to Billy was the equivalent of a kings ransom.

'Anyway, after handin' the seven bob over she was informed there was someone there from the 'other side' anxious to contact her, so naturally, who should spring to mind but 'er ould lady. Now, when this so-called medium tried fishin' for details of her mother's likes and dislikes, well, she smelt a rat straight away. And instead of feedin' genuine info, she gave her a load of duff stuff, just to see if she was the real article. Oh, she's no, mug, is my Maisie. Never 'as been and never will be,' Billy said, beaming with pride.'

'And then, as soon as this medium - Rosie Lee, or worr ever her name really is - went under, she began describin' a grey haired sprinkly old fella, who, of course, only she could see. It seems that this bloke was saying that he belonged to the family. And that's when Maisie stepped in and began stringin' her along in earnest, saying perhaps it was her dad who'd been an army officer in the great war.'

'Hang on dear, be patient, he's becomin' clearer,' the old fraud said. 'In fact he's standin' smilin', right behind you now. Can you feel his presence?'

'Oh yes' Maisie said, kiddin' on, 'I definitely felt something brush past me shoulder.'

'Ah! I can see him clearly now,' the psychic said suddenly. 'At least six-foot tall, dressed in khaki uniform, with a row of medals on his chest. A real military man, yes a real military man, dear. He's standin' next to a much smaller grey-haired lady; and something tells me it could be your mother, or maybe your grandmother.' She gazed round the empty room then asked, 'has you're mother passed over dear?'

'Yes,' but not so long ago,' Maisie told her; and then, in an effort to catch her on the hop and almost as an afterthought, she asked the old rogue, 'what did she say her name was? 'And you know what lad?'

'What?' I blurted.

'She only went right through the bloody alphabet guessing at names, until finally she got to Wilhelmena. At that point Maisie told her mother's name was Annie and her ould fella was five-foot nothin' and had died an alco, before the war began. And that ended that session right there and then.'

'An' did she get 'er seven bob back?'

'Don't be daft lad. That disappeared quicker than 'er old lady's spirit. So you see, Jim, that little experience put paid to all the crap about ghosts and the likes. Now wait lad, 'cos there's more… just listen to this. Remember me tellin' you about the time I heard footsteps on me landin', and the light in the bathroom flickin' on an' off? Believe it or not, but I've managed to get to the bottom of that mystery as well. Between you, me and the gatepost, son, for the past six months me and Maisie 'ave been sleepin' in separate rooms.'

'Separate rooms?'

'Yeah separate rooms. Now don't get the wrong idea, lad, there's nothin' the marrer with us. But week days she's started goin' to bed early - at nine o'clock - an' she didn't like me disturbin' her when I turned in, that's all.'

'What's separate rooms got to do with hearin' footsteps and seein' the light flickin' on an' off,' I asked, unsure how all this fitted in with the resolution to Billy's problems.

'Believe it or not, Jim, it took ages to work this one out. Y'see, we've been married twenty-three years, and in all that time Maisie's never once had to get up in the night to go to the lavvie. As soon as her head hits the pillow she's out like a log. Even when next door went on fire an' was nearly burnt down to the ground, she slept right through it all.'

'So worra you sayin'?' I asked.

'Worr I'm sayin', Jim, is that when I heard those footsteps I didn't even consider for a moment it could've been Maisie. Then, last night, when we were gabbin' about spooks and ghosts and the like, right out of the blue, she mentioned she'd been havin' trouble with her waterworks for the past month or so; and the penny dropped. Y'know what lad, when she told me she'd been gettin' up in the night an' dashin' to the lavvie, I threw me arms round her an' hugged her as if there was no tomorrow.'

'An that led me to consider the tale Willie was tellin' us last week; that yarn about the time he worked in Lancaster. An' so I decided to use reason and logic like I've told you to do when there's a problem - like Maisie did with the spook who said she had her ould man and her ould lady there from the other side, but then couldn't get the name without goin' through the whole of the alphabet, an' didn't know her ould fella had been a piss-artist an' not some war hero. Y'see, Willie slipped up, Jim, when he mentioned he'd had to use Tommy as his accomplice. If you think about it son, an' how easy it can be to kid someone if you're usin' an accomplice with a hidden microphone or mirrors; or someone who's causin' things to move, or who's blowin' cold breezes from behind some curtain, or just takin' light bulbs out; well, it's not a question of it bein' spirits or ghosts or anything from the astral plane. It's just a matter of dressin' up as a ghoul - or in this case as a monk - and pullin' a flanker. 'No, take it from me Jim, this spiritualism lark is just one big racket!'

'Y'see, I realised that Willie had to use Tommy, 'cos he just isn't big enough himself to reach the light bulbs - so some spook eh lad? Some mystic happenings!'

'D'yer know what Jim, I'm grateful to my Maisie for sussing these buggers out. She's a wise old owl, and she certainly put me on the right track with Willie.'

'I hope you're as lucky as me Jim, when you start moochin' around for someone decent to settle down with, 'cos both me and Maisie are extremely fond of you - you know that don't yer lad?'

'I do Billy, I do,' I told him, as we reached the cabin door.

Re-union

The first six months of the final year of my apprenticeship passed more quickly than any period since I'd left school. As the weeks ticked ominously on towards my twenty first birthday, my dreams of evading Her Majesty's ultimate request for the pleasure of my company for two years began to fade as quickly as the tan from an Indian summer.

One late September morning my hopes were dashed again when I received yet another knock-back to my plans to escape by the only safe and available route, via the Merchant Navy. Although I'd offered my experience to a number of shipping companies over the previous months they'd all regretfully declined my services. Of course, when I think back now, my wealth of experience could have been contained on the back of an empty fag packet.

'What's the matter lad? What's all the fuss about? Two years! That's bugger all. It'll be over in no time. So straighten your face an' spare a thought for the poor sergeant major who has to make real men out of you'se lot of smart Aleck's and Teddy fella's,' dad joked.

His sarcastic comments rang in my ears as I glumly ticked off another lowly tramp ship outfit from a long list of possible employers who'd now decided they could well do without my presence.

Despite horror stories of barrack room fatigues and medieval punishment bandied around the site by a stream of closely-cropped new starters who'd returned to civilisation after a couple of years in the mob, I hadn't given much thought to the prospect of being called up for National Service; a compulsory obligation for all young men between the ages of eighteen and twenty four. However my laid-back approach and couldn't-care-less attitude changed dramatically when, within a fortnight big Don and Louie, received their marching orders and were conscripted into the R.A.F.

Watching them traipse out through the main gate on the last Friday of the month quickly brought me back to my senses, and within a matter of days, I'd resumed my task of scouring the docks and searching the telephone directories for the names and addresses of companies plying their trade through the Port of Liverpool.

There was no hiding the fact that a majority of the sparks were of the opinion that contracting apprentices who applied to the merchant navy for positions of junior engineers were wasting their time. It wasn't anything to do with ability on the tools, or indeed with the levels of qualifications we'd attained at night school, but down to the fact that we had little or no knowledge or experience of the intricate workings and the lay outs of ships. Besides, we knew little or nothing about 'D.C motor control' a handicap that gave the shipyard lads a distinctive advantage.

Of course, working with 'Willie the Spook' I'd developed a high opinion of myself, and stoked up enough self-confidence to last more than a lifetime. What's more I had adopted a 'nothing-ventured - nothing-gained' attitude; and even more importantly, I had my own set of supporters to back me up - though strangely enough, they were less than certain when it came to re-assuring me it was only a matter of time before some merchant marine outfit would snap me up.

Naturally, the usual clique of jokers had a field day, constantly reminding me that my nautical ambition was unlikely to secure me the roll of a Chief Engineer, or even Admiral and betting that the nearest sea breeze I was likely to get into my lungs, would be from treading the decks of the ferry as it sailed back and forwards across The Mersey.

Nevertheless, with the help of Robbo, Sid Shortwick, Billy Chancer and a few others who appeared to show interest in my plans to dodge the call to military service, I drafted enough begging letters to as many companies as I could muster, glossing up references and pleading my case. Then, pushing the points of view of the pessimists firmly under the carpet, I sat back and waited for a flood of offers to arrive, confident they would soon be demanding access to my undoubted skills.

In the meantime I began cramming my beleaguered brain-box with as much theory on D.C motor control, generators, marine turbines and the like, soaking up information from the numerous tradesmen who'd spent as many years at sea as I'd had hot dinners.

Those lads who did manage to join the Merchant navy, of course, were committed to a five-year stint, instead of the two years obligatory period of National service. But the higher rate of pay was a major incentive in opting for a sea going career. It was common knowledge that a young engineering officer was usually paid as much as a tradesmen working on shore, and would earn far more than the mere pittance of three quid a week that a national service conscript received. What's more, the chance to travel the world and visit exotic ports was probably the main attraction to those lads joining the Merchant marine. But for the likes of myself who lived and breathed football, there was no doubt that five years away would ultimately end any ambition I had of becoming a reasonable player or a cup-winner for any of the top local amateur teams. And so, in a half-hearted way, while there was part of me that wanted to sample the spirit of adventure by travelling the world, the other half was reluctant to be separated for such a long period from a place and a way of life that I felt was deep rooted in my bones.

On a bleak October afternoon Chunkie and I left Goodison Park having watched an enthralling battle against an Aston Villa side who somehow or other managed to scrape a two-goal draw, a score entirely against the run of play I might add. Seconds before the ref had blown the final whistle to signal the end of the ninety minutes, we had edged our way towards the Gladwys Street exit before falling in line with the massed cavalcade of supporters streaming from the ground towards the town centre. Passing Everton Valley we drifted into Kirkdale Road, where, just before entering the top end of Scottie Road we suddenly spotted the unmistakable bow-legged Arnie Royal, walking in front of us, heading in the same direction.

Within minutes we'd caught up and were alongside our old mate from Pitts. This was our first meeting since the night we'd teamed up together at Bonso's fateful wedding. Chunkie fell in beside him and slapped him hard on the back, so hard that Arnie's specs bounced on his nose.

'Hello Arnie, me old son,' he greeted jovially. 'Howya doin'? What d'yer think - was we robbed back there or what like?'

Judging by the look of surprise on Arnie's face, it was clear he was as pleased to see us as we were to see him. However, the bustling crowd and the hungry and excitable football fans swept us along, so there was neither the time nor the space to stop for a gossip. And so we carried on down the hill, where we drifted into nearest oasis - the popular Throstles Nest - always reckoned to be a prime watering hole for hoarse and dry necked - Evertonians like us. To our surprise the bar was still quiet so we quickly shuffled in from the cold, collared an empty table near the open fire and settled down to enjoy a quiet session, re-live the highlights of the match, and gab about the ups and downs of the past twenty one months since we'd last met. After we'd agreed that the Villa had stolen a point, and the ref's parents were definitely never married, and how the next time, we'd skin the Midlanders alive, Arnie suddenly dropped a bombshell.

'Have you heard,' he said?' 'Bonso's time's about up. An' he's coming home on leave before he gets demobbed.'

Bonso, it seemed, was due home on the following Friday for his penultimate leave before being discharged from the Army.

'That's it then,' Chunkie decided, 'we've got to celebrate.'

'We could have a re-union,' Arnie suggested, and all three of us agreed this was a great idea. Any chance for a bit of a do, and we were always up for it.

'Let's get all the lads from Pitts and hit the town and have a proper skin full,' I said. 'How about Ma Edgies? Bonso always liked it there.'

'We all did,' Arnie agreed, slurping his pint.

After the arrangements were finalised and confirmed, we began the serious business of drip feeding our bellies with pints of best bitter, laughing and joking, recalling our hopeless and futile attempts under Bonso's guidance to latch onto the girls in the local dancehalls. As the night wore on the stories of our romantic achievements became more exaggerated - but we were all the better for it. And our recollection of the part Bonso played in all this had mounted, along with the pile of empty pint glasses on the table.

'And worrabout Eggo,' Chunkie suddenly reminded us; and once again the tales of how the big fella had given the posh-nosed Marmaduke of Waring's the run-around were trotted out; and enjoyed as much as they'd ever been.

Yet another round lay before us, when Chunkie nudged my arm.

'Go on, Jim, fill Anie in about your new craze at the Mardi,' he said, leaning back, pursing his lips and sending a thin wisp of smoke curling up towards the brown stained ceiling.

'The Mardi Gras?' Arnie asked.

'You've heard of it?' I said. It didn't seem to me to be the sort of place Arnie would usually be interested in.

'Yeah, someone at work mentioned it. But don't tell me you're into all that jazz crap, Reilly?' and he laughed.

'Broader horizons,' I said, tapping the side of my nose to suggest it was all about knowledge. 'You'll get nowhere unless you broaden your horizons,' I told him. 'And anyway you should see all the loose skirt that gets in there. Y'don't know what you're missin' Arnie. Nearly all of them are students, not your average Cardboard Factory girls,' I continued, my face red and glowing from the heat of the fire and the effects of the ale. 'And what's more,' I told him knowingly, adding the final and conclusive thrust to my argument, 'most of 'em have their own flats.'

'Tell Arnie about your horny little blonde,' Chunkie said, trying to set - me up, and nudging Arnie at the same time.

'You mean Maggie, the horny ornithologist?' I said calmly, in a matter-of- fact voice.

I knew what Chunkie's game was - he was hoping I'd slip up after half a dozen pints and reveal to Arnie how I'd joined the library to pick up bits and pieces about the subjects that Maggie and her friends were studying. And how, by using short quotes and long words, I planned to use this new knowledge to impress them.

As a strategy it had not been without success - or so I liked to kid myself - and as a means for placing me in the limelight it had certainly put me at the forefront, especially when I turned up at work with a haversack loaded with a pile of heavy hardback books on subjects ranging from anthropology to ornithology and Greek philosophy. The uproar when I laid them out during dinner hour break and began flicking through the pages trying to look intelligent was worth a million dollars.

'See what Reilly's got to do to gerrin with all the posh judy's at the Mardi Gras,' Chunkie yelled round the cabin, while I could only sit back and give him the traditional retort of 'jealousy will get you nowhere, Chunks'.

However, my mention to Arnie that this wealth of academic talent mostly had their own flats, appeared to perk him up, because he suddenly wanted to know all about this part of town which he and his mates had previously avoided like the plague and let slip through their fingers. So I told him how Timmy M'Cain and I had happened to come across the Mardi, after stumbling, half-pissed down Mount Pleasant. We'd stopped round the corner from Renshaw Street, outside this unknown venue, after hearing loud music and the sound of clapping coming from inside.

'What's that they're playin'? ' I asked Timmy, 'cos you know how thick I am when it comes to music.'

'It's trad Jazz, 'he said. 'Come on let's pop in and give it the once over.'

'Trade jazz or any other jazz for that matter, didn't mean a thing to me. But I had nowt to lose, and it couldn't be any worse than Reeces Tea dance, with all the ould girls cockin' their legs and doin' the Hokey Cokey. Remember that fiasco Arnie?' I said, jogging his memory.

Arnie nodded, sipped his pint, but said nothing, waiting for me to continue.

'Thinking back, I'm sure Timmy steered me there on purpose. 'Cos when we staggered in he knew the score and paid for both of us without even checkin' his change. And inside, well, there was that much talent hangin' around on their own, I don't mind admitting I sobered up straight away.

I was exaggerating again, watching Chunkie smile as he gulped down the remainder of his pint in one swoop. He'd heard the tale before from both Timmy and me.

'I just couldn't keep me eyes off them Arnie,' I continued. 'It's a strange place inside, though, not very big. Nothin' like any of the gaffs we're used to. And out front, on some sort of stage, a few fella's were blastin' away, playing this honky-tonk music, like you get in the old gangster pictures. And everyone was sittin' down, nodding their heads, clappin' their hands and stampin' their feet. All of a sudden Timmy said, 'come on Jim, let's show 'em what us rough and ready contractors are made of.' So without needin' to be asked a second time I followed him and dived right in and plonked me'self in the middle of half a dozen of these gorgeous looking' birds.'

'Half a dozen?' Chunkie sniggered.

'Well, maybe five - or four - or it could've been three. Remember I was half pissed at the time. Any road, Arnie, since then I've become a regular, an' I more or less know everyone in there now. So if you fancy a change from the Grafton or the Loccie, well, I'll fix you up with a bit of talent if you like; and talent with a brain - for a change!'

As the night wore on, and even I began to realise I'd reached my limit, I saw that Chunkie was twiddling his hair, which was something he always did when he'd had enough ale or was nodding off.

So shortly before half eight, after confirming the time and date for the re-union, the three of us split up and I headed down Scottie towards Lime Street, where I popped into the 'Legs of Man' just for good measure, and a swift one for the road.

As usual at the breaktime on the following Monday morning every ball was re-kicked, every goal was argued over, every sitter missed was re-visited, and the referee and linesmen's performance, was discussed in minute detail. But, on this morning, our meeting with Arnie Royal and the forthcoming re-union with Bonso was perhaps the most important news to add to the conversation.

Of course only Chunkie and myself among the apprentices had worked with Bonso, but the likes of Robbo, Trunkie Davies, Podgy Hogan and few other sparks recalled how he'd got the bullet, then lost his apprenticeship before being nabbed almost immediately by the army. Billy Chancer had also known Bonso when he'd worked at Pitts; and indeed when he first arrived at Tanjon's he'd openly voiced concerns about the unacceptable behaviour of our ex- mentor and leader. Now, though, for some reason he seemed to have changed his tune - or perhaps he'd mellowed since his outburst - because he asked us to pass on his best regards to Bonso, and said he would put out feelers to see if he could get him a spark's mate's job as soon as he'd completed his army service

On the great night itself we set off earlier than usual, full of the joys of spring and ready to paint the town red. At a quarter to eight, after wetting our palettes with a couple of small whites in Yates Wine Lodge, Chunkie and I and Timmy M'Cain - who'd tagged along for a laugh - ambled into Ma Edgie's and ordered three pints of bitter, then sat at a table facing the door so we could blimp everyone coming in. But it was still early, and there wasn't many in, perhaps half a dozen or so at the most. Half way down the room, leaning against the middle of the bar, a couple of old fella's were deep in conversation. Their wives, with their shopping bags next to their feet, were gassing to each other at the table directly behind where their husbands were standing.

At the far end of the bar a 'Ted,' in full drape was posing, his thumbs hidden behind his blue velvet lapels. Like us, he appeared to be watching everyone who came through the front door.

Arnie, was the first of the team to land. A huge grin spanned his face as he marched in and headed straight towards us followed by two other lads.

'Remember Caulie and Scullo?' he said, and then stood aside and boomed, 'well here they are almost two years on.'

We shook hands with the two long, gangling, smart looking lads, who had shot up since I'd last seen them, changing from pint-sized- pimply faced school leavers into tall, clean-shaven young adults. Arnie, however, had a bigger surprise up his sleeve when he turned round then beckoned across to the Teddy boy who was now leaning at the end of the bar.

'You'll never guess who this, is?' he said, as the heavily built 'Ted' with massive sideburns and a jet black moustache picked up his pint glass in a huge fist as though it was a small whisky tumbler, and then swaggered across towards us.

'Don't worry lads, it's only the bold 'arry,' Arnie laughed.

We almost dropped our pints with shock, as Harry Burkey clasped my puny hand and then took Chunkie's in his massive paw.   We stared long and hard at Harry - never in a million years would we have recognised him. The last time we'd seen him at Pitts he was working with Ginger Morefield and was a five foot four, eight stone weakling. Now, in what seemed be a mere snap of the fingers, he'd zoomed up and had become a six-foot, thirteen and a half stone giant.

As we waited for Bonso we had a whip-round to pay for the drinks for our old colleague. Even Timmy - who'd never met Bonso - threw five bob into the hat, and soon the two tables we'd managed to capture were cluttered with pints of bitter. At a quarter past eight when Bonso arrived and stepped through the doorway and into the bar, we all stood up to give him a welcoming rally.

Bonso had changed, like everyone else. Always tall and lanky, he looked more muscular and confident, swinging broad and well-developed shoulders, and was sporting an unfamiliar short-cropped military haircut that clearly distinguished him from our bold civilian fashions.

We stood besides the tables grinning like a pack of hyenas as he came smartly to attention in front of us, stamping his feet in real army style before throwing us a full salute.

'Lads,' he said with feeling, 'it's great to back amongst me own kind again after - worr is it - twenty one months and two and a half days. And I must say how prosperous you'se lot look.' He was grinning, casting his eye over us, inspecting us from top to bottom, like a fearsome sergeant major on parade.

'Look at little Jimmy Reilly dressed to the hilt. Just like a nine bob note,' he said, shaking my hand warmly.

'And Chunkie's no better.

'Trust Arnie to be still wearin' that old sports jacket he got from that jumble sale when he was fifteen,' he chuckled. 'And the state of these two bean poles, Scullo and Caulie.'

'But worr about our old mate 'arry Burkey over 'ere. A friggin Teddy fella, an' a fat one at that,' he laughed, running his fingers playfully around Harry's velvet lapels, feeling the quality of the material.

It was just like old times as we crowded round Bonso and he automatically took the perch at the end of the larger of the two tables. 'Okay then,' he said, as he picked up one of the spare pints and took his first sip, 'fill me in what you've all been up too, and don't spare the dirty details,' and he laughed wickedly. As the banter began and the ale flowed we were in good spirits, telling jokes, trying to outdo each other with outrageous claims as to our extraordinary sexual encounters, never exaggerating more than was expected of us.

Meanwhile, like a wise old owl, Bonso sat back and listened until we'd exhausted our boastful pretensions. Then, after a little prompting from Harry, who was only weeks from finally finishing his time and next in line for call-up, he began his own account of what it was like to be a soldier.

'First of all Harry, I must tell you that the army will just love capturin' you. For some reason they're at war with hair - they just don't like it. And they seem to take their spite out on the Ted's and the Rockers. So that D.A, well, the barber will 'ave a field day shiftin' that lot. I reckon it'll be off within seconds.' Harry looked downcast, as if he didn't quite believe what he'd heard.

'Seriously Bonso, tell us what the army's really like, 'cos you don't look so bad on it?' Harry asked, as Bonso rested his broad shoulders against the panelled wall and lit a ciggie.

'It's okay now that I'm in me workin' unit, but when I went in I didn't know me arse from me elbow for the first six weeks,' he began. 'Talk about humiliation. Bloody 'ell, I experienced the lot an' I'm not kiddin' either. For starters we all had our heads clipped to the bone, then we were marched to the Quartermasters store, where a bunch of squaddies threw clobber at us, whether it fitted or not. After luggin' these bundles back to our barrack room an' trying the uniforms on, we all looked like village plonkers. The big fella's had small sizes, the midgets had large ones. It was a bleedin' shambles. And the state of the underkecks we were expected to wear. In winter they're thick woolly, itchy John L's. The same kind ould fella's use. And for summer, pissy green ones. 'Drawers cellular for the use of,' they call 'em. Bleedin' drawers Dracula, if you ask me. I mean ter say, imagine paradin' round in drawers with no elastic in the waist.'

'No elastic?' Chunkie asked, 'how do they stay up?'

'They 'ave little cloth tags that you wrap round your braces

just like the old gunslingers you see in the cowie pictures,'
Bonso replied

'That's a bit primitive,' said Chunkie, 'every time you
wanna crap and undo the buttons on yer braces both pair of
kecks must fall down.'

'Correct,' said Bonso. Then he placed his finger across his
lips.

'Shush, a minute lads, did you hear what I've just heard?'

We stopped nattering and listened. Then, the unmistakable
voice of the man who'd given so much pleasure to all of us in
the past, came roaring before him into the pub through the open
door.

'My Duchess,' we heard the voice boom, 'the finest woman
to walk these city streets. I'll just drop in for a moment to see
how old Ma Edgy is going on. So if you would make your way
to the executive seats my dear, I'll see if the ale is still as fine as
it's always been, and then I'll be with you in a jiffy.'

We all turned as one to the door as Eggo stepped into the
bar, displaying the knowing smirk that never seemed to change.
His eyes darting here, there and everywhere fell on our little
team at the far end of the room, all of us staring at the apparition
with a mixture of surprise and jubilation.

Just for a fleeting moment he seemed to hesitate, then he
strode across to our speck in the corner, roaring out a greeting.

'Good Evening Gentlemen!' he hollered, like a compere
introducing a bunch of up and coming stars, and spreading his
hands out in a theatrical manner. 'Have you ever set eyes on
such a fine body of men as we have assembled here?' he said,
addressing a party sitting across the room from us. 'Now then
lads, tell me how are you coping in this wild and wicked world,
without me, the GREAT EGGO?' He'd yelled and yodelled so
loudly that one of the old bloke's leaning on the bar turned to his
mate and said in a droll voice, 'The Empire or The Playhouse?
Take yer pick Frankie, which one d'yer reckon he's playin' at
tonight?'

'I'd say the Nut House, me'self,' his mate replied, as Eggo
bawled at the barman - who he obviously knew - 'Charlie, these
young proteges of mine - give 'em a drink on the house.'

The next ten minutes were hilarious, with Eggo prancing up

and down, squeezing his huge frame between us, asking each in turn what we'd been up to, and taking the mickey. Then, despite failing to grip Bonso's now none-existent side burns he still managed to walk him round the room, gripping his ears and exhibiting him as a product of the military might to the assembled punters. With all the hilarity and the place in an uproar, none of us noticed a smartly dressed, good looking woman walk in the bar. That is until she addressed Eggo with a smile on her face.

'Come on James, were going to lose our seats if you don't hurry along.'

Dropping Bonso back on his seat, Eggo scooped up his wife.

'Come over here Duchess and let me introduce you to the next generation of Liverpool's electrical hero's. Here they are,' he bawled, EGGO'S ARMY OF BLACK PUDDIN' BENDERS.' And Mrs Eggo giggled and waved her hand at us.

After Eggo had slapped each of our shoulders and wished us all the best, he re-joined his wife. Then, as he left the room, he shouted to the two old timers at the bar. 'I don't suppose you gents would happen to know the whereabouts of a couple of good sausage straighteners who would suit my lads over there?'

'Sausage straighteners? Worra yer talkin' about La?'

We all laughed as Eggo departed in his usual crazy and enigmatic way. Here he was again leaving behind a trail of chaos, with the two elderly customers and Charlie the barman shaking their heads in disbelief, and probably no idea what Eggo was rambling on about.

When we'd recovered from the excitement and shock of Eggo's sudden and altogether coincidental appearance, Bonso took a further large mouthful of yet another pint and then continued his tale of the army's tried and trusted methods of knocking everyone into shape during the six-week square-bashing period.

'The first thing you learn is to keep your trap shut. Don't answer back. Salute everyone with pips on their shoulders, an' call them Sir. And get fit, because apart from learning' to march properly and runnin' here, there an' everywhere in full kit, they expect everything to be done in double quick time.

'And if you're daft enough to complain or kick up a fuss, or forget to clean your bed space, or have an untidy locker; or worse still, if you don't bull your brasses up 'til 'they shine like an angels arse, well they dish out what's known as 'jankers.' And believe me lads, I speak from experience and can tell you straight, seven days jankers cures even the hardest of cases.'

'Oh shite that for a lark,' Harry said, nervously running his hand down the back of his well-groomed D.A hairstyle.

'And you paint coal white to keep it clean, and peel more spuds than you believe possible, and flog the barrack Square 'til your feet bleed,' Bonso added. He sipped at his pint again. And you, Jimmy Reilly, they love a little 'un. So watch out for the barrack room bully, there's always one - and he leaves his henchmen to do his dirty work. Tip you out of yer bunk at three in the mornin', stand on yer bulled up boots for a laugh. That sort of thing.' I gulped at my pint and said nothing.

'And I'll never forget me medical,' Bonso continued, obviously enjoying the opportunity to emphasise the worst parts of his army experience.

'Oh Bonso,' Harry groaned, 'don't tell us about it if it's anymore bad news,' and he spluttered spilling a mouthful of bitter onto his frilly shirt and bootlace tie.

'It's not that bad, just a bit embarrassin', that's all,' Bonso said, more or less implying we were going to hear about the medical whether we wanted to or not.

'It stands to reason that you need to 'ave a proper medical before you go in. What with all that square bashin' every day from the crack of dawn. They 'ave to make sure you're not flat-footed or you 'aven't a dicky ticker,' Bonso added with an air of authority. 'I mean, you're on the square with a full pack and rifle for hours, often in the howlin' wind or pissin' rain, so it's obvious they have to check you out first.'

A long legged peroxide blonde swaggered to the bar at this point, slowly easing herself onto a long stool, just behind where Arnie was perched and crossed her legs provocatively.

'Where was I?' Bonso asked, as all our eyes strayed over Arnie's shoulder. Clocking something had happened, Arnie spun round fast to see what we were ogling and his glasses slipped down his nose and he almost fell off his seat.

As we all dragged ourselves round and focussed once more on our military informant, Bonso continued his tale. 'The medical, the one you 'ave in Civvie Street before you're called up and report to barracks, that's the one I mean.'

'Civvie Street! When d'yer get to know about that, Bonso?' Chunkie asked.

'In Harry's case, it'll be very soon,' Private Bonso said, looking at his watch and grinning at the now stricken Teddy boy

'But let me just finish tellin' you'se lads about me medical, then we'll liven the place up an' 'ave a bit of a sing song.' Bonso sneaked a shifty blimp at Blondie's legs as Arnie turned round for another look.

'I had to report to Leece Street. First thing Monday mornin', if me memory serves me right,' Bonso continued his tale. 'I checked in an' gave this po-faced Judy me appointment card, an' she told me to go into this big room at the back of the buildin'and strip off ready for the doctor's examination. What she didn't say was that there was already eight other lads in there strippin' off as well. And when we were all bollicko we stood in a line facin' the front. I had to laugh though,' Bonso said chuckling loudly; 'there we were, all complete strangers standin' bare-bollick and facing these large open windows. An' for some reason it crossed me mind wonderin' how we'd all feel if a window cleaner suddenly appeared on top of his ladder an' blimped the lot of us. What would you do if he happened to know yer? You'd never live it down, would yer? But worse still, say they had women window cleaners? There's be a friggin riot, and a few red faces and broken legs, wouldn't there?'

'Spare us the dramatics, Bonso,' Harry interrupted, and as Bonso stretched his right arm over Harrry's shoulder I could see that Bonso was really enjoying re-living his medical at Leece Street.

'Then this doctor in a white smock bowled in. He was followed by another divvie, who was pushin' a medical trolley which had all kinds of bottles and tubes and bits and pieces on it,' Bonso continued. 'The Doc began his inspection at the far end of the line, but worrever it was he was doin' I couldn't make out, not from where I was standin'. Anyway, it didn't take him long to reach me and the first thing he asked was me name, and if I'd ever had this or that wrong with me. An' all the time his sidekick took notes. Then he listened to me ticker with his stethoscope, tapped me knees and ankles with a rubber mallet, before suddenly demanding that I open my legs. He said it in such a posh voice that I shuffled me feet a couple of inches apart, when, quick as a flash, he grabbed hold of me bollocks and told me to cough.'

'Cough! Christ, Just you try it when someone's grippin' your nackers as if they were trapped in a pipe vice,' our hero said, wincing at the memory of it. We all giggled nervously

'Then he walked behind me and told me to bend over an' then he shone a torch up me arse.'

'Don't tell us any more,' Harry pleaded. But Chunkie wanted to know why should a doctor want to shine a torch up someone's arse, unless he was a pervert.

'I feel sorry for you'se poor lads, avin' to go through all that lark,' the blonde said, speaking in a broad, local accent.

Ignoring 'the' peroxide's' untimely intrusion, Bonso turned to Chunkie. 'Y'know Chunkie 'I asked the same question me'self later. An' I was told it was just to make sure your dukes weren't hangin' too low.' He paused, sipped his pint, then continued. 'An' then there's the injections.' But Harry had had enough.

'Can't we change the subject Bonso,' Harry pleaded, beads of sweat forming on his forehead. 'You know I'm next in line for the army an' with all this kind of crap, you're puttin' me off me ale.'

'How's Molly and the kids? ' I asked, trying to steer Bonso away from his confidence-boosting mission.

'A.1 Jim A.1. You wanna see the size of me young fella - our Bobby - he's massive.'

'Bobby! Why not call him Berty like yourself?' Harry said, delighted at the chance to get a bit of his own back after Bonso's deliberate mission to put the wind up him by exaggerating every detail of the medical.

'Come off it,' Bonso replied, 'you'se lot would 'ave changed your name if you'd taken the stick I did when I was at Primary School. I was always called Dirty Berty Bonson, and there's no way my lad's going to put up with that kind of crap.'

'You've got to blame your ould fella for that, Bonso,' Arnie said.

'Me ould lady more like it.'

'How is your ould fella doin' these days?' asked Chunkie.

'He's popped off.'

'What! When?' we all asked simultaneously.

'I'm sorry to hear about that,' Arnie added, 'when did he snuff it?'

As Bonso lifted yet another fresh pint from the table, he burst out laughing, splattering the creamy head of froth over Harry Burkey's jacket.

'He hasn't snuffed it you daft buggers, he's finally left me ould lady, that's all. And I don't blame 'im', Bonso chuckled. 'He sent me a note after I was called up sayin' he was havin' a dog's life. The girls and me ma were always gangin' up on him, an' every time there was an argument - which is all the time in our house - he was either getting' the blame for startin' the rows, or was bein' accused of takin' sides. So he decided to throw the towel in an' told me old girl he was thinkin' of leavin' her.'

'Don't bother thinkin' lad, ' she bawled at him. 'Piss off, an' don't forget to close the door on yer way out.'

'And when he went to collect 'is gear, she told 'im it was already packed, an' to hang on while she went upstairs to gerrit. The next thing there was a loud thud, an' when he looked outside he found his case an' all his clobber spread across the pavement.'

'Christ! That was a lousy thing to do,' Arnie said.

'He soon gorr over it. He's got 'imself a little flat off Smithdown Road an' he's happy as Larry. And don't laugh, lads,' Bonso said trying to keep a straight face, 'but he's just gone and gorr 'imself a highland jig.'

'What! A highland jig? Yer jokin'. It's not a ginger one, is it?' Harry asked. We were all in stitches at the thought of Mr B with a dead moggy slapped on top of his baldy head.

'Ginger or not, he seems to be doin' well' Bonso told us, 'cos he's latched on to a bit of fluff. And he's out dancin' with her every weekend.'

'Next time you see your old man Bonz tell 'im we'll meet him in town an' take a trip to Reeces. Maybe he could tag on to one of those ould beauties who got me an' Reilly up.

Remember that night Jimmy?' Arnie was chuckling as he recalled our tea-dance experience.

'Who could forget,' I answered.

As the night wore on we tried to outdo each others stories of our early days at Pitts, and of the indomitable Eggo, and of the tricks he got up to, and of the big influence he'd had on our lives. Snypy was also mentioned by one of the lads, though no one had a good word to say about him; especially Bonso, who'd been the main recipient of the old bully's lack of compassion when Pitts were sacking the eighteen-year-olds, and Bonso got the bullet. The last anyone had heard of Snypy was about a year previous, when Scullo came across him. He'd been arguing with a couple of ould fella's at the Pier Head over who held the rights to sit on the wooden bench nearest the water's edge, a seat he snaffled every morning for his own private use.

Y'know, with his temperament and attitude, Snypy could easily upset someone and end up floating face-down in the river,' Bonso said with relish, obviously thinking he could well be that someone, given half a chance.

The long legged blonde who earlier had tried to butt in on Bonso's tale of his army medical must have slipped out while we were telling these stories of our glory days, because now she was missing from her speck at the end of the bar. Then, just before quarter to ten, there she was again, back in the bar, easing her long legs up onto the same stool behind Arnie. But before she had chance to order the bold Arnie sprang up like a jack-in-the-box. Quick as lightning he flushed a pound note from the depths of his pocket and offered to get her a drink along with the round he was buying for us.

As the pints were being pulled, Arnie turned with a triumphant look. Before he'd even arrived back at the table, however, and Bonso could give him the benefit of his vast experience with blondes - both in the civilian and the military worlds - Blondie swallowed the large gin and tonic that the barman set before her, and was off in the direction of the toilets. Wiping the steam from his glasses with a crumpled hankie, Arnie staggered the couple of yards back to where we waited for our pints, looking very pleased with himself.

'I think I'm on to a tail there lads,' he announced in a slurred voice. 'That fella servin' behind the bar reckons she's a right good thing. So that's me fixed up for the night.'

'Don't count your chickens, ' Bonso warned. 'She is what I'd call a genuine sausage straightener that one - probably on the game too.'

'You've gorrit wrong there pal. She's too refined to be a brass nail,' Arnie retorted, the drink obviously clouding his judgement..

'It's your bacon lad,' Bonso told him with a shrug, 'but use your loaf. Look, she's bin on 'er own all night, then slips away for a bag of chips or worrever else is on the menu. Then she shows her face just in time for last orders, an' then she knocks you for a friggin large G&T. I'd say you want your ollies feeling, Arnie, fallin' for a trick like that.'

'That's what he's hopin' ter get aren't yer Arnie?' Harry chuckled.

Bonso was right as usual. After the towels were placed across the pumps and everyone had disappeared, only our small party was left in the bar. And even Arnie had to admit that Blondie, the sausage straightener, had indeed done a runner.

'Some you win, some you lose,' Bonso sympathised, placing an affectionate arm across Arnie's shoulder as we staggered along Casey Street, searching for a late night chippie.

'See yer lads - take care, and remember that in a couple of months from now I'll be a free man,' Bonso yelled at the top of his voice when the time came for us to go our separate ways.

'We're all free now, Bonso,' I yelled back. 'Don't forget none of us are shackled yet - except you, of course.'

'Bugger off Reilly,' he bellowed, as he wandered off to join his wife and kids.

Suddenly, across the gloomy and badly-lit streets, we heard a voice ring out in the darkness, reverberating and echoing beyond anything Bonso or I could achieve. Out of the past and perhaps from half a mile away, Eggo's war cry 'SO THIS IS AFRICA,' came booming out of the night to complete the evening.

Electrocution

December began with rumours circulating the site that redundancies were imminent. Despite Tanjon's having a reputation for being one of the more reasonable firms, when it came to enforcing the one- hour notice to those lads who were 'going up the road,' they used the same tough policy as other contractors. Also with the festive season creeping closer and the threat of a 'pump-list' hanging over them, many contractors opted for security and headed for the safe haven of the shipyards, an industry generally crying out for skilled labour at this time of the year. It transpired that the rumours were well founded, and when the axe was finally wielded on the second Friday of the month, most of us were surprised that it only affected eight sparks. However, showing total disregard for the firm's strict redundancy rules, a couple of the chargehands endeared themselves to the workforce by leaking the names of the eight to be given the chop on the Thursday afternoon, a gesture which gave the lads involved a reasonable chance to contact prospective employers during the course of the Friday.

Meanwhile, I was now entering the final three months of my time and despite my optimism that I'd be inundated with calls from shipping lines clambering for my signature, the sparse responses that landed on the mat were all negative knockbacks

As the beginning of the Christmas period approached, Robbo surprised me, and, I suspect, a few others when he arrived one morning carrying a brand new wooden toolbox with the initials J.R prominently displayed in bold brass letters. The box, painted black, complete with small draws for drill bits, had been made by a joiner, a fellow drinking colleague of Robbo's, who shared his company most evenings in the Castle bar.

I was made up by the present and could hardly wait to swap my tools from the tattered army haversack, salvaged some months earlier from the site dump, though most of what I had were rusted relics

'You've got some decent plant here, Reilly,' Podgy Hogan remarked sarcastically, stretching his flabby neck to inspect my humble possessions. 'What was that you were puttin' in there just now - a knife, fork, spoon - and screwdriver?'

'An' worrabout the two pound hammer and that rusty file that went missin' from the stores a few weeks ago?' Jimmy 'H' joked, keen to get in on the act. 'I spotted you Reilly,' he jeered, 'sneakin' them in your toolbox when you thought no one was lookin'.

'An' what happened to those drill bits that seem to'ave done a runner from the workshop?' someone else yelled from way down the cabin.

'In a few weeks time I'll 'ave a better set of tools than the whole lorr of yer put together,' I retaliated, striding out of the cabin in a huff and slamming the door, my tantrum bringing an immediate burst of applause from the lads.

As the cold morning air whipped into my sweating brow I walked a couple of yards, then stopped dead in my tracks. 'What are you doin' slammin' the door, you soft bugger,' I muttered to myself, as I recalled Robbo's words of wisdom, 'that you have to be able to take the flak, as well as dish it out.'

Turning sharply on my heels I flung open the door grinning like a Cheshire cat, and yelled 'Now then, which one of you lads wants the pleasure of workin' with me today.'

There was no response, so I yelled again, 'be careful you don't all get crushed in the rush lads. Or better still, toss a coin if you can't make your minds up.' The only offer to come my way, however, was from Nipper Hollerhead, the youngest apprentice on site.

Within minutes the chargehands trundled into the cabin, all set to move us out and onto the job as quickly as possible, ready for yet another shift.

'Right young fella me lad,' Sailor Waverley bellowed, 'you're joining my crew for your first proper voyage on the crown jewels.'

Hearing these magical words, a feeling of pride rose up inside my chest as I lifted the brand new toolbox onto my shoulder to hump it to the site. But half-way across the rugged cinder path that led to the mill, I felt a slight tug at the toolbox, and spun round to find George Sharkey treading suspiciously in my shadow. I knew straight away I was a victim, and that he'd fitted a tail; he just couldn't resist a soft touch. When he mumbled he had something for me, seeing I was almost a spark, I stopped to listen. Like everyone, I was wary of anything George offered, though on this occasion he almost seemed genuine and sincere. Then, with a mischievous smile on his face, he began unwrapping a newspaper package to reveal a rusty cold chisel, an old rat-tail file and a worn out wire brush, which he told me he'd found on the girders after Plonker had sent him up to remove a few pigeons nests.

'They probably belonged to some long forgotten painter,' I thought to myself, 'and about as much use as a wet Echo.'

'Here you go, now remember to take good care of these Reilly,' he said. 'And seeing I'm lookin' after you like an older brother, perhaps you could ask Sailor if I can work with yer to give you the benefit of my worldly experience.'

'But I don't want to be a professional 'tail-or' George, I wanna be a spark,' I said, laughing at his feeble attempt to bribe me into helping him escape from his prolonged exile in the cable gang. To appease him, and get him off my back, I promised to have a word to see if Sailor would allow him to team up with me, although I didn't have much hope of success.

'No chance,' Sailor replied firmly, when I mentioned Sharkey's name. 'I'll get bugger all done if you'se pair are workin' together.'

A few minutes later we stopped at the top of the stairs leading from the rear entrance of the mill to the cellar where I'd be working. 'You can drop your gear down the hold Jimmy,' Sailor said, pointing to the dank, rat infested place where very few worker would willingly venture. Then, after showing me the best way to tackle the job, I was left to set about wiring the lights in the 'starboard' section of the dungeon that ran beneath the main passageway of the mill.

By late afternoon on the Wednesday Sailor casually mentioned that it was perhaps too much to expect a young lad to spend long days talking to himself, and shortly after four o'clock he brought along a delighted Nipper to assist me.

On the following Monday morning, keen to show off my abilities and sense of responsibility I began the task of training Nipper, using the same techniques I'd been taught by Robbo, even though my new found enthusiasm brought sniggers from Chunkie and Billy Constable. They seemed to think I was going too far with my keenness and passion, but undeterred by their snide remarks I carried on giving Nipper the benefit of my vast experience.

At the start of a shift, the first task for any apprentice or a mate would be to head for the compound to collect the tools for their respective tradesmen. They'd then cart the toolbox to the cabin, and if it was bulky or heavy, slip a piece of conduit through the handle to allow it to be carried jointly. Nipper had managed to do this easily on the Monday and Tuesday, but on Wednesday he returned to the cabin empty handed and looking frustrated.

'What's happened? Where's me crown jewels?' I asked

'I don't know why, Jim,' he replied despondently, 'but for some reason I can't lift the tools off the deck.'

'It's probably all that old junk and the bits of metal you've been collectin' all week,' Podgy Hogan laughed. Ignoring him, I strode out of the cabin and headed to the compound, with Nipper a yard or two behind me. As usual, the tool cabin was chock-a-block when we arrived, so we hung round waiting for the crowd to move out and when the shack emptied, we ambled in. My box was still lying in the corner where I'd left it the night before, so I bent down and grabbed hold of the handle. Despite yanking with all my might, I failed to lift it even a midge's off the floor. Bugsy Corker, who was standing by the door watching me struggle, stepped back inside the shack, knelt down and taking a large screwdriver he prised up the bottom corner of the box before peering underneath.

'It looks as though someone's screwed your box to the deck, lad,' he said with a sigh.

'You're jokin'.'

'No lad, it's well an' truly fixed. Kneel down 'ere an' have a decko yourself if you don't believe me. And if you were to ask who the culprit's likely to be, then I'd be inclined to say - no names - no pack drill - but look no further than the fella sittin' almost opposite Billy Chancer in our cabin. D'yer follow me drift lad?'

'Sharkey,' I muttered to myself angrily. 'One of these fine days George, I'll set you up good style; you just wait and see.'

Christmas and the New Year breezed in and breezed out, with the usual booze-ups and parties; then it was all hands to the pumps as the second week of January approached. By now I was excuding confidence with an abundance of knowledge under my belt from working in different gangs, and because I was entering the final weeks of my apprenticeship, Bootsy concluded that it was time for a final polish. In order to extend my experience, he decided I was ready to carry out a priority job in a contractor's compound at the far side of the Fibre factory.

As this venture was away from the main body of men - and mainly to keep an eye on me - Teddy Roberts, one of the older and trusted mates, was seconded to help out with the job. Before we began, however, Bootsy took us to the site to explain how the installation had been set-up. Apart from instructions on how to tackle the job, he identified the route of the overhead power supply which began in the Fibre factory and was then looped on wooden poles stretching into what was called Matthew Hall's compound.

Trooping along a wet and muddy road we headed through a pair of metal gates onto a path that led us to the main distribution board and all the ancillaries that went with it. These had been installed between two of the larger cabins and were well protected from the weather. To complete his brief visit, Bootsy finally popped his head into a Nissan hut, pointing to a thick black cable, the crucial part of the job to be undertaken. We then trudged back to our end of the site to fetch the tools and gather other bits and pieces needed for the task.

After finishing our morning tea break, and having collected the necessary gear for the job, we once again set off for Matty Hall's compound. This time though, because Bootsy was no longer tagging along with us, we moseyed through the Fibre factory so I could weigh up the talent. Of course, Teddy had seen it all before and knew all my tricks. So while I deliberately strayed from the main walkway to mooch at a new batch of girls, he ambled behind, smoking a fag, hoping to pick up any tit-bit of conversation that might suggest I was in with a chance.

We finally arrived at the compound just as the Matty's workers were having their eleven o'clock break. With having time on our hands we dropped our gear by the switchboard then traipsed round, curious to see what kind of set-up they had, and whether there were any short cuts to the main road, similar to the one we'd used when our cabin was across this part of the site. After nosing round the joint as if we owned it, we then popped into the workshop where Teddy stopped to pass the time of day with a couple of mates from the Dingle. Eventually, we came to a large, cold, damp, semi-circular corrugated Nissen hut, now in the process of being converted to accommodate the management team. This was the spot where I'd be jointing the cable to provide a new power feed that would allow them brighten and warm the place up.

As soon as the cabins had been emptied, we began the first stage of our task by scrutinising the over-head feeders dangling some twenty feet from the poles. Once inside the compound we followed their route back to the main switchboard to complete the first of our operations. After tackling the auxiliary board which was already crammed tight with cables and removing the front covers, we tried tracing them through a tangled mess back to a set of isolators fitted in the bottom section.

Before knocking the power off, and to make sure there was sufficient hot water for the dinner-time brew, Teddy nipped round to the mess hut to explain to the Peggies we were about to switch the juice off for roughly half an hour. As soon as he returned, and because we were still concerned about the unusual number of cables packed inside the board, we decided to play safe and to switch off every isolator in sight. Satisfied that all circuits in the compound were now dead, we then made our way to the Nissen hut to carry out the task of breaking into the main feeder.

With the power isolated, and only a couple of windows and the open doorway to provide us with light, we entered the hut and were made up to discovered that part of the main cable was conveniently routed round the wall at chest height, so there was no need to use a step ladder.

Like all good and experienced mates, Teddy had laid out my tools beside the job.

'Okay Ted, I yelled, 'let's get this show on the road, my voice crackling with confidence, mainly for the benefit of a Matty Hall's civil engineer, who was perched at a desk a few feet away munging into a bag of fish and chips. Looking up from his newspaper he grinned and winked across at me as I began nibbling away at the cable. Using an extra large pair of un-insulated pliers, I could feel the damp from the concrete floor penetrating my cheap and well-worn shoes, and I remember chatting to Teddy as he leaned against an old metal cabinet, warbling on about something or other.

Suddenly there was an almighty explosion followed by a blinding flash, and I went hurtling backwards through the air, screaming like a demented demon heading towards the gates of hell. My back and shoulders clattered some way up the opposite wall, and then I began to slide slowly to the floor, my eyes open and transfixed, my mouth and jaw jammed wide and rigid.

As stiff as a board, I lay prostrate on the floor, while poor old Teddy almost collapsed on the spot and the engineer, choking on his chips, shot out of his chair. As the power dipped some of the factory lights went out, and a large part of the site was plunged into darkness. Hearing distressing screams coming from the Nissen hut, following the almighty sound of the explosion, a couple of Matty's workmen had already dashed from the compound to summon the Bowies nurse and to phone for an ambulance.

The loss of power in part of the building, together with the emergence of the nurse and the sight of two contractors dashing towards the door was enough to convince most of the factory workers that some kind of accident had taken place. From what I was told later, the bush telephone broke all records that day, with news of the accident travelling faster than the speed of light. When it was rumoured that Nobby Alcock's young side-kick was the victim, all the girls whose machines had been affected by the black-out, congregated at the entrance facing the compound to check on the buzz ; something which chuffed me no end when I heard about it.

Bootsy, who was first to hear the news, had hurtled out of the site office like a man possessed and almost flattened old Tom Perry who was carrying two buckets of cold water for the tea urns. Without stopping to apologise Bootsy leapt into his old convertible and roared off disappearing within seconds in a cloud of dust..

'Christ what was all that about?' Tom muttered as he'd struggled towards the cabin, but stopped in his tracks when he'd heard voices from the site office discussing my demise. Resting his half-empty buckets on the deck, he'd strained to gather details and thought he'd heard the term 'electrocution' being mentioned. At this moment the appearance of young Nipper Hollerhead jogged him back to reality.

'Nipper come 'ere a minute,' he beckoned excitedly. 'I've just heard that your mate, Jimmy Reilly's been electrocuted.'

'No!?' Nipper cried, when Tom told him what he'd just heard, and how Bootsy had taken off like a rocket. Dropping a full bottle of Tizer on the deck, my young mate then legged it towards the queues where everyone was waiting for the hooter to give the go-ahead for the dinner break to commence. Within seconds Nipper was among the queues yelling, 'Reilly's dead. He's been electrocuted.'

Everything went deathly quiet, but when Robbo saw tears running down Nipper's cheeks he knew something really serious had taken place, and that immediate action was required. Followed by Podgy, he broke from the queue, triggering a chain reaction as a dozen or more of the fittest workers dashed towards the site huts. Reaching the end of the cinder path their worst fears were confirmed as they clocked a number of the office workers standing in groups conversing with the peggies. Sailor Waverley, looking grim and dejected, came out of the main office to tell Robbo I was being attended by a nurse and a doctor, and that an ambulance was standing by to whiz me off to the Cottage hospital. Hearing this, Robbo and a number of the lads dashed to the main gate, arriving there just as I was being carted off at great speed.

From what Chunkie said later the cabins were like morgues that day, as the workforce waited for the stewards appearance and the inevitable 'half-chop' - the unscheduled end to normal work when a fatality occurs.

Timmy M'Cain, who was first away after hearing Nipper's devastating news had arrived at the cabin with tears in his eyes, his face tripping him.

'Worr ave yer heard?' Podgy asked urgently.

'I saw them carry poor Jimmy into the ambulance on the stretcher, but all I could see was the top of his head,' he cried.

'Are you sure the blankets were coverin' his face?' Robbo asked.

'Yeah, 'onest ter God. All I could see was his hair and feet.'

My demise, it seemed, had a devastating effect on those closest to me. Billy Chancer wailed that he was feeling emotionally sick and had baulked nervously as he searched his lunchbox for a Rennie or an aspirin, something that Maisie - with an almost uncanny insight - always slipped inside his bag when she predicted he was about to have a bad day.

For once it seemed Jimmy 'H' couldn't find the inspiration to muster any worthwhile quips to raise the spirits of his colleagues.

P&W burped, followed by a rasper, but no one passed comment.

Robbo kept muttering about the number of times he'd emphasised to me the dangers of cutting into a cable without properly testing it.

Podgy Hogan swallowed four boiled eggs on the trot, without a thought for his doctor's advice concerning his weight problem.

Billy the Minge had been inconsolable, moaning about the loss of half day's pay, and the possibility of having to donate a further full day's wage to the deceased - a figure usually recommended by the stewards

Willie the Spook had tried in vain to meditate, hoping to contact his guide to find out if there was any sign yet of a scally named Reilly landing on the other side.

Sid Shortwick, for once, had nothing to say, until Crusthead McGinty asked how many volts were needed to see you off. 'In your case it would be about ten,' Sid replied sarcastically.

Chinless, tugging nervously at a clump of stubble aggravating his Adam's apple, had pulled too hard at it and nearly swallowed his false teeth.

Surprisingly, I heard later that Chunkie was the calmest in

the cabin, declaring that he'd known me for years, and I was like a cat with nine lives. 'Besides,' he said, 'I borrowed ten bob off Reilly last week, an' there's no chance of him popping off with me owing him that much.'

I also heard that there'd been similar reflections from Tanjon's other cabin.

Nobby Alcock recalled the time he'd left me stranded in the Port. Though his guilty conscience hadn't lasted long, when he'd lustily returned to the present wondering loudly 'if the nurse who tried to resuscitate Jim was wearing suzzies.'

The Pope, clasping his hands had prayed aloud, muttering 'God help him Lord.' Coming at it from an entirely different angle, Trunkie Davies worried about the girls in my life and how they would react now that I was no longer on this planet - and whether he might be the person to step in and console them.

George Sharkey missed it all. He was attending the doctors, getting his piles seen to. This was caused, as the lads said, by sitting too long on the cold girders waiting to bomb some unsuspecting victim with the bags of contaminated flour, supplied by his mate from Rank's flour mill.

Eventually, the chargehands converged on the cabin and the place went quiet, but as there was no further news to report, the lads continued their reminiscences. It was noted that Bob wasn't whistling, and although Plonker Parson still had his right hand in his trouser pocket, he kept it motionless, which was assumed to be his way of showing respect.

Meanwhile, as the ambulance sped away towards the Cottage hospital, the front wheel hit a large crater in the road with such a force that I was catapulted into the air from the stretcher. Landing back in a heap on the hairy blankets, I began to shake like a pneumatic drill, my heart pounding relentlessly. Suddenly I found I could blink my eyes and move my jaw, and started yelling as loud as I could. Bootsy and the doctor, who had been flung across the back end of the ambulance and onto the floor, leapt up and grabbed hold of me, though they couldn't stop me trembling or my teeth chattering.

At the hospital I was immediately stretchered into casualty and examined by two doctors. Bootsy, still shaking from the on-going drama, stayed outside to smoke a fag to calm his nerves. After pacing up and down the pathway for a few minutes he eventually plucked up courage to come back inside where the doctor told him I was suffering from severe shock. However, because I was young and healthy it seemed there was every expectation I would make a full recovery. In the meantime, I was to stay in hospital for a few days while they kept me under observation.

Bootsy then drove back to the site in record time and headed straight for the management office, his first priority being to inform the site agent - Cockney Jack - of my condition. The news was then relayed to the shop stewards who immediately contacted their compatriots representing the other contractors on the site, telling them a 'half-chop' wouldn't be necessary after all.

Alf Wilson, the senior shop steward, made his way to the main cabin, while his deputy slipped across to the other shack to inform the lads to move next door for an update on the accident. Eager to hear the latest news, everyone had quickly shuffled in besides their fellow workers.

'Right brothers. First priority, and this is straight from the horses mouth. The lad's goin' to be okay, 'Alf announced. 'That's the good news.'

An excited and relieved murmur rang round the cabin as the steward continued. 'From what Bootsy tells me it's nothing short of a miracle that Reilly survived at all. Now I'm not in receipt of all the facts yet, but from what I can gather he sliced through a mains cable carryin' a full load current; enough to see off a herd of African elephants never mind a bloody nine stone stripplin'. And brothers, this is only second hand, but he managed to do it without getting frizzled or burnt in any way.'

Again an excited gaggle of voices reverberated around the cabin. 'Order brothers, order,' the deputy yelled, and as soon as silence was restored Alf announced that in view of the seriousness of the incident an official meeting would be called immediately after dinner hour, when he expected to be able to relay the full facts of the case.

Once the stewards departed, the sound of laughter soon replaced the sombre atmosphere that had prevailed only a few minutes earlier, with a cheerful clatter of cups rattling amongst the din of the excited conversations.

Billy the Minge, by far the most jubilant of the squad, roared above the noise, 'By God Reilly gave the bloody lorr of us a shock there lads, didn't he? Christ, hearing he was dead could've sent us all to the hozzie with nervous breakdowns.'

'You're right there Billy' Jimmy 'H' replied. 'You'd 'ave been admitted straight away - not with your nerves though - but for an operation on your wallet'

Like everyone else, the apprentices were overjoyed by the news.

'It could 'ave been any of us,' Timmy McCain said, polishing the rosy side of a huge apple on the arm of his jersey, then sinking his teeth right into the core. Chunkie, of course, had a smug smile on his face. 'What did I tell yer,' he chuckled. 'I know Reilly better than anyone. And it'll take more than four forty volts to see him off, particularly with me owin' him a tenner.'

The union meeting took place directly after an extended dinner break, with Teddy Roberts, still looking pale and ill, plonked right at the front of the cabin alongside the stewards and committee members. Placing a well-worn pair of glasses on his Roman nose, Alf Wilson tilted them first up then down, until they were straight. Then, grasping a bundle of notes he rose to his feet and with more than a touch of anger began to address the meeting.

'You're goin' to find this hard to believe, brothers,' he began icily - 'but that cable young Reilly sliced into had its own local isolator, way across the road, in the bloody factory! of all places.'

'Y'mean it had its own direct feed?' Robbo roared.

'Correct brother.' A direct feed, that passed straight through the distribution board in Matty's compound. And, as Teddy here will tell yer, young Reilly had followed procedure by knocking off all the isolators before he began. That's right, isn't Ted?'

'Spot on Alf, spot on,' Teddy answered, his voice barely audible to those sitting near the back.

'Excuse me interrupting', said Billy the Minge, 'but I think poor old Teddy should be taken home, after the trauma he's been through. You never know, he could very well keel over and we'd have another casualty on our hands,' he added quickly.

'I've no intention of keelin' over at this moment in time,' Teddy answered sharply. Ignoring the interruption from Billy, and with his voice rising in anger, Alf continued his report. 'Apart from being bloody dangerous practice, it doesn't conform to I.E.E regulations in any way, place or form. So all I can say - and I know you'se lads would agree - but for the grace of God we're lucky we haven't got a fatality on our hands.'

'Hear, 'ear,' said Billy the Minge; and as Chunkie told me later, he could have sworn the old minge bag even blessed himself.

Podgy Hogan then leapt to his feet, demanding to know the name of the culprit who'd installed the supply, and what action would be taken against him.

A heated debate followed with everyone voicing their furious concerns, as to how some cowboy outfit could operate on site, and perhaps get away with not being penalised. The next item discussed related to the need to get Tanjon's to vindicate Teddy's reputation and to exonerate me from any blame. This, the stewards claimed, was just a formality.

Finally, before the lads dispersed, someone proposed having a whip-round to me buy a few odds and ends to help me on my road to recovery.

At this point Billy the Minge almost caused a few fatalities when he produced a two bob bit, startling everyone by declaring, 'here you go lads, I'll set the ball rollin' for young Reilly's collection.'

That night as I stretched out on my bed gathering my wits amongst a ward full of older fella's, suffering from hernias and heart attacks, a bell rang and the visitors began arriving. To be honest, I wasn't really expecting anyone. It was a tidy trip on public transport from Woodchurch to the Port, so I closed my eyes, and tried dozing off; then suddenly I felt a massive hand grip my foot and shake it like a rag doll.

'Come on Shorty, wake up, you're not dead yet,' a gruff but familiar voice rang in my ears. When I opened my eyes I nearly passed out with fright, for standing at the side of the bed towering above me like some V.I.P bodyguard was the bold and fearsome Rocky.

She must have noticed the colour drain from my face, because the first thing she did was to slip a box of chocolates from a brown paper bag and place them on the top of my locker. 'There you are,' she said, in that loud, gravel voice that had terrified me in the past. 'Unlike some I could mention, I don't forget me friends easily, and as I only live round the corner I thought I'd pop in an' see what damage you've done to yourself.' She then plonked herself down on the side of the bed, which dipped significantly under the extra pressure.

I said nothing, but I thought to myself. 'Me? A friend of Rocky's?' That's worth remembering.

'Christ Reilly, what d'yer think you were playin' at. D'yer know you nearly closed the bloody factory down altogether with your heroics,' she rattled on. 'Everyone thought you'd snuffed it. I couldn't believe you had so many fans until I heard all the yellin' that was goin' on.'

'It wasn't by choice Rocky, it was just an accident,' I muttered, my heart beating, ten to the dozen.

'I don't expect we'll see your friend Nobby Alcock out here tonight,' she said carefully, arousing my curiosity with her sudden change of tone.

'Nobby Alcock, The boss poser? There's no chance of him coming, unless he's gorra bit of skirt lined up,' I said. Rocky looked at me in a funny, almost angelic way, which left me wondering for a second if perhaps, I was hallucinating. What she said next gave me almost as big a shock as my electrocution had.

'I'll let you into a little secret Jimmy,' she whispered, moving her giant gnashers close to my ear. 'We've been seein' each other on an' off for the past six months, and when Norman gets his divorce through we're thinking of getting' hitched.'

To say I was shocked would be the understatement of the year. I almost had to pinch myself to check I wasn't dreaming.

'Hitched..you, ..an'.. Nobby,' I gasped, looking into her cold, dark calculating eyes, and all the while trying to find a suitable complimentary reply that wouldn't get me into lumber. But even as my fumbled brain searched in vain, she beat me to it.

'Don't bother with sweet talk or congratulations Reilly,

just remember to tell all your mates not to book any holidays next year. And if he lets me down, then take it from me this hospital will be the first of many such places he'll end up in. I'll guarantee that.'

'I believe yer,' I muttered to myself as she playfully tapped my head and swaggered out of the ward, yelling over her shoulder that she'd pop in later in the week to see me if I was still in.

Afterwards, I lay trying to fathom how Nobby had managed to cop off with Rocky after the mauling she'd given him earlier in the year. 'He's got to be stringin her along,' I thought. But then again, I knew she was more than capable of seeing him off altogether if he messed her around. And as I concluded, with the death penalty having recently been abolished she wouldn't swing for it and could easily do fifteen years standing on her head. Finally, I turned over and dropped off to a fitful sleep, vividly recalling my own encounter with the Queen of the 'Sacky' when I'd first wandered through the factory and strayed into her territory without permission.

After a couple of days lying round doing nothing in particular, my confinement came to an abrupt end when I was declared fit for action and allowed to return home. From what I heard later, Jimmy 'H' had been spot on with his prediction that I'd only be in hospital for two days. This was in reply to Crusthead, who'd asked how long he reckoned it would take to discharge me. To which, Jimmy 'H' had come straight back with the quip, 'roughly two days at a rate of a quarter of an amp per hour.'

During the time I was recuperating at home, enjoying my enforced holiday, the accident seemed to become an inspiration for several budding poets. The first ode to appear on the wall of the other cabin was probably written by Nobby Alcock or one of his cronies, and was sung to the tune of Bobby Shafto.

> *Jimmy Reilly almost died,*
> *Chopped a cable nearly fried,*
> *All the girls broke down and cried,*
> *Poor old Jimmy Reilly.*

Not to be outdone by the low life in the other cabin, the apprentices in our shack had then released their own combined effort to their eager public.

> *Jimmy Reilly's tale of woe,*
> *Sliced a main and stopped the flow,*
> *All is dark but he's aglow,*
> *Poor old Jimmy Reilly.*

So popular and so constantly repeated were these odes that Bob Baines spent most days whistling the tune over again. Ironically, not one of his squad was able to turn him off and steer him away from the Bobby Shafto tune, a task that would have been easy in the past.

On the following Monday, a week to the day since I'd brightened up the atmosphere and darkened part of the Fibre plant, I returned to work wearing a cumbersome pair of rubber soled boots. These not only increased my height by an extra inch and a half, but were guaranteed to protect me from the hazards of any stray or extraneous currents that happened to be lurking around.

With Chunkie on one side and Timmy the other I moseyed into the cabin in my usual nonchalant manner, grinning broadly and acting as if nothing had happened. Immediately I was knocked back by a rapturous round of applause. Chunkie grabbed hold of my wrist and raised it like a referee lifting a boxer's hand in victory.

It was then that I piped my toolbox resting on a spare table under the window at the far end of the cabin, clean as a whistle and looking as if someone had taken the trouble to polish it ready for my return.

As the noise subsided I made my way towards my prized possession, then realised everyone seemed to be waiting for a reaction, or for me to say something.

Just then I spotted a crude cross made from two pieces of wooden batten, propped against my box. Bending down I read out the inscription in a loud clear voice.

Reilly with pliers,
Electric wires,
Blue flashes,
Reilly's ashes.
R.I.P.

After repeating the details of how I'd almost made an early celestial arrival and thanking my colleagues for their generous collection of four pounds, six shillings and three pence, I was summoned to the office. There, Jack and Bootsy informed me that I was totally blameless for the accident and would be paid a full week's wage. This gesture, according to the stewards, was the least the firm could do, considering it was one of their own sub-contractors who'd had been responsible for fitting the dodgy installation in the first place.

With the talk and banter regarding my electrocution taking centre stage I still hadn't mentioned the startling news of Rocky's relationship with Nobby Alcock. The following day, as I made my way to the stores, I suddenly blimped the Boss Poser heading in the same direction. Catching him up, I mentioned Rocky's visit to the hospital, which immediately slowed him down considerably. In a round about way I then let slip how she'd revealed their date's together and future plans - which, naturally, I exaggerated. This, of course, stopped him dead in his tracks, and as I stood back and watched the colour drain from his face, I felt quite chuffed with my performance.

'Don't talk daft Reilly! With all those classy Judy's workin' there to choose from, d'yer think I'd lower me standards an' go out with the likes of Rocky? Christ lad, I wouldn't fight her, never mind goose her.' But I knew he was bluffing and playing the big shot because his colour still hadn't returned.

'Why would she talk about weddin' dresses, an' bridesmaids an' all that then?' I asked; and this rattled him badly.

'Weddin' dresses? You're kiddin' me! What else did she tell yer Jim? 'he asked, placing his hand on my shoulder and guiding me into an empty doorway near the stores.

'She told me to tell your mates not to book their holidays next year, just in case it clashes with the big day' I said, slightly exaggerating on what the formidable Rocky had said. Nobby squirmed as he tried to convince me that there was perhaps, some mis-understanding, or that maybe she'd lost her marbles.

'Just weigh it up yourself lad, I'm not even divorced yet. An' once is more than enough for any normal fella to put up with. Another thing, can you imagine me being drivin' round in me danny with the likes of Rocky perched in the front seat? No way lad, no way. It would definitely cramp me style and ruin my image.'

'Anyway Jim, remember we go back a long way me and you. So do me a favour, an' don't mention a word to anyone about the lies she's told yer,' he pleaded. 'Can I rely on you pal?' he said, grabbing my hand with his sweaty palm and shaking it limply.

'I suppose so,' I said, 'but what happens if I bump into Rocky when I'm over at the cannie. I can't very well ignore her after all the chocolates she brought into the hozzie, now can I?'

'You're a smart lad Jimmy. Use your loaf and play it cool, just play it cool,' he said wandering slowly away, his head bowed low, weighed down no doubt with a combination of pressure and lies.

Two days later, on the Wednesday, Plonker Parson's broke the news that he was about to lose one of his best worker's, Nobby Alcock. Without a word to any of his workmates, Nobby had handed in is his notice and was heading down south to work on a nuclear power station for N.G.Bailey's.

As dinner hour approached, and with this latest news tucked under my belt, I slipped across to Bowies canteen hoping to see Rocky. But by the time I got there, she'd been and gone. On the Friday, I deliberately waited outside the canteen opposite the Sack factory entrance until Rocky eventually appeared and watched, as she plonked herself on one of the huge paper reels that a stacker-truck driver had just dropped off. Glaring across she stuffed two fingers from each hand into either side of her mouth, and whistled two sharp notes, which I acknowledging by raising my right thumb. I took a deep breath and then ambled across, not at all sure of the reception I would get now that Nobby had done a runner.

'Sit there, Reilly,' she ordered, so I climbed up and sat besides her, feeling like little Stan Laurel perched next to the oversized Oliver Hardy.

'A little bird tells me you've been spoutin' on about the private conversation we had at the Cottage Hospital,' she said, staring me in the face, her jaw wide-open showing her bent and twisted bottom teeth.

'Honest ter God, I didn't know it was meant to be a secret, Rocky,' I pleaded, knowing full well just how precarious my position was, balanced up on a paper reel some five foot or more above the deck.

'Don't worry lad, it wasn't meant to be,' she said smiling, almost breaking into chuckle. I felt a nervous laugh coming over me, but I managed to suppress it until I was completely satisfied that her smile wasn't because she was suffering from a bad dose of wind or indigestion.

'Y'see, I got the bastard at last,' she said grinning broadly. And so, with a feeling I was really treading on safe ground now, I followed suit and chuckled openly. 'You mean to say it was all a pack of lies about you an' Nobby goin'out together?' I asked.

'No, not all of it. But the bit about us getting hitched was. You see, I'd collared the creep moochin' outside the cannie one day, and I told him his life wouldn't be worth a fart in a tea cup if he didn't take me out. An' guess what?'

'He took you out,' I said.

'He did just that. But I wouldn't let the greasy turd near me with a friggin' barge pole. It was only after I told him I was saving myself for me weddin' night that he started giving me the bull-shit about getting' hitched when he was a free man. As if I'd fall for that kind of crap.'

'Bloody hell,' I whispered to myself, stunned by what I'd heard - 'she's a virgin.' Even as I said this, I realised I'd spoken in more than a whisper, and in desperation, I bit on my tongue hoping my words would come out in a garbled and incoherent way.

Rocky didn't seem to notice though, as she ploughed on with her version of events. 'But of course he was knockin' off a few others at the same time, including our Josie. 'And he didn't know they couldn't be trusted to keep their mouths shut about his divorce, or his empty promises of buying engagement rings. I wasn't bothered though, 'cos by then he was well and truly hooked. And so as I strung him along I made sure it cost him a small fortune every time he came to the Port to see me, hammering him for large gin's and tonics all night.' She smiled another crooked grin at the recollection. And because you did it the hard way and nearly got frizzled Jimmy, you happened to be the means of me getting' rid of that cock-sure bastard once an' for all.'

'Me?' I said, edging closer to my new found friend.

'Yes you Reilly.' An' get that skinny little arse of yours back where it belongs,' she said, nudging me with the side of her massive thigh. 'So you see, for the price of a mingy box of chocolates, we've managed to get rid of Nob- head Alcock for good.'

'And Reilly,' she said, gripping me like a grizzly bear, 'from now on you've got the freedom of the Sack factory. But, remember,' she cautioned, 'keep well away from our Josie, me twin sister.'

'Your twin sister!' I stuttered. 'I will Rocky, I will,' I replied, going a bit overboard in the gratitude I was showing her for the warning. 'And, by the way,' she added as I scarpered back towards the safety of Tanjon's site huts, that also goes for any of the younger girls that I might fancy.'

Meanwhile I was happy to be back in Whistling Bob's gang working alongside Billy Chancer, who, for once, had stopped offering me any more fatherly advice. And, of course, I was now extra vigilant whenever I was near to or likely to come into contact with live equipment; and my tester never left my side.

Curtains

'I wonder whereabouts we'll be this time next year?' I said to Chunkie as the number ten bus clattered over the cobbles by the Duke Street Bridge making its way to New Brighton. It was the last week in January and we were on our way to the Pier Hotel to meet Billy Constable and Timmy McCain. With less than a month to go before I finished my apprenticeship, Chunkie had come up with the idea of giving the Tower ballroom the 'once over' as a change from our normal routine and hangouts, reminding me 'to make hay while the sun shines 'cos there's not many days left on the calendar for nights out on the town.'

As we kind of expected, the pub was heaving with bodies when we got there, but it didn't take long for us to get organised with a decent space by the bar. After downing a couple of swift pints we joined in the action, and within minutes, we were wallowing in the highly charged atmosphere that only Saturday nights at The Pier seemed capable of providing.

It was a great night and we were in tip-top form, laughing and joking and falling all over the place, when suddenly we realised it was a quarter to ten. Having feasted all night on a concoction of Black Velvets, a mix of Guinness and cider, followed by rum and pep chasers, we left the Pier to stagger up the short, steep hill to the Tower ballroom.

We could see the bouncers weighing us up as we approached the last half dozen steps to the entrance and judging by the scowls on their grim looking faces, there seemed a strong possibility we'd be back-heeled. Then, Timmy, the most sober in our party, stepped forward and somehow managed to convince them there was no one in our small team capable of causing trouble. Compared to the usual gangs of hard-knocks who rolled up at the week-ends, ready to test the water, we were like mice.

After paying the entrance fee and receiving our tickets from the cloakroom attendant, we traipsed into the ballroom full of confidence and glowing with effects of the booze. The place, as usual, was chock - a - block, with the regulars hugging the prime spaces in front of the band. Meanwhile, all we could do was shuffle around the perimeter of the hall, weighing up the talent and trying our best not to reveal the state we were in.

With the amount of ale I'd supped, coupled with the intense heat rising from the throngs of dancers and spectators, and my head now spinning like a top, I swayed unsteadily as I wandered amongst the crowds, until somehow or other I landed at the back of the stage, behind the band. Leaning against, what seemed like a marble type pillar, my blurred eyes followed the spotlights flashing from corner to corner, then from floor to ceiling; until, like a ray from heaven, it hovered invitingly over the one empty chair in the back row of the hall, flanked on either side by two gorgeous girls.

Setting off in a mad and drunken state, I staggered, stumbled and lurched sideways, until, sprawling clumsily, I fell across the empty seat; my sole intention, to snatch forty winks before my legs packed in altogether. Instead of nodding off though, I sat for ages staring ahead, talking gibberish, unable to stop my head falling onto my chest, until eventually I crashed out.

In no time at all I was trotting out on the lush green grass of Goodison Park' in front of a 70,000 crowd who were all yelling 'Come on Jimmy lad show us what you can do.' The noise was deafening. I could hear the sound of sweet music drifting softly in my ears, and there I was - flying down the right wing - cutting into the penalty area - heading straight for goal – with the keeper hopelessly committed - and no one to beat. Then - just as I was about to put the ball in the empty net - I was punched savagely in the ribs, and brought down. Before I had time to scream 'foul ref, penno,' I heard a defender yell in a high pitched voice, 'hey lad, 'ave yer 'ad your dinner yet?'

'Dinner? Wha..wha... what d'yer mean like?... 'I think so..I think so,' I stuttered, as my bleary eyes stared at a bunch of hostile, shadowy faces.

'Well try leanin' on your own for a change lad,' the wallflower sitting next to me growled, before elbowing me once again in the ribs.

I took the hint and staggered away towards the dance floor, searching for the lads. When I reached the front, I could hardly believe my eyes - the night had flown and everyone was lined up waiting for the compere to announce the last waltz and the band to strike up.

As the waltzers circled, clinging together and the lights

dimmed, my bloodshot peepers frantically scanned the dance floor, until finally they rested on the huge mahogany clock hanging between the top of the main doors and the ornate gold painted ceiling coves.

'Christ! It's twenty to twelve, I'll miss me last bus if I don't get a move on, 'I stuttered, dashing into the crowded cloakroom where a long queue had formed.

With just over ten minutes before the number ten left the terminal, I knew it was touch and go as to whether I'd make it, or again have to face the prospect of relying on my trusted right thumb to get me home. As I searched my pockets for the cloakroom ticket, I spotted the lads way up front, holding onto their coats and jackets and looking sheepishly back at me. When they saw how far I was from them, they weaved their way through the waiting crowd towards me.

'Worr 'appened to you Reilly, where've you been hiding all night? We've searched high and low for you. Timmy here thought you must've copped off, vanishin' like that. Come on worr 'ave yer been playin' at? ' Chunkie rattled on.

I almost told them I'd been playing at Goodison Park, but this wasn't the time or the place, my main concern was to move as quickly as possible along to the front and get my overcoat. So I said I'd tell them later.

As I edged nearer I still hadn't found my ticket, but I wasn't too bothered. Despite the amount of ale I'd supped, I vaguely remembered my ticket number was 239, probably because that was the number of our house in down-town Brookie.

'Ticket!' a heavily built lad on the other side of the counter yelled when finally I reached the hatch. I told him I must have dropped it somewhere' in the hall, and calmly mentioned the number 239, and the colour and style of my cavalry tweed overcoat. Then, pointing behind him to where the coat was hanging on a peg, I said 'that's it there.'

'No ticket, no coat, so hard luck lad. You'll just have to wait 'til everyone's got theirs,' he said dismissively. And though I pleaded that I'd miss the last bus home, he gave me the cold shoulder and began serving the next person in the line.

After he'd served a couple more lads he came across to where I was still parked at the end of the counter and in a low whisper said, 'I'll tell yer what pal, slip me five bob an' it's all yours.'

'Five bob,' I replied, astounded. 'Your kiddin' aren't yer?' But then I began thinking of the seven mile hike, and how sore my feet had been the last time I'd been stranded out here in New Brighton. So I gave in to his extortionate demand and fiddled in my pockets looking for two half crowns, while he went to retrieve my overcoat.

'Is this it?' he said, holding the coat in one hand, his other palm open, ready to collect the back-hander.

'Here you go, arsole,' I hissed, passing the coins across. Then just as he was about to take the five bob, I purposely dropped one of the half crowns, which bounced down on his side of the hatch. Placing my overcoat on the counter but still holding it firmly, he glared aggressively at me then bent down to pick up the coin. Suddenly, memories of my successful boxing championship at Butlins came flooding back, and as he stood up, I let fly, just as I'd done on that night in the Finals, whipping across a right-hander that caught him totally by surprise. As he fell back I grabbed my coat and made off. Or to be more precise, I tried to; But how was I to know the bouncers protected the cloakroom area as well as the main entrance.

The next thing I knew I was being lifted off the deck by a mean-looking giant who pummelled me around the face and then propelled me along the full length of the queue, far quicker than it took the cabin to empty when the shift ended on a Friday night. He then tossed me from the doorway and I flew through the air without touching any of the half-dozen marbled steps leading down from the main entrance.

Because of the speed of my eviction, and the fact my overcoat had somehow or other wrapped itself around my face and head, at first, the lads didn't recognise the crumpled body lying in a heap on the muddy pathway. Then Timmy spotted a pair of flashy Italian shoes and a torn midnight-blue trouser leg sticking out from under the coat.

'Bloody 'ell, it's Jimmy,' he yelled. Chunkie and Billy then dashed across to where I was lying, wailing like someone trapped in a car, upside down, drowning in a river.

'Help..help! 'Where am I? Me head! Me head,' I cried,

trying to free myself from the wet and mud-covered coat which somehow, I now seemed to think was a death shroud.

'Christ, Reilly. Can't we take you anywhere without you up-setting the natives,' Chunkie growled, tugging the overcoat from my head and pulling me to my feet.

Bruised and battered, with Billy on one side and Chunkie on the other, I was forcibly dragged the few hundred yards to the bus terminal.

We were dead stuffy that night - the number ten had been delayed and was running late - and we even managed to claim the side seat next to the conductor. This was just as well, for after the bus moved off and rumbled across some rough and un-even road surfaces, my stomach began to rebel and I began to puke violently.

'Stand here lad and get some fresh air down yer,' the conductor said consolingly, placing the leather strap barrier across the platform, as the smell of grease from the fish and chip suppers of a group of passengers drifted back down the aisle of the bottom deck.

Just as we were crossing the Dock Road the bus hit a row of cobbles, then bounced and skidded on the railway lines and sent me lurching against the leather barrier strap. This sudden impact caused my head to drop lower than my stomach and I heaved and threw up what looked and felt like three days dinners. My noisy and continuous puking must have upset the passengers enjoying the last of their fish suppers because they began throwing rolled-up paper missiles at me. My misfortune also attracted comments from a few of the older passengers, many of whom had probably been in the same predicament when they were my age.

'Don't jump lad, unless you're in the parra's,' one old fella yelled as the bus picked up speed and I tottered and swayed on the platform next to the conductor, gripping the rail like grim death.

'Leave 'im alone an' let him jump Fred, his ould lady's probably got 'im insured for a few bob,' a friend sitting alongside him joked

'There's a bloody good nicker's worth of ale gone down the drain there lad,' a blue nosed guy added, shaking his head at the sheer waste, and at my inability to keep it down.

Finally, we reached the bus stop opposite the Black Fella's pub in Clevie, the end of the road for me and Chunkie and just three stops away from Hamilton Square for Billy and Timmy.

Although Chunkie offered to let me doss down on his couch for the night, I decided to face the six mile trek to the Woodchurch, just in case my old man was waiting up for me; something he did on occasions when he couldn't sleep and worried about one thing or another.

With very little traffic on the road I plodded on and even though I'd covered no more than a mile, for some reason my head now seemed as clear as a bell and my limbs were no longer aching; although the lump under my eye was still swelling considerably and was sore to touch.

Next morning, however, I felt as if though I'd been kicked by a mule, my face was bruised and swollen, my suit and overcoat looked as if they'd spent the night wrapped round a scarecrow in a muddy field, and Dad, as usual, didn't show much pity.

'It's about time you learnt that if you play with fire you're liable to burn the bloody house down m'lad, and as for tanglin' with bouncers, Christ! Why don't you pick on someone your own size before you think of taking on those big fellas? Oh, and by the way,' he added in a much sterner tone, 'Don't think of using this bit of a dust-up as an excuse for not going to work tomorrow. 'Cos I've got news for you - you've no chance.'

For the rest of the day I took it easy, recovering bit by bit. At bedtime I was still feeling ropey, and when I crawled carefully downstairs on Monday morning, dad – uncharacteristically - relented. Even he could see I'd be neither use nor ornament in the state I was in. But as usual, before he went to work, he had the last word, warning me to control my excess drinking and to steer clear of trouble when I was out with the lads; otherwise I'd better start looking for new digs.

I didn't reply. There was no point in arguing, I knew it wasn't worth while. What's more, within a matter of weeks the army would be lurking, ready to pounce, and then I'd be provided with a different kind of digs.

Despite being waited on hand and foot by mam, I spent the next couple of days lolling round the house feeling sorry for myself, then on the Wednesday I returned to work ready to face my mates. Of course, if past experience was anything to go by, I knew they'd be raring to have a go at me about my eventful night out at the Tower, but surprisingly not a word was said when I stumbled into the cabin just before eight o'clock. As soon as the last of the teapots were drained and the cups and mugs were emptied, the mood changed and the piss-taking took over.

'What's this we've been hearin' about you sparring with one of the seven foot bouncers outside the Tower?' George Sharkey scoffed.

'I didn't even see him,' I protested. 'All I remember was flyin' through the air and landin' in a heap on me arse.'

'I thought you held a good bevvy Reilly?' Podgy Hogan grumbled. 'After listening to you braggin' about how much you and your mates supped at that re-union you went to the other week, I'd have thought you could 'ave handled at least ten pints?' Instead of being his usually jolly self, Podgy still had a bee in his bonnet. He'd been moody and miserable for weeks, ever since his doctor had warned him of the effects that his heavy drinking was having on his health.

'You try drinkin' black velvets and rum and pep chasers all night, an' see how long you last,' I replied, ignoring his personal problems.

'Jimmy you surprise me,' Robbo said, shaking his head and tutting loudly. 'You know I speak from the heart and mean what I say. It's something I've always drummed it into you since you were a sixteen year old.'

'Go on Robbo,' I said, 'fire away.' I knew I was in for some wise words and I probably wasn't going to like what I heard

'First of all I find it hard to believe that an apprentice I've trained diligently like a son ends up suppin' fancy playboy drinks. Full sessions of black velvets and rum an' pep chasers, I ask yer! Christ lad, it's enough to blow the brains off anyone, even those hardy old piss artists you find staggerin' along Skid Row on a Saturday night.'

'If I were you Jimmy,' he continued, 'I'd revert to basics, and seriously consider going back on the bitter. And if that's too strong, why not try the boy's beer, the Birkenhead mild, to see if that agrees with yer?' There were chuckles all round, but Robbo hadn't finished yet.

'What with nearly getting' yourself electrocuted a couple of months back, then fallin' down a ladder in the switchroom, and the time you almost sliced half your thumb off on Willie's jack knife,' He paused, lit a ciggie, then carried on, a hint of sadness and even despair in his voice. 'But now this performance of yours takes the biscuit. Here you are, five foot six - an' what weight are yer, eight or nine stone - an' comin' in here battered and bruised after tanglin' with a bouncer, an' just weeks before you get your full ticket and your call-up! 'Bloody 'ell lad,' he concluded, 'by the time the army sends for you there'll be nowt left for them to practice on.'

With this final thrust he subsided into a chair, shaking his head sadly. I said nothing. There was nowt I could say. But I did manage to look slightly down hearted.

The fifteenth of February finally arrived, and against all the odds I officially became a tradesman. At seven thirty on the following Monday evening I presented myself at the Park Hotel's branch of the E.T.U to proudly receive my skilled Electrician's union card from the Treasurer, George Paris. This small card was like a passport. Without it, there was no chance of working on any of the union organised jobs, either in contracting, shipping or maintenance.

I was then tactfully reminded by George of how fortunate I was to be working for Tanjon's, who had not followed the line of many other contractors by dismissing me on my birthday. A number of firms, particularly shipbuilding companies, simply sacked their apprentices when they reached the age of twenty-one and were out of their time. It was, according to those firms, a practice designed to encourage young tradesmen to spread their wings and gain experience and confidence with new and different kinds of employers. There again there were as many who claimed that the policy was merely a cheap way for the firms to get rid of inexperienced lads.

But now, even though I was a tradesman of a kind, I knew I was living on borrowed time. And as each week passed the suspense of not knowing whether some shipping company would offer me a job, or the army would suddenly pounce, reduced me to living in dread of the postman's delivery.

Meanwhile, sensing a chance to make some extra cash, our Tommy took to hanging round the bus stop waiting for me to arrive from work. As soon my feet touched the pavement, there he was in my shadow, furnishing me with an up-date on all the mail delivered to our house that day. Of course, I knew he mooched through my belongings when I was out on the town and would know I was earning top wages, so I wasn't surprised to see him grasping this opportunity to increase his pocket money by a few extra bob.

One morning in late March, news filtered in that Harry Burkey had been 'captured' and was now a resident - or inmate, depending on how it was viewed - down south at the Aldershot barracks. As usual it was Chunkie who broke the news, grinning with pleasure at the anguish it caused. Chunks was a few months younger than me, and wasn't too bothered about the army, as his 'date of execution' wasn't even on the horizon.

Easter arrived with its church parades and regalia, and was no sooner on us than it had passed like the wind. As Whit and the bank holiday approached, I still hadn't heard from the army or from any shipping company - British or foreign; a dilemma that prompted the betting fraternity in the cabin to make the armed forces the odds on favourite to get my scalp.

Rumours were also flying around that National Service was soon to be abolished, news that certainly raised my spirits, and many lads of a similar age. However, the bar-room politicians in our cabin were not impressed by the gossip, arguing that it was just a political ploy to attract young men to the polls. Despite their pessimism I still retained a glimmer of hope that by the skin of my teeth I might just escape the long arm of the military machine.

As the warmth of May drifted into the full summer of June I began to believe that maybe a miracle had indeed taken place, and that somehow or other the ministry had misplaced my file. Such was my optimism I even considered booking another holiday at Butlin's, but not with the famous Star boxing team now that Don was away doing his bit for Queen and country.

While I was floating on this wave of fantasy, my hopes were given a significant boost when I received a letter from British Petroleum informing me they were arranging interviews for junior electrical engineering positions for their tanker fleet, and would be contacting me to arrange a suitable date.

'Fourteen months is along time at sea,' Sid Shortwick warned, as I buzzed in next morning, flashing my letter round the cabin to prove B.P. had indeed been in touch.

That weekend - regardless of Robbo's advice - like a man possessed I celebrated my good fortune with Chunkie, Timmy McCain and Billy Constable. Supping ale by the gallon and squandering money as if it were going out of fashion, we staggered from pub to pub shouting through the barmy Sunday night and singing 'til we were hoarse and totally incapable. No wonder it took me all of Monday to recover from a hangover far greater than any I'd experienced in my short drinking career.

But then, as many of the older workers would often preach, no two days are ever alike; and on the next day, Tuesday, everything went well for me. An awkward job I'd struggled for weeks with in the boilerhouse came together perfectly. Then I won a tenner on the horses. Nipper, who'd been dossing in an empty trap in the bogs over-heard Pat, the bookies runner, discussing a 'dead cert' which bolted in at ten to one. What's more, despite the cash spent during the weekend extravaganza, I found my wallet was still healthy enough to allow us to plan for another big night out on the coming Friday, with no expense spared. My good fortune even continued when the half-five bus departed from Ellesmere Port on time, enabling me to catch the on-going connection at Woodside without the usual half-hour wait. To crown a perfect day, I saw that our Tommy wasn't hanging around the bus stop when I arrived at the Woodchurch.

With a bounce in my step and a 'good to be alive' feeling sweeping over me, I set off at a steady pace to climb the steep slope up to our road.

'No news is good news,' I remember thinking to myself as I reached the top of the hill, and turned into Schoolfield. But then my heart missed a beat as I spotted our kid galloping towards me like mad, waving something in his hand. Suddenly I had a feeling that maybe I'd counted my chickens long before they'd hatched. 'You've 'ad it Jimmy, it's curtains,' he yelled, as soon as he was within shouting distance. Breathlessly, he thrust out an official looking envelope that looked as if it had been savaged by a tin opener.

Who told you to open this?' was all I could think to say,

my eyes darting across the large brown envelope which had the official looking crown instead of a stamp on one side, and O.H.M.S in bold letters on the other.

He didn't reply. He didn't need to. He knew if I was called-up his weekly pocket money would dip considerably; that's why he looked as dejected as me.

Ignoring our kid's grubby fingerprints, I eased the single white folded sheet from the brown envelope, scrutinising each word for an escape clause, but the content was short, blunt and straight to the point,

For the attention of James Reilly. By order of H.M government. Sir, you are summoned to present yourself at Leece Street Medical Centre, Liverpool, Monday, 9am, 18th June 1959 to undergo a medical examination for conscription into H.M.Forces.

'That's it, I've been captured,' I mumbled, crumpling the letter and stuffing it into my trouser pocket before covering the last hundred yards to our house like a condemned man taking his final steps to the gallows. Tommy, who was trailing behind me, kicked a tin can with such force that it flew over old Mrs Green's hedge, clattering noisily along her concrete path. Before she had chance to set her Alsatian dog on him he was up and away, leaving me to face her wrath and the angry dog; and, of course, totally lost for words. Burdened as I was with this extra weight on my shoulders, I merely shrugged, gave her a sympathetic nod, then opened the front door and sloped inside.

I couldn't really face my dinner, despite Ma having cooked my favourite hot pot. And before dad trooped wearily up the path after a long twelve hour shift at the docks, I'd nipped upstairs, had a swift bath and within half an hour I was propped against the bar of the Arrowe Park Hotel drowning my sorrows. During the next few hours I sat drinking in the company of a couple of down and out ex- army veterans. By the time last orders were called, these two old soldiers had almost convinced me that when compared to their long and illustrious careers spent fighting for the mighty British Empire, two years in the mob would be like a mere holiday at Butlin's.

During the session, I'd been enthralled by their tales of heroic deeds and battles, and I thanked my new found friends for lifting my morale sky high, before staggering from the hotel well and truly bladdered.

As for my workmates in the morning, well, they could take the mickey all they liked, because 'Reilly has all the answers now,' I muttered to myself - hoping I could remember these fine words in the morning!

Bleary-eyed and nursing a very thick sore head, I arrived at work next morning feeling as if I'd been dragged through a hedge backwards half a dozen times. At first I couldn't face telling the lads about my misfortune, but as nine o'clock approached and with my faculties now more or less on the mend, I nipped across to see Robbo, working on a panel in the workshop, to tell him my bad news.

'Bloody 'ell lad,' he said, placing his tools on the bench, 'that's what I'd call lousy luck. Take a tip from me and go an' find the lads and let them know. Its better they find out sooner than later, and don't forget to make a joke of it. I'm sure you'll be appreciated if you do.'

I made my way to the mill, searching for Chunkie and the rest of the lads working in Sailors squad, and found them larking about on top of a large scaffolding platform.

'Guess who's been captured?' I yelled as loud as I could. Chunkie, Timmy McCain and Nipper Hollerhead stopped what they were doing, climbed down and came across. As usual, Chunkie was laughing and seemed to think I had something up my sleeve and was stringing them along. Then I fished the letter from my jacket pocket and passed it across to him.

'Next Monday! Bloody 'ell Reilly, that must 'ave put you right off your dinner last night?'

'You're tellin'me,'I replied.

By breaktime everyone knew about the letter, and the floodgates were now open for the jokers to take centre stage.

'What day did you say you were goin' for your medical Jim?' Podgy Hogan asked on the Thursday.

'Nine o'clock, on the dot, at Leece Street, next Monday mornin'. Why?' I answered, cautiously.

'If mine was anything to go by Reilly, then you're in for a rough ride, so be prepared,' George Sharkey' butted in.

'Come off it Sharkey, I've heard all about Leece Street from me mate Bonso,' I replied, full of confidence, knowing he was setting me up for a laugh.

'So you know all about the short arm inspections, then?' he drawled cockily.

'Short arm inspections?' I hesitated, scratching my head, giving him a slight advantage. 'Worr are they when they're out?'

'You'll find out soon enough,' he said, and I noticed Sid Shortwick and Crusthead McGinty move a couple of seats nearer, a sign there was something on the cards worth listening to.

'For starters Jim, don't listen to all the crap that it's like a doctor's cosy surgery and you're in your own private cubical on your jaxie; 'cos there's always a batch of half a dozen the quack inspects in one full swoop, okay?'

'I know that, I'm not thick y'know. Bonso told me all about his medical. And for your information there could be as many as eight or even ten. Anyway, what's the problem? They're all fella's aren't they?' I said, pleased at the way I was handling the situation.

'Don't get narked lad, I'm just puttin' you in the picture, that's all,' Sharkey said, smiling broadly. 'Remember when you were still saggin' school and playin' tiddlywinks in the back jiggers, I was over in Leece Street havin' me own medical. So d'yer want hear my account, or what?'

'Carry on get it over and done with. I can easily take anything you've got to offer,' I replied, noting Robbo's smile of approval.

'As I've already said there was six in our group,' he began, 'and without exaggerating I can picture everyone one of them now, just as if it was yesterday. But Reilly, before I start, listen to what I've got to say and maybe you'll get something out of my tale; and not the hairy ones I hang on everyone round here.

'Go on, I'm all ears Sharkey. Though it's probably a load of bull shit as usual,' I said, winking at Chunkie.

'Now the quack, he wasn't your ordinary back street, run-of-the-mill local doctor,' he began. 'No! he was a real Jack the Lad, a right rum bugger, probably ex-Navy the way he breezed in with his side kick

'RIGHT LAD'S LET'S HAVE YOU STRIPPED, READY FOR SHORT ARM INSPECTIONS,' he bawled.

Still puzzled as to what was coming, I kept quiet as Sharkey turned and said, 'you've still no idea, have yer Jim?' By now I could hear sniggers from a few of the lads sitting behind us, so I knew there was something about to land

'Anyway,' Sharkey said, continuing the story, 'we stripped off, dumped our clobber on some chairs in the corner and stood in a straight line while the quack walked slowly in front of us, casting his eye up and down as if he was weighing us up. After a few seconds he seemed to falter in front of a lad farthest away from me at the end of the line. Now this kid was long and skinny, except for his nudger, which was massive. An' I mean massive. In fact I wouldn't be exaggerating if I said it was the biggest part of him.'

The penny dropped. 'Short arm inspection, eh Sharkey? Now I know what you mean,' I yelled. But George carried on talking, showing no surprise that it had taken me so long to catch on to his wind-up.

'Don't think I'm bent Jimmy, 'cos everyone looks down to blimp worr everyone else's got,' he said, seeing the look of surprise on my face. 'You'll find out for yourself next week when you're in there. It can't be helped, there's nowhere else to look.'

Sharkey was up on his feet and holding the floor now, acting out his own experience at the medical. And with everyone anticipating a theatrical performance from the maestro, the bold George was not one to let them down.

'Name?' the doc asked, after performing his cold-handed, three-cough operation.

'Timpson Sir,' the lad with the exceptional nudger replied

'Christian name?'

'Dickie.'

A few hearty chuckles rippled around the cabin.

'It's obvious you didn't have any toys to play with when you were a lad,' the doc rebuked Timpson. 'But give your parents their due lad, they were spot on with your Christian name.'

'Status?' the Doc's sidekick asked, his pen poised above a clip-board'

Half roundhead, half cavalier' the doc replied, scribbling something on his pad and then moving onto the next fella in line. Now this guy was small and stocky, with the biggest beer belly I've ever seen in me life.' Sharkey told his audience. 'In fact from where I was standin' he looked as if he was eight month's pregnant and carryin' quads. But the doctor must've been sufferin' from spinal trouble, 'cos when he bent down to reach out and grip this little fella's balls, well, he nearly dislocated his back. So he did no more than to hand the task to his mate, telling him not to forget to check shorty's status while he was down there.'

The way the tale was unfolding brought sniggers from Sharkey's audience, while George, I could see, was thoroughly enjoying his place in the limelight. A few older sparks however, muttered that as far as they knew, Sharkey had never even been in the army in the first place.

'Now the third fella along; guess worr he was lads? Come on I'll bet there's no one in this cabin who can give me the right answer?' Sharkey said with some conviction.

'A Martian with three knobs?' Jimmy 'H' said.

'A one legged arse kicking champion?' Sid Shortwick joked.

'Nope, he was a bloody Evertonian,' Sharkey yelled, a revelation that alerted the minority of red supporters in the cabin that a blue nose was perhaps about to be slated.

'How did yer make that out George?' Crusthead asked, speaking from somewhere behind us. 'How could yer tell?'

'Well, Crusthead, seein' you're the only one who wants to know, I'll put you wise. Y'see he'd been well and truly scalped and his plums were painted blue.'

'Painted blue? What for?'

'That's what the doctor queried when he spotted them.'

'Crabs,?' he'd asked sternly. 'Where did you get these from young man?'

'I didn't get them Sir, they got me - when I wasn't lookin'. Gorr 'em from the lavvie at work even though I didn't sit down on the seat. So they must 'ave jumped Sir.'

'Jumped? Don't talk nonsense man,' said the doctor. 'Those old wives tales that say these little beasties can jump six feet are well off the mark. Take it from me my boy, it's three inches at the most. And on a good day, in a strong wind, then perhaps four.'

'Honest Sir I gorr em from the lavvie, an' so did our kid.'

'Well as long as you've got rid of the little buggers that's the main thing,' the doc replied, poking the affected area with his pencil.

'Of course, as soon as he mentioned crabs everyone started scratchin' Sharkey added. 'It wasn't half embarrassing.'

'It's a good job Plonker Parson's wasn't there, he'd 'ave been in his element,' Jimmy 'H' remarked. 'He'd 'ave probably been done for indecent exposure for showing that dodgy right hand of his.'

We all laughed at Jimmy's dry sense of humour.

To keep everyone focussed on his narrative and to keep centre stage, George pushed on with the story of what happened to the lad standing next to him.

'When the exam team stopped in front of this fella, me bloody sides were achin' with laughin,' George said. 'Y'see he'd cupped both hands over his tackle, so naturally, we thought it was because he was timid and shy.'

'Okay lad, let's see what you're hiding under there?' Doc Holiday asked sternly. 'Magnifying glass and tweezers Albert, we may have an I.G.P on our hands,' he ordered, addressing his buddy with a sense of urgency.

'I.G.P, what's that? said Crusthead.

'In growing penis,' George chortled loudly, looking pleased that he'd sucked someone into his bait, even if it was just Crusthead.

'Of course,' Sharkey continued, 'the lad was deeply embarrassed and obviously relieved when, after finishing his inspection, the doc declared him to be a round head. Later on, when he was dressed with his kecks back on, he pinned the blame for his shrinkage on a bad bout of nerves and the temperature in the room.

'Finally, the doc stood before me,' Sharkey declared, grinning like a hyena. 'You could tell at once he was impressed, by the way he looked me up and down.'

'Now Albert, this is what I call a fine specimen of youth,' he said. 'With your physique young man, I'm going to recommend you for a position in the Royal Marines.'

'The Royal Marines! Bugger off George. Now you're really getting carried away,' I yelled at Sharkey - though I knew it was all part of the crack.

'Bear in mind I was only eighteen at the time, Reilly, not twenty-one, like you. And, of course I hadn't developed the muscular body I've got now,' George added, expanding his chest fully. 'Nevertheless, it was quite a compliment from the doc for a young fella like me.'

The tale seemed to be over, with George headed for the Royal Marines, perhaps even for the Commando's. But then, after the pride came the fall, when Podgy broke the silence.

'Is that why you landed in the Pioneer Corps, Sharkey?' he asked our hero.

'No Podgy,' Sharkey responded in an instant, not at all bothered by Podgy's revelation.

'Y'see the Marines wanted me to sign on for three years as a Regular, so I volunteered to dig trenches for the old thunder boxes instead.'

'Hey George, did you manage to hang a tail on the doctor while you were there?' Chunkie enquired.

'No, kid, unfortunately I didn't have one with me at the time.'

Then, turning back to me he added, 'that's another thing you'll have to beware of Jimmy, lad, when you're traipsing round in the nude.'

'What's that?'

'That no one hangs a tail on you.'

'If you're not there, Sharkey it's highly unlikely to happen,' I replied with a grin.

My medical on the Monday was almost as embarrassing as Bonso and Sharkey predicted, except that in my case the doctor didn't resort to the use of a torch to aid the investigation.

I was also surprised to discover that Sharkey was spot on when he said there was nowhere else to look when we were all standing in a line in our birthday suits. After scanning the ceiling for any sign of subsidence, then following the fine wallpaper pattern from top to bottom, my eyes finally strayed across to the lad who was standing next to me. Sharkey's description of the I.G.P leapt into my mind, and naturally I burst out laughing.

'Worra you laughin' at la?' the lad snapped.

'Nowt mate, just nerves, that's all,' I told him, stifling a final guffaw.

His eyes wandered down my lily-white frame, past my belly button before he chuckled loudly.

'Yeah, you're right there lad, I see what you mean. Snap!'

A week later another envelope from the Ministry of Defence landed on the mat. This time it lay unopened until I came in from work. Since the call to attend my medical, I'd noticed our kid's enthusiasm for hanging round the bus stop had petered out; and I was more than pleasantly surprised to learn that he'd developed an interest in girls instead of extortion.

The letter was formal and straight to the point. I'd passed my medical without a hitch, had been classed as A1, and was instructed to report to Catterick barracks by 1400 hours on Thursday 28th June 1959, to join the Royal Signals Regiment. A railway voucher from Lime Street to Richmond was enclosed with the letter.

My last day at work was a memorable affair. Nipper managed to scrounge a couple bacon and egg butties from the canteen, long before the start of the first shift, which in itself was no mean feat considering the girls never began serving until nine o'clock. As we munched on the butties, I looked round at my colleagues, most had been with me now for a good part of my apprenticeship.

Jimmy'H's absence from the cabin was noticeable. He'd left Tanjon's only days after my medical taking a job with Troughton & Young, a well-known London outfit who were recruiting sparks to work on the new university building in Liverpool city centre. Everyone agreed that his sense of humour and dry-wit would be sorely missed, so we were all ears when Robbo related a tale he'd heard at the branch union meeting about our ex-colleague.

'On the morning he was due at his new job,' Robbo began, 'Jimmy 'H' was seen leaving his house wearing a posh, double-breasted brown suit, with a matching silk tie.

This raised more than a few eyebrows - with few washing or changing room facilities sparks rarely dressed up for work unless they were finishing early for a funeral or some other important event. It was common practice for the lads to travel to the job, then spend the day working in the clobber they stood up in, before heading home covered in grime and grit. What's more, in an environment such as the Bowies mill refurbishment, we were usually covered in a thick paper dust which seeped deep into the grain of our clothes by the end of each shift. Of course, most of us wore ovies to protect our clothes though Jimmy 'H' never seemed to bother, and to be honest, had always looked more than comfortable grafting in what some of the older workers referred to as 'his demob suit.'

Robbo continued his tale, interrupting my train of thought.

'Closing his front door, Jimmy 'H' fell in line with his neighbour, who, from what I've been told, is one of those fella's that never misses a trick.'

'Mornin', he said to Jimmy 'H'. 'My word, you're lookin' smart this mornin'; Whereabouts are you at now?'

'Oh,' said Jimmy, in a deeply pompous voice, 'I'm at the Liverpool University.'

'THE LIVERPOOL UNIVERSITY?" his neighbour gasped loudly. 'I didn't know that, Jim. What are you taking?'

'Corn beef sarnies,' Jimmy 'H' answered, before climbing into Tommy Mac's old Austin banger and roarin' off towards the tunnel entrance.

'Tommy told me the tale at the branch,' said Robbo, laughing along with the rest of us in the cabin.

Later in the day, full of the joys of spring, I trooped out of the stores looking forward to my final shift, but then, as I turned the corner, I walked slap-bang into Jack Poulson, the site engineer.

'Watch where you're walkin' son,' he grumbled, casting a disapproving eye over me as I dodged out of his way, struggling to muster some sort of a late apology.

'Oh, it's you Young Reilly. I hear you're leaving us at last?' he said, his mood changing within seconds. As I spluttered a mumbled 'yes,' he then told me to stop off at his office and wait for him there. A few minutes later he appeared carrying a bunch of rolled-up drawings under his arm. After placing them on a rack behind his desk he turned to me with a grin. 'So young man, the army's captured you at last,' he declared.

'Well, Jack,' I said lightly, 'someone's got to fight for the nation, and who better equipped than me after all the action I've had since I came here.' I was surprised at my 'off the cuff' reply and the rare show of bravado - which was something I'd lacked since my victory at Butlin's boxing tournament.

'Did you hear that gentlemen?' Jack said, turning to the rest of the office staff and laughing loudly. 'All I can say is God help the country if it's stooped so low that it has to rely on the likes of you to defend us, Jimmy Reilly.' At which point some creep at the back of the office muttered, 'Hear ...Hear!'

'Now then,' Jack continued, 'after you've finished your afternoon break, son, pack your tools away and get yourself off,' then he shook my hand warmly and wished me all the best for the future. 'By the way,' he added with a smile, 'if you manage to get through the next two years and return in one piece, there could be a job waiting here for you.'

When Norman the timekeeper joined those wishing me well muttered that from what he could make of me I was sufficiently street-wise to do well in the army, I had the sneaky feeling that he was referring to past misdeeds and implying I was largely responsible for the time-book fiddle.

Having done the rounds in the main office, I then nipped along to the chargehands cabin to say my farewells. After rattling the door for a few seconds, I heard the usual 'come on in' response and stepped inside their warm cosy shack to be welcomed cordially by Bob Bains who'd been whistling 'Your in the army now,' for over a week. When he saw who it was, he immediately changed his tune to the less well-known number 'I'm nobody's child,' probably out of sheer devilment.

I was totally shocked when Plonker eased himself from behind his desk, removed his mysterious right hand from deep in his pocket and offered it to me. Meanwhile, Sailor, bounced from his chair like a jack-in-the-box, placed a heavily tattooed arm across my bony shoulders, and said he'd keep a sharp look-out for any sea-going opportunities while I was away. He then urged me to have a good trip and, more importantly, never to let my shipmates down. Tear arse, his head buried in a bunch of drawings, muttered it was the army that had sharpened him up and reflected consolingly that if I kept my nose clean there was perhaps a slight chance I could reach the same dizzy heights that he had.

'Have a good time, me old cocker,' Old Shep croaked, blowing his nose loudly, as he shuffled from of the office he shared with Bootsy; while Bootsy himself, after embracing me like a younger brother, told me not to forget how close I'd come to meeting my maker, and to double check everything I touched in future.

An hour later, after finishing the last of my butties and receiving all kinds of advice and suggestions from those stalwart veterans who'd trodden the same road that I was about to tread, it was time to leave the cabin.

'Keep the crack goin' Jimmy, remember a good yarn is worth its weight in gold,' Sid Shortwick said, slapping me hard across my shoulders.

'Take it from me lad - from one of the few in here who's seen proper enemy action - keep yer chin up an' yer head down an' you'll be alright,' Chinless Brady advised.

'Christ, Brady,' Podgy Hogan, butted in, 'he's not goin' to war yer know. The only action he's likely to get involved in is fightin' his way to the front of the N.A.F.F.I queue for a jam doughnut or a cream bun.'

The Pope, tottering in from Tanjon's other cabin, as sanctimonious as ever, thanked God that I was still in one piece, and told me the army was lucky to have me after all I'd been through in the last year.'

'Four forty volts, that's nowt to him,' Chunkie said, pulling my ear playfully.

Shifty then bagged my po-sized tea mug, upsetting Nipper who'd wanted it as a memento.

'Willy the Spook,' as keen as ever for me to retain some interest in his beliefs and teachings, slid me a copy of 'Forty years of Psychic research' by Hamlin Garland; but Billy Chancer intervened, saying, 'leave it son, don't take any notice of him; just remember all I've told you about analysin' everything before drawing your own conclusions.'

To save face and not wishing to hurt 'The Spook's' feelings, I managed to slip the book across to Chunkie to mind for me while I was away.

Looking like a man who'd lost everything on some money making scam, Billy Chancer took a sheet of paper from his pocket, handed it to me and said, 'here's me address lad. If you get a chance, drop me an' Maisie a line, 'cos we'd both like to hear from you. And by the way Jim, you've turned out just as I expected, and all I can say is I'm proud of yer.'

Sharkey, who'd been fiddling with something or other, reacted immediately to this somewhat over-the-top eulogy. Rolling up his sleeve, he pursed his lips, took a deep breath, then blew against his forearm and elbow, producing a loud squirting noise just like one of Podgy Hogan's fart's; and identical to those which had scattered everyone working behind the panels in the switchroom. Billy Chancer was far from amused and glared contemptuously at Sharkey, though some of the younger lads found it hilarious.

After collecting my bits and pieces, then shaking hands with everyone, I left the cabin for the last time. Carrying my toolbox firmly across my shoulder, I swaggered proudly towards the gatehouse. Having reached the red and white barrier, I turned to wave once more to my cheering colleagues, and, as I ducked under the pole and stepped away from the site, a coiled-up paper tail, which had been concealed under the bottom of my donkey jacket, slipped out and fluttered like a kite in the wind. From way behind, on the other side of the fence, I heard another resounding cheer.

This wasn't the end of the farewells though. Earlier in the day Robbo had arranged a meet in the popular Luke Lee's bar at five o'clock, along with a couple of his regular drinking partners who didn't need much of an excuse for a session on the ale; and to give me what he called 'a proper send-off.'

When the bus reached Rock Ferry, I dropped off by the traffic lights and walked up Bedford Road towards Luke's only to find the doors closed. To kill time, I crossed the road to the Railway café where I settled down to admire the passing talent until Robbo and his team landed.

The send-off that night was something I'll never forget, as pint after pint arrived at our table, ordered and paid for by complete strangers, most of whom seemed to be friends and drinking partners of Robbo and his mates. In this kind of drinking company I was well out of my league, and though I offered to get a round in to 'pay my way,' I was told to 'hang onto my money' and reminded that 'before long son, you'll be paid in buttons.'

At eight thirty I tottered and swayed the last hundred yards of our road. Our Tommy, who must have been watching me staggering from pavement to gutter crept up behind me and insisted he carry my toolbox the rest of the way home, despite his size.

'Give me your key Jim,' he said when we reached the back gate, and I'll clean the rust from your tools before I put them away in the shed.' But even before I'd had time to take off my boots or my jacket he came hurtling back into the kitchen, frowning.

'What's up?' I asked, in a beer-sodden voice.

'Someone's filled your toolbox with a couple of bricks and a load of old junk,' he replied.

'Sharkey!' I chuckled, what a fella!'

'Sharkey, who's he? I don't get yer,' Tommy said, scratching his head in puzzlement.

'It's nowt worth bothering about, Tommy. Just throw 'em in the bin.'

Leaving home was a quiet affair. Dad, as usual, was up at the crack of dawn, and I wasn't far behind him. Before he set off to catch the ten to seven bus he didn't lecture me as I'd expected, but just shook hands, placed his arm across my back, squeezed my shoulders and told me to keep in touch and look after myself. Then off he went, closing the front door behind him. Ma, whose temperament was different to dad's in every way, fussed around with my gear before cooking me a huge breakfast and all the while worried as to whether my clothes were correctly ironed and properly packed. She'd also made a pile of sandwiches and scones to sustain me on the long train journey to the far side of Yorkshire; which, as far as she was concerned, could have been somewhere on the other side of the world.

'Now don't forget to let me know when you get there, son,' she said, pecking me on the cheek and throwing her short, heavy arms round my shoulders, hugging me as if I was leaving home for good. After struggling free, I finally set off, and from out of the corner of my eye I spotted that young scally, our Tommy, hiding in an entry half-way up the road.

'Why aren't you at school?' I yelled when I caught up with him.

'I just wanted to walk with you to the bus stop for the last time, that's all.'

'Why? D'yer think I'm gonna get shot or somethin'?'

'You never know. Worr if war breaks out and you don't come back home? Mam would go nuts. And worr about me?' he grinned 'I'd have our bedroom all to me'self.' Playfully, I swung my canvass holdall at him, but he dodged out of range.

Within minutes we arrived at the bus stop, when the 'Tommy Reilly' road show really began.

As we stood waiting I pretended not to notice him fiddling in his pockets, pulling out the empty linings and looking as if he'd lost his last tanner. When he'd finally finished larking about, I asked him who he was trying to kid and if he was on the scrounge again.

'No, 'onest Jim,' he pleaded, displaying a well-rehearsed doleful look. 'I must 'ave dropped a threepenny joey somewhere, 'cos it was in me pocket last night before I went to bed.'

'Don't tell bloody lies, you've been skint all week,' I said, rattling the loose change in my jacket pocket just to aggravate him. I knew eventually he'd be able to twist my arm - he'd become something of an expert at getting his own way with me.

After cadging two bob Tommy promised he'd go straight to school, even though, as he was quick to point out, there was every chance he'd be caned for being late. He wasn't fooling me though, I knew he wouldn't go to school. As soon as the bus pulled away, there he was, dodging from behind the shelter, and I watched him legging his way back home. Mam was always an easy touch with sob stories - still, who was I to lecture anyone, especially when I recalled my own school record.

It was far too early for a 'livener' in the Legs of Man so I ambled into Lime Street Station, boarded the steamer and managed to claim a window seat in one of the compartments. This was the first time I'd travelled the Pennine route and it was something I was looking forward too. Mind you, the reception I'd be facing at the other end of the line, well, that was another matter.

From station to station the train slowly puffed its way through the heart of industrial Lancashire and then across the border into a rugged Yorkshire, where every station seemed to be crammed with passengers. I looked out on the cotton mills with their solid chimney stacks disappearing into the polluted skies, scattered across the vast moors as far as the naked eye could see. This was a part of England that was totally alien to someone like me, who'd been born and lived his whole life on the North West coast.

As the train entered the final stage of its journey, for some reason or other I had the sneaky feeling that I was being scrutinised by two short close-cropped individuals who were parked almost opposite. My instinct seemed to be spot on when I clocked them weighing me up again. But rather than get involved in a staring match, I closed my eyes and leaned back to enjoy that favourite pastime I'd carefully developed over the years - day dreaming!

Before long, I was reliving some of the eventful memories from the past six years, remembering the many conscientious workers who had gone out of their way to help to build and develop my character.

My mind drifted back to the time I left school for my first proper job at Pitts, and to the great man himself - Eggo! He was some character, and what about those capers and the pranks he got up to, and the way he'd handled those supercilious types who tended to look down on us lowly workers! I smiled, thinking fondly of his 'screw-ball' personality, his encounters with management, and his unorthodox attitude to life.

As the train trundled on, lost in thought, I drifted back to recall the ever-helpful Robbo, remembering the many occasions he'd used his experience to guide and help me at the Cape, and then at Bowies. Then there was Billy Chancer, the self-styled philosopher who also treated me like a son. I chuckled, recalling Rock Ferry Frank, Jimmy 'H', Willie the Spook, and storytellers such as Sid Shortwick, whose tales and antics had brightened up many a miserable day. There were others, of course. The Pope, Crusthead McGinty, the grossly overweight Podgy Hogan, Trunkie Davies, Nobby Alcock and his sparring partner Rocky - just a few of the names that ran fleetingly through my mind.

As the train rattled rhythmically along I began thinking of my fellow apprentices. Our mentor, the bold Bonso, was first to spring to mind. It was Bonso who'd showed us the ropes at the local dance halls and who'd led us to pubs where we could get a bevvie when we were still under-age. I grimaced with embarrassment as I recalled our immaturity and how he'd shepherded us round town, as we meandered like lost sheep, sporting Teddy boy gear and feeling seven foot tall. Then there was my side-kick, Chunkie Harlowe, who'd been responsible for getting me into the electrical game in the first place, and a mate since we were kids at school. And I wondered how Timmy McCain, Billy Constable and the loyal Nipper would fare at Tanjon's now that I'd left; and whether Arnie Royal who was the same age as me, would get his call-up papers in the next few days.

I chuckled thinking of George Sharkey, with his tail hanging obsession and the outrageous pranks that drove Billy Chancer, his mate at the time, up the wall. Fresh in my mind was the time he'd hurtled down the hill at Woodside to catch the ten past seven bus and had claimed his seat by wriggling his bum into the tiny space and farting. I smiled when I recalled the Chancer's feeble attempts to apply a little psychology in order to embarrass Sharkey, and his old fashioned quotes, 'decorum George, decorum, that's what your lacking in life my friend.' This, like the majority of Billy Chancer's well-meaning utterances had tended to fall on deaf ears.

It was all so vivid in my memory that I forgot for a moment where I was and burst out laughing. Opening my eyes to dab away the tears, I heard someone mutter, 'I reckon he's definitely trying to work his ticket, Archie.'

'Aye, you might be right there, Gerry. I hope he's in my intake. I'll soon straighten him out,' the sharp-featured individual sitting next to him replied.

'You and who's army,' I muttered under my breath, before closing my eyes to dream on about Sharkey and some more of his other crazy antics.

'All off for Richmond,' a guard yelled, his deep Yorkshire voice reverberating as he plodded slowly along the length of the platform. Whether it was a sixth sense or something else - such as one of 'Willie the Spook's' phantoms watching over me - I had a gut feeling of impending danger, so I kept my eyes shut until the compartment was completely emptied.

When I was satisfied everyone for Richmond had left the carriage, I grabbed my bag from the roof rack, ran my fingers through my mop of shoulder-length curly hair, then coolly disembarked just in time to see a sergeant come to attention and salute the two miserable passengers who'd shown more than a curious interest in my appearance. From a position concealed behind the open waiting room door, I watched through a tiny gap as they climbed into an army jeep then shot off, leaving a cloud of muddy coloured dust rising upwards.

Looking up at the clear blue sky I stopped for a moment to thank my guardian angel - or whoever - for steering me out of the path of those un-smiling individuals. For those two, I realised, probably had the power to make my life in the Signals a misery.

'Hey you, what 'd'yer think you're doing skiving over there,'someone barked. Turning sharply, I nearly jumped out of my skin as a mean and truculent looking soldier with a single stripe on his arm approached like a whirlwind, his hob-nailed boots clattering on the flagstones.

'Nowt,' I said, taken back a bit by surprise

'Nowt what lad?'

'Nowt Sir…Sergeant… Captain, ' I spluttered, as he grabbed me by my collar and frog-marched me towards a bunch of crestfallen recruits congregated alongside a convoy of army lorries. Glancing at their sullen faces reminded me of a herd of cattle about to be sent off to the local abattoir to be slaughtered.

After our bags had been tossed unceremoniously on to the back end of the open lorries, we scrambled up in much the same way, landing wherever we could find an empty speck. For the next ten minutes or so a small team of officious squaddies with clipboards in their hands began checking our names. When they were satisfied no one had escaped or had vanished across the fields and open countryside, the lorries began to move off and away from the Railway station.

As we bounced up and down on the narrow, un-even country lanes, I took a swift blimp at the glum faces of my fellow detainees and decided to cheer them up.

'It's not the end of the world lads; try looking on the bright side, we're only here for six weeks,' I yelled, but my feeble words of encouragement were lost in the gloomy atmosphere. Everyone, it seemed, was wrapped up in his own little world, and all with one common denominator in mind. There was no turning back now. It was goodbye to Civvie Street.